A GUIDE [illegible]

UNITED STATES TYPE COINS

Third Edition

History • Values • Collecting

Q. David Bowers

Foreword by

Eric P. Newman

A GUIDE BOOK OF

UNITED STATES TYPE COINS

Third Edition

1974 Chandalar Drive, Suite D, Pelham, AL 35124

Correspondence concerning this book may be directed to
Whitman Publishing, Attn: Type Coins, at the address above.

ISBN: 079484636X
Printed in China

Disclaimer: Expert opinion should be sought in any significant numismatic purchase. This book is presented as a guide only. No warranty or representation of any kind is made concerning the completeness of the information presented. The author, a professional numismatist, regularly buys, sells, and holds certain of the items discussed in this book.

Caveat: The value estimates given are subject to variation and differences of opinion. Before making decisions to buy or sell, consult the latest information. Past performance of the rare-coin market or any coin or series within that market is not necessarily an indication of future performance, as the future is unknown. Such factors as changing demand, popularity, grading interpretations, strength of the overall coin market, and economic conditions will continue to be influences.

Other books in the Bowers Series include: *A Guide Book of Morgan Silver Dollars; A Guide Book of Double Eagle Gold Coins; A Guide Book of Modern United States Proof Coin Sets; A Guide Book of Shield and Liberty Head Nickels; A Guide Book of Flying Eagle and Indian Head Cents; A Guide Book of Washington Quarters; A Guide Book of Buffalo and Jefferson Nickels; A Guide Book of Lincoln Cents; A Guide Book of United States Commemorative Coins; A Guide Book of United States Tokens and Medals; A Guide Book of Gold Dollars; A Guide Book of Peace Dollars; A Guide Book of the Official Red Book of United States Coins; A Guide Book of Franklin and Kennedy Half Dollars; A Guide Book of Civil War Tokens; A Guide Book of Hard Times Tokens; A Guide Book of Mercury Dimes, Standing Liberty Quarters, and Liberty Walking Half Dollars; A Guide Book of Half Cents and Large Cents; A Guide Book of Barber Silver Coins; A Guide Book of Liberty Seated Silver Coins; A Guide Book of Modern United States Dollar Coins; A Guide Book of the United States Mint;* and *A Guide Book of Gold Eagles.*

Whitman®

Contents

FOREWORD

In the extensive current enthusiasm for the collection and study of numismatic objects, an emphasis on United States coins has brought about great satisfaction and pleasure to many of us. The depth of specialization and resulting understanding that has developed covering over two centuries of such issues has steadily broadened to include economics, history, art, metallurgy, mechanics, commemoration, patriotism, usage, counterfeiting, forgery, and replicas.

The universal appeal of American numismatics has so many avenues of interest that it is difficult to be an informed generalist because of the complexities within each division and time period of such coinage. The multiple dates, mint marks, styles, denominations, minting techniques, varieties, usages, restriking, conditions, rarity, etc., of each type need careful analysis. For that reason, many collectors and writers have often set their goals to one or more particular types of American coinage. This has created a need for a comprehensive detailing of those types to assist a collector or writer in delving more deeply into the attributes of such coinage. It enables both the comparison of coins to a standard within a type and a comparison of types of one period with those of another.

Numismatic literature in the past has continually added to clarification of various American coin types, but at present computer science has widened the availability and storage of knowledge of old and new manuscripts, printed records, and images to such an extent that the opportunity of enlarged fact sources and corrections of assumptions is open to everyone with a desire to investigate.

My friend, Q. David Bowers, whom I have watched develop and use his abilities for over half a century, has crystallized the United States coin type distinctions in this volume. It will be a standard to help collectors and scholars to enjoy their endeavors more fully. It is a privilege to welcome another of his masterful pieces of numismatic literature.

Eric P. Newman
St. Louis, Missouri

Eric P. Newman (1911–2017), born in St. Louis, Missouri, was drawn to numismatics as a child after his maternal grandfather gave him an 1859 Indian Head cent. Later, St. Louis coin dealer Burdette G. Johnson encouraged him to learn more about coins than simply how to form a collection. In the 1940s Newman acquired significant portions of the collection of Colonel E.H.R. Green. In that decade he also embarked on becoming one of the greatest scholars in American numismatics: his first publication in the field, on paper currency of Missouri, came in 1941. In the years that followed he wrote on colonial coinage, early American paper money, counterfeit detection, and many other topics. The Eric P. Newman Numismatic Education Society describes his methods: "Newman's research activities were pure 'old school'—personal visits to libraries and historical societies scattered throughout the country, voluminous correspondence with archivists and fellow collectors, and the accumulation of research files on hundreds of topics." Newman and his wife Evelyn (married in 1939) supported each other in a variety of philanthropic efforts focusing on medical research, academia, and St. Louis cultural affairs. After he spent nearly a century as a collector, his holdings were featured in a series of sales by Heritage Auctions beginning in 2013. Today, the Newman Numismatic Portal (online at https://nnp.wustl.edu) extends his legacy of scholarly research by making freely available the largest online archive of numismatic information in the world.

PREFACE

A New Kind of Type-Coin Book

The first edition of the *Guide Book of United States Type Coins*, by Q. David Bowers, was published in early 2005. This wasn't the first time the broad panoply of American coinage had been gathered into a single volume. A few predecessors include the following:

- *Walter Breen's Complete Encyclopedia of U.S. and Colonial Coins*, popularly known in the hobby simply as "Breen," was published in 1988.
- Before that, *The History of United States Coinage as Illustrated by the Garrett Collection*, also by Bowers, had debuted in 1979.
- And of course, the granddaddies of all hobby-oriented single-volume U.S. coin books had been published, more or less annually, since 1946 (the *Guide Book of United States Coins*, a retail price guide known as the "Red Book") and, before that, since 1942 (the *Handbook of United States Coins*, a wholesale guide called the "Blue Book").

So, this was not the first publication of every American coinage type in a single reference. But it was the first book to approach, specifically and with the hobbyist in mind, the subject of building a collection of U.S. "type coins"—that is, a grouping of specimens, each one carefully chosen to represent an entire design type. This is distinct from building a collection of every date and mintmark within those types.

The Popularity of Collecting By Type

Collecting U.S. coins by type has been popular for generations. "Such a pursuit is hardly new," Bowers would write years later in the foreword to Robert W. Shippee's *Pleasure and Profit: 100 Lessons for Building and Selling a Collection of Rare Coins*. "In fact, it is one of the most popular ways to collect." Since the boom in U.S. coin folders and albums started in the 1930s, most major manufacturers have included "type set" holders in their product lines.

Collecting in this way gives a hobbyist well-defined goals. It is affordable. It also offers many ways to customize a personally meaningful collection. "Such a display would be a virtual panorama of American coinage from the earliest days to the present," as Bowers says. "Along the way, you would have specimens from each of the major engravers, examples of each denomination, and all of the different design variations. You could flip through the pages of any reference book and, upon seeing a picture of a type, say, 'I have one of those!'"

A date-and-mintmark collection of Liberty Head gold eagles would consist of nearly 200 coins and would cost hundreds of thousands of dollars. In a type collection a single beautiful example represents the entire series, much more affordably.

Creating the *Guide Book*

We billed the *Guide Book of United States Type Coins* as "A Complete History and Price Guide for the Collector and

Investor." In true Bowers style, it was just that, with historical overviews of more than 20 coin denominations, from copper half cents through gold double eagles; and advice on collecting the 100-plus coin types within each of those denominations. Bowers offered a lifetime career's worth of ideas, inspiration, and guidance on how to build a significant coin collection while learning a heck of a lot about American history and having fun along the way.

Large cents of 1816 to 1857 used to be classified as the Coronet type, further described as Matron Head (1816–1835) and Young Head (1835–1857). Today they're categorized as the Liberty Head design, of the Matron Head (1816–1835), Matron Head Modified (1835–1839, the old "Young Head"), and Braided Hair (1839–1857) types.

The process of organizing, writing, and editing the first edition of the *Guide Book of United States Type Coins* was an immersion in numismatic master-planning. This was one of the earliest books released in the modern renaissance of numismatic publishing that started around 2003, the year Dave Bowers took the role of numismatic director at Whitman Publishing. I joined the company as its publisher in 2004, and, together with *Red Book* editor Kenneth Bressett, valuations editor Jeff Garrett, Whitman senior editor Diana Plattner, and others, we carefully studied our flagship book (the *Red Book*) and its terminology, organization, and information architecture.

I remember well the many conversations we had on what constitutes a "type" versus a "subtype" or "variety." Nomenclature wasn't completely standardized within the hobby community. (It still isn't, today.) Was the Braided Hair large cent properly divided into the Young Head and Matron Head types? Was the half cent of 1840 to 1857 the Coronet type, or the Braided Hair type? Did Christian Gobrecht's nineteenth-century silver coins show "Seated Liberty" or "Liberty Seated"? Some writers referred to Franklin half dollars as the "Franklin Head" type. Should *trade dollar* be capitalized or not? Much of this terminology had long been standardized within the *Red Book* and the *Blue Book*, but Dave Bowers's study and classification of coin types for his new book revealed opportunities for clarification and, in some cases, change.

All of this discussion was very useful as we were also organizing a comprehensive new "Whitman Style Guide" to apply across the width and breadth of all the company's books, folders, albums, and other hobby products.

Launches, Updates, and Companions

We published the first edition of the *Guide Book of United States Type Coins* in January 2005, debuting it at the Florida United Numismatists convention held in Fort Lauderdale. It was a popular and critical success, selling briskly and earning the Numismatic Literary Guild's award for "Best Specialized Book on United States Coins."

The second edition followed in 2008, with updated market values, auction records, and certified-population data; improved photographs; cleaner typesetting; the addition of new coin types (Presidential dollars, Westward Journey nickels, and State quarters); a new section on "Great Collectors and Collections of the Past" (by Ron Guth and Jeff Garrett); new historical illustrations; a bibliography; and a bullion-value chart for determining the precious-metal values of common-date gold and silver coins.

In the meantime, Whitman published another book that addresses hobbyists' interest in the type-set approach to collecting. Ron Guth and Jeff Garrett wrote the beautifully illustrated coffee-table book *United States Coinage: A Study by Type*, which was also published in 2005. "One need not own a single cent to possess a wealth of knowledge about it," retired Louisiana congressman Jimmy Hayes observed in that book's foreword.

Robert W. Shippee's *Pleasure and Profit* debuted in 2014. Shippee, over the course of several years, had assembled a remarkable collection of about 150 U.S. coins by type, from half cents to double eagles. In his book he shared the lessons he learned along the way—lessons that came from costly mistakes as well as from profitable purchases. His collection sold for more than $1.5 million; his total gain after commissions, holding the coins for about 10 years, was nearly 40 percent. As you read *Pleasure and Profit*, though, you come to realize that his "profits" were far greater than just financial.

Type-Coin Collecting Today

Type-coin collecting is as popular as ever today. In an informal survey of 100 coin collectors in early 2019, I found that 15 percent had formed a "one of everything" type-coin collection, and almost as many had assembled the same collection except, more affordably, without gold coins. One out of every four had formed a nineteenth- or twentieth-century type set. Nearly 20 percent had built more than one kind of type set. Respondents talked enthusiastically about their rainbow-toned dollar type sets, their slabbed type sets, Proof Barber types, and other personally significant collections. Some mentioned the competitive registry sets maintained by PCGS and NGC, which have thousands of active participants in their "Type Set" categories. (In April 2019 PCGS had 10,427 type sets registered, and NGC had 5,713. Categories include complete sets of U.S. circulation-strike coins; nineteenth- and twentieth-century Proof types; first-year-of-issue type sets; and many others—more than 100 different ways to form a type collection by design, era, denomination, mint, and other classifications.)

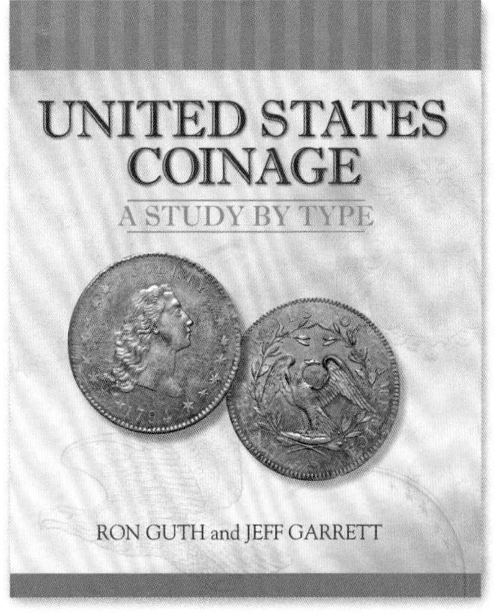

85 percent of the collectors I polled had completed or at least started a collection of U.S. coins by type.

For these enthusiasts and thousands of others actively collecting in 2019, we've updated the entirety of the *Guide Book of United States Type Coins* in a substantially revised third edition. The entire book has been reformatted to make it easier to read and navigate. Market values have been updated to provide a snapshot of the financial side of forming a type-coin collection. The historical price charts, too, have been updated, showing the paths, up and down, of each coin type over the past 70-plus years. We've incorporated the latest numismatic research, modified some of the older editions' categories and chapters, and included the most recent new coin designs. We've also added a new appendix on Philippine coins struck under U.S. sovereignty, which can easily be collected by type and which form an attractive and historically important section of American coinage.

Silver pesos struck for the Philippines under U.S. sovereignty can be collected by date and mint (they were struck in Philadelphia and San Francisco), or by type, just as Morgan dollars can be.

It might be said that a numismatic author starts a book when he writes his manuscript, but his readers finish it when they build their collections. I believe the third edition of the *Guide Book of United States Type Coins* will inspire many collectors to join with Dave Bowers in creating their own unique chapters—their type-coin collections—in this engaging hobby pursuit.

Dennis Tucker
Publisher,
Whitman Publishing, LLC

Introduction

Collecting United States coins by design types is in many ways an *ideal* numismatic pursuit. Such a quest involves finding one of each major motif in the vast and fascinating panorama of American coinage from the first full year of Philadelphia Mint operation in 1793, down to the present day.

The scene is ever changing. Within the past decades, we have had many new design types, including the short-lived and varied statehood reverses on circulating quarter dollars, the innovative Sacagawea dollar begun in 2000, and the new 2004 and 2005 Jefferson nickel designs.

In the best-case scenario, it would be nice to collect one of everything—a specimen of each date and mintmark and major variety from the 1793 copper half cent through other copper coins, plus nickel, silver, and gold, to the present day. In actuality, only one person has ever done this: Louis E. Eliasberg, the famous Baltimore numismatist, began his interest circa 1925, and by 1950 had one each of every known date and mint—including the unique 1870-S $3, one of just three known 1822 $5 gold coins (the other two are presently in the Smithsonian), and more, including such famous rarities as the 1913 Liberty Head nickel, 1894-S dime, 1838-O half dollar, 1804 silver dollar, 1885 trade dollar, and everything else—even the rare 1933 $20.

Eliasberg was in the right place at the right time, as the incredible old-time collections of John H. Clapp, Col. Edward H.R. Green, Virgil M. Brand, and others were coming on the market. Moreover, Eliasberg was both a man of means and an astute numismatist with an eye on investment. I had the honor of knowing Mr. Eliasberg personally, and also his two sons, Louis Jr., and Richard. In autumn 1975 Louis Sr., gave a talk at Evergreen House in Baltimore, the Garrett family home donated in 1942 to The Johns Hopkins University. The title of his presentation was, "Why, When, and How I Assembled the Most Complete Collection of United States Coins." A few selected comments:

> If you are a numismatist or coin collector, I hope you will derive the degree of pleasure and happiness I have in assembling my collection.
>
> In making your purchases you should buy them through reputable dealers. If you invest any significant portion of your assets in rare coins, be sure that you are thoroughly familiar with all aspects of such an operation.
>
> The profitability of collecting coins can be measured in part by my own experience. . . . Based on our recent appraisal [1975] I find that I have averaged a minimum return of over 11.9% a year on the original cost.

After Mr. Eliasberg's passing in 1976, his family selected me and my firm to auction his coins, and what a thrill this was! In sum, all of his United States coins, which had cost him slightly over $300,000, yielded over $40,000,000 at auction! And, perhaps even better from an emotional viewpoint, during his lifetime, he enjoyed numismatics to its fullest—ever willing to display his coins, answer questions, and help in other ways. Numismatics became a very rich and rewarding part of his life.

Today, even if you had an unlimited budget and a quarter century of time to spend, you could not obtain such a complete collection, as some pieces are simply not available. Moreover, prices have risen so much, and distribution of available coins has become so wide, that it would be impossible for this reason as well.

A very nice alternative is to form a type set. You may never own a 1913 Liberty Head nickel. However, you can enjoy the Liberty Head nickel series just the same, by purchasing for your type set a glittering gem Mint State or mirror-finish Proof of 1910, 1911, 1912, or some other date—all being exactly the same as the fabled 1913 except for the last one or two digits. All the elements of the design, lettering, and other aspects are the same.

Once you have your gem 1912 or other Liberty Head nickel tucked away, this type can be crossed off your list, and it is off to seek a specimen of the silver trade dollar, minted 1873 to 1885. The 1885 is super rare, the 1884 is very rare, and even the 1878-CC is hard to find. But such considerations concern you not, for you are seeking a representative of the design type, and that may be a Mint State 1874-S, or a Proof 1878, or some other date that is at once affordable and beautiful.

There is no "right" or "wrong" as to what to include in a type set. In this book, I list different coins that traditionally have been considered as major types, but you can do your own finessing. Similarly, there are no rules as to what grades to buy. If I were building a type set, I would be delighted to have a nice EF-40 example to illustrate the Draped Bust copper cent design of 1796 to 1807, but you might want an AU, someone else might have heard that "Mint State is the best way to go," and another person will be satisfied with a well-worn VG-8 grade.

You might want to collect all coin types from 1793 to date, or you might want to start with issues of the twentieth century. You may want to include gold coins, or perhaps you want to limit your acquisitions to copper, nickel, and silver coins. And, of course, dozens of different types minted in the past few decades are available inexpensively, including in gem grades—giving you a running start!

These choices are all up to you. Whatever you select, each coin is a part not only of numismatic Americana, but also of American life. Each coin is different, and each has its own story to tell.

Although collecting coins by design types is hardly a new idea, it became especially popular circa 1960, a pivotal era in the rare-coin market. In that year, *Coin World* became the first weekly periodical, and its availability spurred unprecedented hobby interest. At the same time, the "rare" 1960 Small Date cent captured the attention of news media and created a nationwide sensation (several bags containing $50 face value of these cents had been sold for over $12,000 per bag—exciting stuff!). In the next few years, hundreds of thousands of new faces entered the market. The supply of coins was spread even wider, and no longer was it feasible to collect Indian Head cents, Morgan silver dollars, Barber silver coins, and just about everything else by date and mint.

At the same time, a new "Library of Coins" album series for copper, nickel, and silver type coins was marketed by the Coin & Currency Institute (Robert Friedberg). These albums were very popular, and I recall selling them about as fast as they could be ordered. In the same era, other albums were available as were many attractive plastic display holders for the type collector.

Today, collecting coins by design types is an established part of numismatics, one that attracts many enthusiasts. The pleasures of forming a type set await you in the pages ahead. Enjoy!

Q. David Bowers
Wolfeboro, New Hampshire

1
A Concise History of U.S. Coinage

Introduction

As you commence building a type set of United States coins, a panorama of American denominations and designs awaits you. In this chapter, I give some basics of United States coinage, including mints, metals, designers, and more—a concise guide to coinage from the 1790s to the present. As you might suspect, there are so many aspects of American coinage that a thousand pages could be devoted to the subject and not cover them all. Here I endeavor to catch the high spots, especially with reference to the evolution of coin designs—the emphasis of the present book.

You can skip this chapter if you are already familiar with the concepts, as you may be if you've been collecting for a year or two, or if you have read and absorbed *A Guide Book of United States Coins* (the Red Book) from cover to cover.

Or, linger here to refresh your memory or perhaps learn a few new things.

Foreign Coins in Early America

After colonists arrived from Europe to settle in what is now the United States, they set about everyday activities including farming, hunting, building homes and stores, and manufacturing useful items. Serving as money were many things, including coins from Europe as well as barter items, the last being quite varied and ranging from musket balls to corn to cows.

In time, the silver and gold issues of Spain and her New World possessions became the most popular foreign coins in American circulation. Most such pieces were made in Central America and South America, at mints in Mexico (in particular), Chile, Peru, and other Spanish possessions, where vast amounts of precious metal were continually mined.

The Spanish-American coins were denominated in *reales* and *escudos.* Silver coins of one real were valued at 12-1/2 cents and were familiarly called *bits.* The eight-real piece was called a dollar, or Spanish dollar, and became the foundation of the monetary system. Years later, during the American Revolution, the paper bills of the Continental Congress were denominated in Spanish dollars. Most popular of the smaller denominations was the two-real coin, or two bits, worth 25¢. The "two bits" term is still in use today for a United States quarter dollar, although few know its origin. Other popular Spanish-American silver coins included the one-half real, called a *medio*, worth 6-1/4 cents, and the four-real piece.

Gold coins of Spanish America were valued in escudos worth $2 each. An eight-escudo coin, valued at $16, was popularly called a *doubloon* (this being worth 16 times more than a dollar in silver). We know this term today in connection with pirate treasure and related lore. The term "pieces of eight" has no precise meaning and can refer either to eight-real or dollar coins or to eight-escudo doubloons, or their fractional parts. In some instances, eight-real coins were cut apart into eight sections, like slicing a pie, and each "piece" was valued at one real, this being done when smaller denomination coins were not readily available. In the early nineteenth century, the Planters Bank of New Orleans produced many such silver wedges from dollar-size coins and stamped each with a distinctive *PB* mark.

Coins of Britain, Holland, Italy, Portugal, and other European nations also circulated widely in colonial America. There were hundreds of different combinations of silver and gold coin denominations, types, and issuers, and the purity (fineness) of coins varied considerably. To keep track of this, merchants relied upon charts listing coin values and used balance scales to be sure that coins were of approximately correct weight. Just about every leading newspaper had a column titled "Prices Current," which listed the values of commodities and, often, silver, and gold coins.

After the Revolution, certain foreign gold and silver coins were given official legal-tender status by the United States government, these including the aforementioned Spanish-American issues. At first there were no federal American coins available. After their production began in 1792 (in the form of silver half dismes), it took decades until there was an abundant supply in circulation. In the meantime, designated silver and gold foreign coins were used widely. The Act of February 21, 1857, provided that the legal tender status of foreign issues would expire in two years (subsequently extended for an additional six months), after which time only United States coins would be used. It might come as a surprise to learn that a person shopping at a dry-goods store in downtown New York City in, say, 1800, was likely to see many Spanish-American silver coins but few if any United States pieces.

EARLY AMERICAN COINAGE

The first coinage produced in what would become the United States was under the aegis of the Massachusetts Bay Colony, which in 1652 provided for the making of silver coins based on the British monetary system. Soon, silver coins of threepence, sixpence, and shilling (12 pence), designated on the coins as III, VI, and XII, were in circulation in and around Boston. These pieces were simple in their appearance and were made under primitive circumstances. An approximately circular planchet was cut from a strip of silver, weighed, and, if it was too heavy, some excess metal was snipped off the edge. A planchet would then be stamped NE (for New England) on one end, then turned over and stamped with XII or another denomination at the opposite end, so as not to obliterate the first stamp. Soon, the Massachusetts coins became more sophisticated, through designs now known as the Willow Tree, Oak Tree, and, finally, Pine Tree motifs. The latter were coined as late as the 1680s, but most retained the 1652 date of their authorization. By this time, they were a familiar sight in commerce throughout the Northeast.

In time, other colonies produced coins or had them made under contract, as did some private individuals and companies. In 1658 and 1659 coins depicting Cecil Calvert were struck in England for the Maryland colony, in denominations of four, six, and 12 pence. During the period 1722 to 1724, William Wood, an English entrepreneur, obtained a license (or patent) from the British Crown allowing him to strike coins for circulation in the New World. These pieces, of halfpenny, penny, and two-pence values, bore the portrait of King George I and, on the reverse, the inscription ROSA AMERICANA, or "American rose." Wood also struck copper halfpennies and pennies for circulation in Ireland, but is said to have shipped many to America as well.

After the Revolutionary War, several states produced their own copper coins, the first being Vermont and Connecticut in 1785, followed by New Jersey in 1786 and Massachusetts in 1787. Each of these coinages was short-lived. The largest production was created by Connecticut under contract with private individuals. Today, well over 300 different die combinations are known for Connecticut coppers of dates from 1785 to 1788, and thousands of pieces exist and are highly prized.

In the 1790s, many different tokens and medalets, mostly struck in England, were made with the portrait of George Washington and were popular in circulation. Many other coinages could be mentioned. In 1875 they formed the focus of a landmark book, *Early Coins of America*, by Sylvester S. Crosby, which, remarkably, remains as the standard text on the subject today, although much other information is to be found elsewhere.

Early Federal Coins

In 1776 a pewter dollar was struck, depicting on one side a sundial and the word FUGIO (for "I fly," referring to the rapid passage of time), with CONTINENTAL CURRENCY around the border. On the reverse, a series of rings bore state names and abbreviations. The design was taken from a paper bill issued by the Continental Congress. Curiously, today no documentation has been found concerning this coinage, how the contract (if there was one) was awarded by the Continental Congress, or how many were made.

In the 1780s, Robert Morris, Thomas Jefferson, and others corresponded about and discussed a national mint. In 1783 a few patterns were made, mostly in silver, the highest value being 1000 units or a mark. However, no federal mint was established at that time.

In 1787 James Jarvis, an entrepreneur, was awarded a federal contract to strike copper coins, today called Fugio cents, and bearing a sundial motif somewhat similar to the design of the 1776 Continental dollar. Many were made, and they circulated widely.

In the 1780s and especially in the early 1790s, there were several proposals for other contract coinages. The federal government had little in the way of manufacturing expertise and owned no buildings. It was logical that the making of coins be delegated to the private sector, similar to the manufacture of guns, furniture, paper, and other items needed. Several individuals and firms in the United States and England produced tokens or coins on speculation, seeking a contract, including several varieties dated 1791 and 1792 depicting President George Washington.

The first Philadelphia Mint, built in 1792, was used until 1833. This photograph was taken in 1854, by which time the building had been converted to other uses. Many coins were struck within its walls.

ESTABLISHING THE MINT

The Mint Act of April 2, 1792, provided for the establishment of a federal coining facility. The legislation also established a monetary system based on dollars and the decimal system, and gave weights and finenesses for various issues from the copper half cent to the gold $10 or eagle.

On July 31, 1792, in Philadelphia, then the seat of the federal government, the cornerstone was laid for the Mint, consisting of two main buildings. In the meantime, in July, silver five-cent pieces, called half dismes (the *disme* designation, used at first, was later changed to dime, the term used today), were struck for the government at the workshop of John Harper, a local sawmaker and machinist. It is believed that 1,500 were made. As to whether they should be included in a type set of United States coins is a matter for discussion, because they were not produced within the Mint. However, they do stand as the first official government coins made after the Mint Act of April 2, 1792, and for that reason I include them here.

WORK AT THE MINT

In 1792 equipment stored with Harper was moved into the partially completed Mint, and limited work began there. Pattern coins dated 1792 were made, although today little is known about them, save for what can be determined by examining the coins themselves. Certain copper cents are signed BIRCH on the obverse, but the first name of Birch is not known. These are of the same general appearance as the aforementioned 1792 half dismes, indicating the dies were probably by the same hand. A pattern disme or ten-cent piece was made, as was a curious small-diameter, silver-center cent, the silver being inserted as a plug to bring the planchet up to nearly a full cent in metal value. We do know that another pattern, this perhaps for a quarter dollar, featuring the head of Miss Liberty on the obverse, and on the reverse an eagle standing on the top of a globe, was done by an unknown artist and engraver. The work was long attributed by numismatists to Joseph Wright, but modern research casts uncertainty.

In the Mint buildings, there were facilities for processing metal, including refining copper, silver, and gold to the purity or alloy proportions required by law, and for rolling metal ingots into long strips from which coinage discs or planchets were cut. Dies were made at the Mint, by hand, using punches and engraving tools, cutting the designs into the end of a tapered soft steel blank. After completion, dies were hardened, then dressed or finished for use. Coins were struck on hand-operated presses. Each had a weighted lever-arm with straps attached. Two men tugged on the straps, causing a screw mechanism to drive the top or *hammer die* down to a blank planchet resting on the fixed bottom or *anvil die.*

Mint Policies for Different Metals

In time, coins would be struck in copper (beginning in 1793), silver (1794), and gold (1795). Copper was purchased by the Mint for its own account, converted into coins, and the Mint would retain any profit made. Accordingly, there was a continual search for copper and an enthusiasm for processing it.

On the other hand, silver and gold coins were produced under a completely different arrangement, whereby banks, merchants, and others would bring metal to the Mint. The deposit would be analyzed (assayed), refined to create alloy suitable for coinage, and, in time, silver and gold coins would be delivered to the depositor in whatever denominations had been requested, a process for which a small fee would be charged. Silver and gold deposits in the early days were mostly composed of foreign coins. Later, bullion from mines and refineries was deposited in quantity.

As depositors of silver and gold could specify the denominations desired, this resulted in erratic production over a long period of time (until after the Act of February 21, 1853, when the government bought silver for its own account). Generally, depositors preferred larger coins as they were more easily stored and counted. Accordingly, during the 1790s, the largest silver denomination, the dollar, was produced in the largest quantities and most consistently. Production of other silver coins was irregular, as, for example, a small quantity of quarter dollars in 1796, but no others until 1804. This Mint policy for silver and gold coins has a direct effect on the availability of many coins needed for a type set, and thus this aspect, not widely mentioned elsewhere in numismatic texts, is worth noting here. Conversely, as copper coins were made for the Mint's own account and usually recorded a profit, production over a long period of years tended to be consistent.

The Coinage of 1793

The Philadelphia Mint was ready for business in February 1793, and in that month, the first copper cents were struck for circulation. These bore on the obverse the head of Miss Liberty and on the reverse a chain of 15 links, one for each state. The dies were simple in their art. The very first reverse was lettered UNITED STATES OF AMERI., as the engraver would have spoiled the symmetry if the last word had been spelled out in full. The next die was done differently, the engraver planned ahead, and UNITED STATES OF AMERICA fit comfortably in the space allotted.

Complaints arose concerning the motif, with the chain viewed as an "ill omen" for a country that had just secured its liberty. The design was changed to what we now know as the Wreath cent, with Miss Liberty restyled on the obverse and with a very ornate wreath on the reverse. The new dies displayed superb artistry, although a botanist would find it quite curious that on the coin olive leaves and maple leaves are attached to the same branch!

In July 1793, copper half cents of the Liberty Cap design were made at the Mint, imitating a motif adapted from the famous Libertas Americana medal commissioned by Benjamin Franklin and struck in Paris from dies engraved by Augustin Dupré. Today, we do not know who cut the dies for the Liberty Cap half cent—whether a Mint employee (there was no designated official engraver on staff) or, more likely, an artist in the private sector, possibly Joseph Wright.

In the summer of 1793, Wright was hired as an engraver. Trained as an artist, Wright was highly skilled. In 1784 he painted the figure of General George Washington from life. In 1792 he may have been the creator of the aforementioned eagle-on-globe pattern quarter dollar, a coin of rare beauty when viewed today. At the Mint in August 1793, Wright cut the dies for the Liberty Cap copper cent, similar to the half cent, but with the head facing to the right instead of to the left. Not long afterward, Philadelphia was ravaged by yellow fever, and in September one of the victims was Wright. No doubt had he lived, the contents of a type set of early Mint coins would appear vastly different from what we know today.

The edges of the first copper cents had a design composed of vines and vertical bars. Soon, this was changed, and edge lettering was employed: TWO HUNDRED FOR A DOLLAR on the half cent and ONE HUNDRED FOR A DOLLAR on the cents.

THE COINAGE OF 1794

The production of copper half cents and cents, begun in 1793, continued with vigor in 1794, both employing the Liberty Cap motif. It was anticipated that the half cent would become a staple in commerce, but by a generation later its use had diminished, and such pieces mostly vanished from the American scene.

In the same year dies were cut for several new denominations—the silver half dime, half dollar, and dollar. The obverse of each depicted Miss Liberty facing right, with rich tresses streaming downward to the back—what today is called the Flowing Hair type. The reverse displayed an eagle perched on a rock, with a wreath and lettering around.

It was important that the blank planchets for silver coins be the correct weight. Those falling short of the standard would be melted down and recycled, in effect wasting the time earlier spent in making ingots and strips. It was more feasible to make the planchets slightly overweight, and then file away the extra metal until the standard was reached. In the early years of the Mint, this was standard practice for silver and, later, gold coins. Today, many of these coins show these "adjustment marks," as they are called, usually at the rims or on the higher parts of the design.

The first silver coin production consisted of 5,300 half dollars and 1,758 silver dollars delivered in October. In February 1795, 18,164 half dollars were delivered from 1794-dated dies. The silver dollar production was an unfortunate affair, as the Mint did not have a press of proper capacity to strike this large-diameter denomination. Accordingly, all known specimens dated 1794 are lightly struck on the star centers at the lower left.

THE COINAGE OF 1795 AND 1796

Although dies for the silver five-cent piece or half dime had been prepared in 1794, no coinage ensued in that year. In 1795, the 1794-dated half dime dies were used for the first time. In the early years, the Mint kept using dies until they cracked or wore out. As the Mint reported its production on a calendar-year basis, but as earlier-dated dies were sometimes used in a later calendar year, mintage figures for the first decade or so cannot be directly related to coins bearing specific dates.

In 1795 the first gold coins were struck at the Mint, half eagles or $5 gold pieces, the first 744 of which were delivered on July 31. Additional half eagles, plus $10 gold eagles, were subsequently made. The obverse featured Miss Liberty wearing a truncated conical cloth cap, and the reverse illustrated a delicately engraved eagle perched on a palm branch and holding a wreath aloft.

In the meantime, the weight standard for copper coins was lowered, and most of the half cents and cents made in 1795 were to the new specifications, on thinner planchets and with plain instead of lettered edges, yielding more profit for the Mint's in-house account. Half dimes were made for the first time, from dies dated 1794, as noted, and also from dies bearing the 1795 date. Half dollars were made from dies with the same two dates, but the majority were from new 1795 dies.

By late spring 1795, a large-capacity press was in operation, and production of silver dollars resumed, this time without any problems. Toward the end of the year, a new motif was prepared, the Draped Bust style, and at least two obverse dies were made for dollars and at least one for the silver half dime. The half dime die was not used, and in the next year, 1796, a 6 was cut over the 5, creating one of the first *overdates* in American coinage, known as the 1796, 6 Over 5, overdate. Certain of the Draped Bust dollars were carefully struck and have mirrorlike surfaces.

In early 1796, copper cents were made of the standard Liberty Cap design. Later in the year, the style was changed to the Draped Bust motif. Given designs were sometimes adopted at different times across various denominations. Draped Bust half dimes, dimes, quarters, half dollars, and dollars were made in 1796, the dime and quarter dollar being new denominations. All of the quarter dollars were made from highly polished dies, as were some of the other silver denominations. Interestingly, the Draped Bust design was not used on half cents until 1800.

The $2.50 gold coin, or quarter eagle, made its debut in 1796, with a reverse design not used elsewhere until later: the Heraldic Eagle motif, patterned after the Great Seal of the United States. This had been used on privately struck tokens before the Mint era, including on copper tokens of Washington made in 1791 and 1792. Later, it would be employed on all silver and gold denominations. The Heraldic Eagle proved to be enduring, and in various incarnations it has been used intermittently ever since.

In 1796, a 1796, 6 Over 5, $5 eagle was created by overpunching an existing 1795 die. It is seen that *sometimes* the Mint overdated earlier dies, as here and also with the earlier-mentioned 1796, 6 Over 5, half dime, but other times used earlier-dated dies without change. Various explanations have been advanced for using two different procedures, one theory being that dies that were engraved, but not hardened for use, could be overdated easily, while dies that had been made and hardened could not be, unless they underwent a softening and rehardening procedure.

During this time, silver and gold coins were valued in commerce by their weight and purity. Certain of the federal denominations, including the silver half dimes, dimes, quarters, and all of the gold coins, bore no indication of their value! On the other hand, a copper cent of 1794 had the value given *three times:* as ONE HUNDRED FOR A DOLLAR on the edge, as ONE CENT within the wreath on the reverse, and also as the fraction 1/100. One of the pleasures of forming a type set is being able to compare the features of many different denominations side by side.

THE COINAGE OF 1797-1806

By 1797 all of the denominations authorized under the Mint Act of April 2, 1792, were in circulation: the copper half cent and cent; the silver half dime, dime, quarter, half dollar, and dollar; and the gold $2.50, $5, and $10. However, quantities were small in comparison to the needs of commerce, and Spanish-American silver and gold coins remained dominant. Half dimes and dimes were still called *half dismes* and *dismes* in some government reports, and would continue to be, with diminishing frequency, for decades afterward, although not on the coins themselves. In the late 1830s, for the first time, coin inscriptions said HALF DIME and DIME.

Copper coins were struck each year, these a mainstay of Mint profits. In calendar year 1799, official records gave the production figure of cents as 904,585, but today cents of the 1799 date are great rarities—by far the most elusive in the entire copper cent series from 1793 to 1857. Likely, all but a few thousand cents struck this year were from still usable 1798-dated dies on hand. No half cents were made with the dates 1798 or 1799.

Most depositors of silver requested dollars, and accordingly, production of lower denominations was sporadic. Among gold coins, half eagles and eagles were both popular, while far fewer quarter eagles, this being the smallest value, were made. In the half eagle series, the Heraldic Eagle reverse made its first appearance in 1798. However, certain 1795 eagles have this motif—the result of a 1795-dated obverse die being on hand in 1798 and used in that year, a curiosity mentioned earlier.

In the early nineteenth century, many American silver and gold coins were exported, this being particularly true of the dollar and eagle. The director of the Mint mandated that no more dollars or eagles be made after 1804. Because of this, no silver dollars were again made until 1836 and no eagles until 1838. The highest silver denomination became the half dollar and the highest gold the half eagle, resulting in these being struck in record quantities afterward.

JOHN REICH'S NEW DESIGNS OF 1807-1808

In 1807 John Reich was hired as an assistant engraver to work with Robert Scot. His "Capped Bust" design, as we call it today, was used on the half dollar and half eagle, followed by employment on the quarter eagle (1808), dime (1809), and quarter (1815). Miss Liberty faces to the left and wears a soft cloth cap, sometimes called a *mob cap.* Half dimes had not been made since 1805, as depositors of silver had not requested them. It was not until 1829 that Capped Bust coins of this denomination were made, the first being struck on July 4 and some used in the cornerstone laying ceremony for the new or second Philadelphia Mint (which would be occupied beginning in 1833).

After the Capped Bust design was used on the quarter eagle in 1808, no more coins of this gold denomination were struck until 1821, by which time the motif had been modified. Thus, the 1808 $2.50, of which only 2,710 were struck, became a rarity well known to later generations of numismatists. Today, it is a key to forming a gold type set, the oriflamme of the entire Capped Bust coinage series.

Reich also created what we call the "Classic Head" design today, featuring Miss Liberty facing to the left, with a band inscribed LIBERTY across her head, with hair tresses visible above. This motif was first used on cents of 1808 and continued there through 1814. On half cents, the Classic Head first appeared in 1809, and it was used for a long time afterward, on the intermittent coinage through 1836. In 1834, when chief engraver William A. Kneass made dies for the new Classic Head quarter eagles and half eagles, he appropriated Reich's motif of 1808.

Reich remained at the Mint until 1817, when he resigned to pursue other interests. In time his coinage became a numismatic specialty. Many of Reich's obverse dies have a small notch in the 13th star, leading to the conclusion that this was his secret sign, called a *privy mark* in numismatic nomenclature, to identify his work.

The Coinage of 1809-1834

The Mint hired Robert Scot after Joseph Wright's death in 1793. Scot remained as chief engraver until his death in 1823. Records are sparse as to the identities of other engravers who may have assisted him after John Reich left in 1817. In any event, in the later years of Scot's tenure, changes in designs were limited, including the preparation of a new quarter eagle die in 1821, by adapting the motif already in use on the half eagle.

As silver dollars and gold eagles were not being coined, the half dollar and half eagle were the basis for commerce. From 1821 through and including July 1834, no gold coins were seen in domestic circulation, as the value of gold had risen in relation to silver, and newly-minted quarter eagles and half eagles were worth more than face value. Large numbers of half eagles were struck, plus a smaller number of quarter eagles, at the request of depositors of gold bullion. Each of these coins traded at bullion and exchange offices for a premium. Most half eagles were sent overseas, valued at their gold content and not at face amount, where they were used to settle accounts. Many were hoarded in the Philadelphia vaults of the Second Bank of the United States, not exchanged for paper money, then turned into the Mint in 1834 at a profit (the Mint paid the bullion value, which was more than the face value).

At their foreign destinations, nearly all half eagles exported from America were melted and the metal used to strike other coins. As an example, half eagles sent to England, Europe's main commercial center, would be melted down and the bullion used to strike British gold sovereigns. Accordingly, absolutely no half eagles were used in domestic commerce, but all went into the hands of speculators, were stored in bank vaults, or were employed in foreign exchange, and all half eagles of the 1821 to 1834 era are extremely rare today, despite high mintages. Perhaps most remarkable in this context is the 1822 half eagle, for which a production figure of 17,176 is listed in the *Annual*

Report of the Director of the Mint. Only three specimens are known today, of which two are in the Smithsonian Institution and the third is the highlight of a private collection.

Members of the Senate and House of Representatives had the privilege of requesting and obtaining their salaries in gold coins. Probably, most quarter eagles of the 1820s and early 1830s were used for this purpose. However, they were not spent at face value, but realized a profit for their owners by being sold to exchange dealers. In the meantime, silver half dollars of the Capped Bust design were made in large quantities and were the main larger-denomination federal coins in commerce. Still, there were not enough such coins to supply the need, and the majority of silver issues in circulation, overwhelming the Capped Bust halves, were Spanish-American two-real ("two bit") and eight-real (dollar) coins. Just about every ship sailing out of New Orleans, Charleston, Baltimore, Philadelphia, New York City, Boston, Salem, or Portsmouth, and destined to buy goods in China, the East Indies, the Caribbean, or elsewhere, carried thousands of Spanish silver dollars for this purpose.

The aforementioned William Kneass, an engraver of bank-note plates and other items, was appointed chief engraver on January 29, 1824, after the death of Robert Scot. He engaged in various routine duties and is not known to have turned out any coin or medal designs of lasting artistic note. Indeed, certain creative work was farmed out to local engravers in the private sector, most notably the talented Christian Gobrecht, who furnished letter punches and who cut the dies for the highly acclaimed Franklin Institute medal, the Charles Carroll medal, and others.

In 1825 Mint Director Samuel Moore wrote to President John Quincy Adams and solicited his permission "to introduce, in the character of assistant engraver, Christian Gobrecht of this city, an artist of great merit." However, Gobrecht remained as a private contractor, and routine engraving work at the Mint continued to be performed by Kneass. In 1833 the Philadelphia Mint was relocated to a handsome new building in the Greek Revival architectural style, designed by William Strickland, where operations continued for many years (until the third Mint was occupied in the autumn of 1902).

Senator Thomas Hart Benton, of Missouri, one of the best known and most powerful figures in that legislative body, spearheaded the Act of June 28, 1834. Nicknamed "Old Bullion," Benton had demanded his salary in gold coins and was a staunch foe of paper money, much of which was worthless, causing great distress to the country. He was also a friend of President Andrew Jackson, who, beginning in 1829, almost single-handedly destroyed the Second Bank of the United States by vetoing in 1830 its charter renewal (set to expire in 1836). While Jackson and other Democrats viewed the Bank of the United States as a corrupt and greedy monster, the opposition considered it to be the very foundation of American financial stability. Actually, a careful study of that bank today reveals that it had both its good and bad points. In the 1830s the concept of paper money had its own strong political backing, as the officers, directors, and shareholders of banks enjoyed the privilege of issuing their own paper and used political influence to protect their franchise.

Although in the absence of gold coins in commerce paper money continued to circulate, and in vast quantities, the Act of 1834 reduced the authorized weight of gold coins, effective August 1, after which they were again used in domestic trade. Now, newly minted gold coins were worth face value, not a premium. It fell to William

Kneass to create new designs for the quarter eagle and half eagle. As noted, he did this by copying and modifying John Reich's Classic Head first used on the cents of 1808.

These new Classic Head coins were made in large quantities through 1838 for the half eagle and 1839 for the quarter eagle. Many have survived to the present day.

The Gobrecht Coinage: 1835-1844

On August 27, 1835, Chief Engraver Kneass suffered an incapacitating stroke. Fortunately, Christian Gobrecht was hired at the Mint soon thereafter, under the title of "second" (not assistant) engraver, as the talented and long-admired Gobrecht did not want to be considered lower in position than Kneass.

Gobrecht soon embarked on an ambitious program to modify coin designs. His major project was to create a new motif for the silver issues. The obverse, from a sketch by well-known artist Thomas Sully, featured Miss Liberty seated on a rock, holding a pole in her left hand, the pole surmounted by a liberty cap. Her right hand rested on the corner of a vertical shield inscribed LIBERTY. The use of a seated goddess as a coin motif had a tradition dating back to ancient Roman times, and at the time was used on coins of England.

The reverse, from a sketch by Titian Peale (a son of local museum proprietor Charles Willson Peale, who named his children after famous personages, including Titian, Rembrandt, Rubens, and Franklin), featured an eagle in flight and was modeled after "Peter," a mascot kept at the Mint.

In the meantime, while Gobrecht was perfecting his designs, new steam-powered equipment was installed at the Mint to replace horsepower and human effort, this through the research and effort of Franklin Peale (brother of Titian), who later became chief coiner at the Mint. On March 23, 1836, the first steam-powered coining press was dedicated in a special ceremony. Soon, copper cents were being produced in this manner, and in November, Gobrecht's newly modified Capped Bust half dollar, smaller in diameter and with a reeded edge, was struck.

In December 1836, the Liberty Seated motif, without stars on the obverse, made its debut on 1,000 silver dollars, struck with mirror Proof finish, but 600 of these were deposited in the Bank of the United States and were subsequently paid out for use in commerce.[1] In January 1837, a further 600 pieces were made from the 1836-dated dies. Although the flying eagle on the reverse was used on later "Gobrecht dollars," including patterns of 1838 and 300 regular issues in 1839, the motif was not employed either on later silver dollars or on other silver coins.

The Liberty Seated design, with a wreath reverse, was used on the half dime and dime beginning in 1837 (featuring for the first time the denominations given as HALF DIME and ONE DIME). The same obverse, with 13 stars around the border, and with a perched eagle reverse, was used on the quarter of 1838 and half dollar of 1839. In 1839 Robert Ball Hughes, an artist, was hired by the Mint to restyle Gobrecht's Liberty Seated figure. On the half dimes and dimes, this makeover was extensive and involved tilting the shield to the right, from its former slant to the left, and adding extra drapery to the elbow. Higher denominations received extra drapery but no major change in the shield.

Meanwhile, Christian Gobrecht made several modifications to the portrait used on the large copper cent, creating variations from 1836 to 1839, including the curiously nicknamed *Silly Head* and *Booby Head* issues of 1839. He also made some adjustments to Kneass's Classic Head motif used on the quarter eagle.

Although the Philadelphia Mint had served the nation's coinage needs since 1792, by 1835 it was felt that branches should be established to reduce the cost of shipping bullion and coins and to take care of needs in distant areas, and appropriate legislation was passed. In 1838 the New Orleans Mint began operations, eventually striking many different silver and gold issues, each with the distinctive mintmark O. In the same year, smaller mints opened at Charlotte, North Carolina, and Dahlonega, Georgia, to strike gold from bullion found in those districts. The two latter mints operated through 1861 and used C and D mintmarks, struck only gold coins, and of no denomination larger than $5, as this was the maximum capacity of the small presses on hand.

In 1838 gold $10 eagles were struck again for the first time since 1804. Christian Gobrecht's Braided Hair design was used. This proved to be popular, and in modified form it was used on the half eagle and cent beginning in 1839 and the half cent and quarter eagle beginning in 1840.

During the late 1830s, there were other improvements at the Mint. In early 1837 a Contamin portrait lathe, ordered in Paris in November 1835, was installed at the Mint. This device was a pantograph mechanism that enabled a large model in brass or iron (cast or electrotyped from an artist's work in wax or plaster), measuring five or six inches in diameter, to be reduced to the size of a half dime, half dollar, or other coin. By successive transfer processes, hub dies could be made with the obverse and reverse designs, plus letters and stars added by punches. These hub dies were used to make working dies, to which only the date had to be added. Previously, working dies were made by hand, by using separate punches for the portrait, eagle, wreath, or other motif, and adding stars and letters individually.

In the early 1840s, American coinage included the Braided Hair design on half cents and cents, the Liberty Seated motif on all silver coins, and the Liberty Head or Coronet Head on the gold issues. "Sameness" was the rule for coins in a given metal, this generally following what mints of Europe, Central America, and South America did with their own coinages.

The New Orleans Mint, opened in 1838, operated intermittently until 1909. This view is circa 1906.

Christian Gobrecht died on July 23, 1844, leaving a rich legacy in the realm of coinage. Certain of his motifs remained in service, in modified form, for many years afterward, the final use being the Liberty Head $5 of 1908, by which time several other chief engravers had come and gone at the Mint.

The Longacre Coinage: 1844-1869

On September 6, 1844, James Barton Longacre was hired as chief engraver. When Longacre came to the Mint, he clashed with Franklin Peale, the chief coiner at the time. In the 1830s, Peale, a brilliant man of high technical and engineering skills, had traveled to Europe to view innovations at the mints there. Upon his return, he set in motion many improvements including steam-powered presses, the Contamin portrait lathe, and other operations. Peale made life at the Mint difficult for Longacre, but he was dismissed in 1854 through the efforts of the new (since June 1853) Mint Director James Ross Snowden.

On January 24, 1848, gold was discovered by John Marshall at Sutter's Mill on the American River. The California Gold Rush ignited in 1849, and large quantities of precious metal arrived at the mints at New Orleans and Philadelphia, affecting operations for a long time afterward and also having a profound impact on Longacre's career. The Mint Act of March 3, 1849, provided for two new denominations to utilize the metal, the gold dollar and $20, the latter called the double eagle for it had a face value of twice the current highest denomination, the eagle.

Longacre began work on the gold dollar and created a head of Miss Liberty facing left and wearing a coronet or tiara inscribed with LIBERTY, with 13 stars around the border. The reverse utilized an open wreath enclosing the denomination in two lines, as 1 / DOLLAR, with the date 1849 below, and UNITED STATES OF AMERICA around the border. This is possibly the first time that the date of a coin was actually used in the hub or master die, from which working dies were made.[2] The traditional procedure at the time was to add the date separately. However, this innovation was short-lived, and on later gold dollars, the dates were added by hand.

Longacre's work on the gold dollar seems to have had some problems. The earlier issues of 1849, with a smaller head of Miss Liberty and with the field flat (rather than basined or gently curved), were soon replaced by a larger head and curved fields. Later in the year, the engraver concentrated on the double eagle die, but difficulties developed concerning the relief of the portrait, and engraver Peter Cross was hired by the Mint to help.

A close examination of the early $1 and $20 dies reveals casual workmanship by Longacre, including a gaffe in the inscription LIBERTY in the headband of the $20, first punched as LLBERTY and then corrected by overpunching an I on the erroneous second L. The word does not fit properly in the space allotted, and thus the Y is incomplete and overlaps other features. It is probably fair to say that Longacre was a coin-die engraver of modest talent at best, at least when compared to his predecessor, Gobrecht or, decades earlier, Joseph Wright.

A new denomination, the trime or silver three-cent piece, was created in 1851. Longacre prepared a simple motif, featuring a six-pointed star and small center shield on the obverse and a C-shaped ornament on the reverse. The arrangement was modified slightly in 1854 and again in 1859.

In 1854 Longacre redesigned the gold dollar, with Miss Liberty having a smaller head and wearing a headdress made of ostrich plumes. The reverse depicted an "agricultural" wreath of cotton, corn, wheat, and tobacco. The same wreath was used for the $3 gold coin, a new denomination that year. Again, the artistry was lacking in the finessing of some details. For example, the word LIBERTY in the headband is not correctly spaced nor properly centered within top and bottom borders of the band. The *facial* features were identical to those used on the 1849 $1 and the 1850 $20.

Also in the year 1854, the San Francisco Mint began producing coins with S mintmarks. The mint has remained active since that time, but in a new building commencing in 1874, and in 1937 in a third facility.

During the 1850s, Chief Engraver Longacre created various patterns for a new cent to replace the heavy copper "large" cent in use since 1793. These efforts culminated in the creation of the 1856 Flying Eagle cent. Although he had the opportunity to place his imprimatur on entirely new designs for the obverse and reverse of America's most ubiquitous coin in circulation, he elected not to do so. For the obverse of the Flying Eagle cent, he borrowed Gobrecht's eagle from the reverse of the silver dollar of 1836, and for the reverse, he copied his own agricultural wreath created for the gold dollar and $3 of 1854.

Problems developed with striking the Flying Eagle cents properly, and in 1859, the design was replaced by Longacre's new motifs, the obverse featuring Miss Liberty (with the same facial features earlier used on the $1, $3, and $20 gold coins), now with an Indian war bonnet (which in real life only *male* Native Americans wore). The reverse depicted a laurel wreath with inscriptions. While the reverse was changed to the oak-wreath-and-shield style in 1860, the Indian Head endured for decades, until 1909, and along the way became an American favorite. Copper-nickel alloy was used for Flying Eagle cents and Indian Head cents, until spring 1864 when bronze was adopted.

The second San Francisco Mint building, opened in 1874, was used until 1937. This view is circa 1904, two years before the earthquake and fire. The Mint was the only building in its district to survive the conflagration.

Longacre went on to create the bronze two-cent piece of 1864, a design featuring a shield on the obverse and a wreath on the reverse, this being the first circulating coin to utilize the motto IN GOD WE TRUST. In 1865 he created the nickel three-cent piece, using a new head of Miss Liberty for the obverse, and copying his laurel wreath reverse from the cent of 1859. In 1866 his Shield-motif nickel five-cent piece was made for circulation, the obverse copying his design on the two-cent coin, and the reverse consisting of a large numeral 5 with stars and rays surrounding.

During his tenure, Longacre had several assistants from time to time, including Anthony Paquet, William Key, and Peter Cross. He died on January 1, 1869, leaving an impressive legacy of designs, some of which continued in use for many years.

The Popularity of Coin Collecting

During Longacre's service as chief engraver, numismatics became a dynamic hobby. Early in 1857 the old large copper cents and half cents were minted for the last time, and the nation was set to receive a new version—the small Flying Eagle cent, released on May 25 of that year. A wave of nostalgia swept across the country, and many citizens scrambled to find as many different dates as possible among the old-style cents still in circulation. Most could be located, dating all the way back to 1793, except for 1815, when none were minted. Early coins might be found worn nearly smooth, and the rare 1799 and 1804 might not be found at all, but it was fun to look for them.

In 1858 the American Numismatic Society was founded in New York City, and in the same year, the Mint made an estimated 210 sets of silver Proof coins for sale to collectors. The hobby continued to grow, and in the 1860s such dealers as W. Elliot Woodward and George Cogan, among others, produced many catalogs of collections and other items to be sold at auction.

During the Civil War, all silver and gold coins disappeared from circulation in the East and Midwest, and their place was taken by Fractional Currency, Legal Tender bills, National Bank bills, bronze tokens, paper scrip, encased postage stamps, and other media. Silver coins reappeared in April 1876 and gold coins in December 1878. In 1861 the New Orleans, Charlotte, and Dahlonega mints came under control of the Confederate States of America. Operations were continued for a time, after which the C and D mints closed forever. The New Orleans Mint ceased operations, but in 1879 reopened for coinage and was used until 1909.

In 1866 the first hobby periodical, the *American Journal of Numismatics*, was published. Coin collecting became a way of life for many, and collectors and dealers devoted time to studying coin designs and the availability of various issues. Interestingly, there was no interest in mintmarked coins at the time, and not even the curators of the Mint Cabinet, an in-house collection begun in June 1838, saved pieces with C, D, O, or S mintmarks.

Beginning in the spring of 1859, officers of the Philadelphia Mint commenced restriking scarce Proof-only half cents (of such dates as 1831, 1836, 1840 to 1848, and 1852), Gobrecht silver dollars (1836, 1838, and 1839), and other coins from old dies still on hand. The operation went "underground" and was conducted in secret. The favorite outlet for the secret coinage was Philadelphia dealer John W. Haseltine, who knew much but said little—while in the meantime a parade of hitherto unknown patterns, Proof restrikes and others, popped up in his auction sales. Today, numismatists are collectively thankful for these shenanigans, for otherwise there would be hardly any pattern coins to collect, and the population of the 1804 silver dollar, dubbed "the King of American Coins," would be just 6, instead of 15, the extra 9 having been later productions.

THE BARBER COINAGE: 1869-1879

Succeeding James B. Longacre as chief engraver in 1869 was William Barber. He had worked in Boston as an engraver for about 10 years, and in 1865 he was noticed by Longacre and hired as an assistant at the Philadelphia Mint.

Today Barber's cachet in the specialty of type coins is limited to two issues, the first being the silver trade dollar of 1873, his version of the Liberty Seated design. On this new denomination, Miss Liberty is seated on bales of merchandise, looking to the left across the sea, in the direction of China, where the American trade dollars were used in maritime commerce. On the reverse was a standing eagle holding an olive branch and arrows.

For the second new denomination by Barber, in 1875, Gobrecht's Liberty Seated motif was modified slightly for use on the new and short-lived silver twenty-cent piece, and for the reverse, he copied the eagle from his own 1873 trade dollar. Now and again, Barber or his assistants did some tweaking and adjustments to regular designs, including adding arrows to the date of certain silver coins in 1873 and 1874 and expanding the inscription on the reverse of the $20 in 1877, but not much in the way of anything major.

The Coinage Act of 1873 terminated the bronze two-cent piece, silver three-cent piece, half dime, and Liberty Seated dollar, and provided for the trade dollar. As *silver* dollars were no longer minted, some nineteenth-century economists who did not do their homework stated that the act also placed the United States on the gold standard. This is not true, and although gold coins had been made under federal auspices since 1795, it was not until the Act of 1900 that the gold standard was formally adopted. Meanwhile, since 1853, gold coins had been of full value, while most silver coins had less than face value in bullion content.

The twenty-cent piece, first in circulation in 1875, was not accepted by the public, as it was easily confused with the quarter of somewhat similar size. It was discontinued in 1876. However, a few Proofs for collectors were struck until 1878.

Mint Director Henry R. Linderman felt that Barber's work was below par and sought to hire a truly talented artist. He secured the services of young George T. Morgan, who came from England to the United States in 1876 and was hired as an assistant engraver. The arrangement was resisted by William Barber and his son Charles (who had been recruited by his father as an assistant in 1869). The surroundings were made uncomfortable for Morgan, who for a time worked away from the Mint premises.

Morgan turned out a series of pattern coins, some of them very beautiful, his half dollars of 1877 being particularly notable in that regard. In 1878 his design for the new silver dollar was chosen over the motif created by Chief Engraver Barber. Thus the "Morgan dollar" was created, first known as the "Bland dollar" (from Richard Bland, co-author of the act that enabled it), today a great numismatic favorite.

The Coinage of 1879–1906

After William Barber's passing in August 1879, it was an open question concerning the selection of the next chief engraver. George T. Morgan was the obvious choice, but the position was made on a political basis, with artistic talent being a distant secondary consideration. Toward the end of the year, Charles E. Barber was chosen. Under his father's watch, he had created the 1879 Flowing Hair pattern $4 gold Stella. Morgan remained as an assistant and had also created another version of the $4 gold coin, but Morgan's work was hidden from view, and only a few were made. Today, it is known as the Coiled Hair style.

In late 1879, the panorama of current American coin designs in circulation included the Indian Head cent; nickel three-cent piece; Shield nickel; Liberty Seated dime, quarter, and half dollar; Morgan silver dollar; trade dollar; and $1, $2.50, $3, $5, $10, and $20 gold coins with various Liberty Heads.

In 1883 Charles E. Barber's design for a new nickel five-cent piece made its appearance: the Liberty Head motif, of classic beauty to beholders today, but not acclaimed in its era. The first issues, lacking the word CENTS on the reverse, were considered by many people to have been minted in error, and a frantic search ensued for them—resulting in millions being saved. As a result, this short-lived type is very common today.

The Coinage Act of 1889 eliminated the nickel three-cent piece, the gold dollar, and the three-dollar gold coins. Numismatic publications as well as the popular press continued to criticize the motifs currently in circulation. In 1891 it was announced that a nationwide competition of artists would be held to replace the old-style Liberty Seated design and, for good measure, the Morgan silver dollar. However, nothing resulted from the effort, and in 1892 Charles E. Barber's new designs for the dime, quarter, and half dollar were selected for use.

In the 1890s, America experienced a great awareness of art and artists, with a great catalyst being the World's Columbian Exposition that opened in Chicago in 1893. During the next decade, *Century Magazine*, *Harper's*, *Leslie's*, and others often featured paintings and sculptures of artists with Augustus Saint-Gaudens receiving especially high acclaim. Publicly, Saint-Gaudens called Barber's work "wretched," a sentiment sometimes echoed by others. A news item from early 1892, published in Boston, included this comment relating to Barber's work:

> During the week which closed last Saturday some of the new coins issued by the United States government crept into circulation and were commented on by beholders from different points of view. The coinage is limited to three pieces, the dime, quarter and half-dollar, and all three present in differing sizes the same designs for obverse and reverse. On one side there appears a spread-eagle and on the other the profile of a head surmounted by the legend: "In God We Trust."
>
> The eagle is a meager and ill-fed specimen of our noble bird and the profile is that of a goddess of liberty, though it looks like the head of the ignoble Emperor Vitellius with a goiter. To be extremely frank, these new coins are not artistic. Even this mild statement is unduly flattering to the designers. . . . The nation has poor luck in getting up designs for coins. The reason is not apparent unless it be that sufficient inducements are not offered to bring our really good designers into competition. . . .

Just as biblical prophets are said to have been without honor in their own countries, many varieties of American coins to this point in time were without honor in the United States. Circulating cents, nickels, dimes, quarter eagles, and other pieces were familiar, perhaps *too* familiar, and became objects of contempt. Collectors (except for those who ordered silver Proof sets each year) generally ignored the Barber dimes, quarters, and half dollars, as well as Morgan silver dollars. Later generations of numismatists would eagerly seek high-grade Barber silver coins, only to find that few had been saved. Coins once despised and ignored became very valuable.

In 1893 Augustus G. Heaton's *Treatise on Mint Marks* was published and encouraged the study and appreciation of coins from the branch mints, including the latest, Carson City, which had opened for business in 1870, but ceased coinage in 1893. However, few heeded his siren call, and in that year, probably no more than half a dozen collectors endeavored to acquire Barber dimes, quarters, and half dollars made for circulation. During the decade, Barber coins were struck each year at the Philadelphia, New Orleans, and San Francisco mints. With few exceptions, gem coins, once available for the asking, are today very rare!

Meanwhile starting in 1903 the Philadelphia and San Francisco mints struck coins for the Philippines, a territory acquired by the United States in 1899. The Denver Mint opened for business in 1906 and began producing coins with D mintmarks, including Barber silver issues.

THE SCENE IN 1907

By 1907 the American scene had changed dramatically from what it had been in 1792 when federal coinage commenced at the Philadelphia Mint. Towns and cities were now linked by rail, the automobile was beginning to replace the horse, and the airplane was a reality. The Union had expanded from sea to sea. Communications were instant via telephone and telegraph, and wireless communication was in its growth stage. Magazines, newspapers, and books were now extensively illustrated, unlike the days of 1792 when books and periodicals had a small selection of woodcuts at best and often had no pictures at all.

The American monetary system changed vastly from 1792 to 1907. The bills of state-chartered banks, the mainstay of American commerce from the early nineteenth century through 1865, were no longer seen. Federal paper money, once distrusted, was now in evidence nearly everywhere. Varieties abounded, including Legal Tender Notes, Silver Certificates, Coin Notes (also called Treasury Notes), Gold Certificates, and thousands of different varieties of National Bank notes bearing the imprints of banks in every state.

By this time, numismatics was a mature hobby, complete with reference books and monographs on selected subjects, many local and regional clubs and societies, and tens of thousands of advocates. However, there was still no regularly issued guide to mintage figures, rarity, and prices. That would not come until years later in 1934 when Wayte Raymond released his *Standard Catalogue.* Nor were there any popular albums or holders to protect, display, and enjoy coins. Numismatists usually stored their collections in shallow wooden drawers in a cabinet (a collection was therefore called a *cabinet* of coins) or in small paper envelopes.

By 1907 the roster of dealers included such names as the Chapman brothers (S. Hudson and Henry, each with his own business, although earlier they had been partners), Thomas L. Elder (recently established in New York City, and destined to become the most active professional there), B. Max Mehl (an up-and-coming young man in Fort Worth, Texas, who excelled in advertising and public relations), and Lyman H. Low (a member of the old guard, active since the early 1880s), among others. Farran Zerbe was among the best-known dealers and in this year set up a sales exhibit at the Jamestown Exposition, a familiar procedure as he had run concessions at earlier events, including the 1904 Louisiana Purchase Exposition (St. Louis World's Fair).

Roosevelt and Saint-Gaudens

It was customary to have the Mint staff make presidential inaugural medals. Newly elected Theodore Roosevelt, however, thought that the work of chief engraver Charles E. Barber was inartistic. Accordingly, he enlisted sculptor Augustus Saint-Gaudens to make a private inauguration medal. Along the way, Saint-Gaudens shared his opinion that Barber's coinage work was not artistic, and that the chief engraver did not have the respect of the American artistic community.

Although Roosevelt was not a numismatist per se, he had a passing familiarity with the coinage of ancient Greece, specimens of which he had examined at the nearby Smithsonian Institution. He contemplated the coins currently in circulation in the United States, and on December 27, 1904, he wrote to Leslie Mortimer Shaw, his secretary of the Treasury: "I think our coinage is artistically of atrocious hideousness. Would it be possible, without asking permission of Congress, to employ a man like Saint-Gaudens to give us a coinage that would have some beauty?"

Indeed, it was possible. The sculptor was contacted, and soon after delivering the inaugural medal, he accepted the commission to redesign all United States coins from the cent to the double eagle. In failing health, Saint-Gaudens was able to do significant work only on the $10 and $20 denominations.

All along the way, Chief Engraver Charles E. Barber protested, but Roosevelt rose to the challenge and sided with Saint-Gaudens in the effort to have $20 coins struck in sculptured-style high relief, Barber's remonstrances notwithstanding. Even if only one coin *per day* can be struck on Mint equipment, the process will go on, Roosevelt stated. Miss Liberty on the coin, designated as "Fame" by the artist, was taken from Saint-Gaudens's *Sherman Victory* monument created for the Grand Army Plaza in New York City. Saint-Gaudens died on August 3, 1907, but his assistant, Henry Hering, finessed the $10 and $20 motifs from the sculptor's models.

The $20 coins, today known as the MCMVII (1907) High Relief issues, were an artistic sensation, although they did require three blows of the press to bring the design up properly. In due course, 12,867 of the High Relief coins were made.[3] Afterward, the low-relief double eagles were made, using a model made by Henry Hering. European ("Arabic" in many listings today) or regular numerals were used. Detail was lost in reducing the model, and Charles Barber restored some of it by re-engraving the hub and master die.[4] In this flattened form the vastly altered design of the late Saint-Gaudens became the standard and was used from 1907 to 1933. In the summer of 1908, it was modified by adding IN GOD WE TRUST to the reverse.

Saint-Gaudens $10 coins of 1907 featured Miss Liberty in a feathered headdress on the obverse, and the reverse showed a standing eagle similar to the one the artist created for Roosevelt's private inaugural medal after the 1904 election. Liberty's face was modeled by Henrietta Anderson. This motif, with modification to add the motto in 1908, was used intermittently through 1933.

The popular press and numismatists alike praised the 1907 designs, and the MCMVII $20 coins were eagerly snapped up after their release through the Treasury Department and banks. Soon, they were selling at a 50% premium.

THE COINAGE OF 1908-1916

Next on Roosevelt's itinerary were the $2.50 and $5 gold coins originally assigned to Saint-Gaudens. William Sturgis Bigelow, an acquaintance of Roosevelt's, contacted Massachusetts artist Bela Lyon Pratt to do the job. He created motifs with an Indian head on the obverse and eagle on the reverse, both incuse and recessed so that the field of the coin was the highest part. The Bigelow-Pratt relationship was a private one at first, as an official commission from the Mint did not come until May 1908.

The Indian Head coins, first made in 1908, were an artistic flop, and columns of *The Numismatist*, the publication of the American Numismatic Association, were filled with letters from collectors and dealers condemning the design. However, they were in demand by the public for use as holiday gifts.[5]

In 1908 Roosevelt enlisted Victor D. Brenner to redesign the one-cent piece, following an attractive portrait of Abraham Lincoln the artist had created as a desk plaque. In celebration of the 100th anniversary of Lincoln's birth, Brenner's Lincoln cent was launched in August, 1909, by which time Roosevelt's successor as president, William Howard Taft, had been in office for several months.

In 1911 and 1912, James Earle Fraser, a well-known sculptor, experimented with designs of an Indian head and bison, which in 1913 were used on the nickel five-cent piece, popularly called the Buffalo nickel, which was well received by nearly everyone.

Thomas L. Elder and the New York Numismatic Club, among others, rallied the coin-collecting community to replace the Barber silver dime, quarter, and half dollar with motifs created by accomplished artists, to round out the spectrum of all denominations currently being minted (silver dollars had not been made since 1904 and would not be struck again until 1921). William H. Woodin, a prominent industrialist and numismatist, was enlisted to help.

In 1916 during the administration of Woodrow Wilson, the final suite of artistic coin designs became a reality. Adolph A. Weinman's Winged Liberty Head or "Mercury" design for the dime and his Walking Liberty motif for the half dollar were made. The Mercury dime required no particular modification and remained standard for many years, through 1945. The Liberty Walking half dollar also remained standard and was used through 1947. Both designs were in high relief, and at the several mints there were problems in striking them up properly—today providing a challenge for numismatists to find sharp examples.

Hermon A. MacNeil designed the Standing Liberty quarter dollar of 1916, featuring Miss Liberty on the obverse, her right breast exposed, not at all unusual in the field of art and sculpture, but a feature that occasionally piques special interest from modern numismatic writers. From antiquity to present, including at the Panama-Pacific International Exposition of 1915, many if not most statues featuring goddesses were partly or entirely nude, without much in the way of adverse public comment. So far as is known, there was not the slightest problem with this on the 1916 coin either. Partway through 1917, the design was modified (called Type II today) to encase the upper part of Miss Liberty in a jacket of armor, to reflect America's military preparedness while the World War (commenced in August 1914) was raging in Europe. However, the United States did not officially join the conflict until 1917. Years later, it became numismatic folklore to say that the cover-up occurred because of American prudery—just another of the many interesting tales scattered along the path of American numismatics.

One of the "fun" things about the new 1916 coins is that the arbiters of numismatic fashion have declared that a Mercury dime with fully-split horizontal bands on the fasces (bundle of sticks) on the reverse is sharply struck. Accordingly, the term FB (Full Bands) has been used. It is indeed curious that an FB coin can be weakly struck elsewhere on the coin, such as near the date. Similarly, a FH (Full Head) Standing Liberty quarter is worth a premium, even if the rivets on the shield are weak. I find all of this to be mildly amusing, and suggest that *you* seek coins that are sharply struck *all over*, not just in a particular place! Perhaps *any* coin with all features sharp could be called FD (Full Details).

With the new dime, quarter, and half dollar of 1916, the old order of coinage had been completely changed. Now the Lincoln cent, Buffalo nickel, Mercury dime, Standing Liberty quarter, Liberty Walking half dollar, Indian Head $2.50 and $5 by Pratt, Saint-Gaudens Indian $10, and Saint-Gaudens $20 were all in use.

The Coinage of 1917 Through World War II

Chief Engraver Charles E. Barber died in 1917, and his long-time assistant, George T. Morgan, was named to the post. He had been at the Mint since 1876, and the recognition was long overdue! Although Morgan had produced many distinguished pattern coins and medals over a long period of time and had done work on commemoratives, there was nothing on the federal agenda for new coins for circulation. All of the designs were fresh, made 1907 to 1916, and coinage laws stated that a period of 25 years must pass before a new motif is used (although over the years this rule had been bent now and then).

In 1921 coinage of the silver dollar denomination was renewed, such pieces not having been struck since 1904. Millions of coins were produced from an adaptation of Morgan's old 1878 design. In December 1921, a new motif was employed, the work of sculptor Anthony de Francisci. Miss Liberty on the obverse seems to have the same facial features as used on Saint-Gaudens's 1907 $10, although de Francisci stated that it was a composite and that his wife Teresa served as a model. On the reverse, an eagle is perched on a rock, with the lettering PEACE below. Both sides were in high relief.

Problems in striking resulted, and the centers of nearly all 1921 Peace dollars were weak. In 1922 the designs were made in shallow relief, and in this revised form, dollars were made through 1935, with a break from 1929 through 1933.

George T. Morgan died in 1925. Soon, he was succeeded by an assistant, John R. Sinnock, who had created the designs for the reverse of the 1918 Illinois Centennial commemorative half dollar, various medals, and other items.

In 1932 the Treasury Department desired to produce a quarter dollar depicting George Washington, on the 200th anniversary of his birth. A motif by sculptor John Flanagan was selected based upon the classic bust by Jean Antoine Houdon, modeled from life by Washington, who had a cast of his face taken at Mount Vernon in October 1785. However, President Herbert Hoover was against commemorative coins, and his veto of any such proposal seemed to be in the offing. Accordingly, this was positioned as a regular issue, which in fact it was.[6] Ignoring the 25-year rule for changing standard coin designs, the Treasury decided to discontinue the Standing Liberty type in use since 1916. Created in fairly shallow relief to begin with, the Washington quarter posed no problems with striking sharpness.

In 1933 the mintage of gold coins was terminated following a production of $10 and $20 pieces early in the year. Quarter eagles and half eagles had not been made since 1929.

In the mid-1930s, in the midst of the Great Depression, inexpensive hobbies came to the forefront. Coins attracted nationwide interest, spurred by several watershed events occurring within a short time. In 1931 the mintage of cents at San Francisco was less than a million coins, the lowest since the rare 1909-S V.D.B. was made in 1909. There was a great rush to acquire them.

In 1934 Wayte Raymond launched the *Standard Catalogue*, to be, at long last, a regularly issued guide to coin varieties, mintage figures, rarity, and values. Raymond also published a line of attractive album pages and binders, making it a pleasure to "fill holes," as in a crossword puzzle, and to admire a collection as it grew coin by coin. "Penny boards," made for J.K. Post by Whitman Publishing Co., were inexpensive and were the foundation of a line that also included large flat panels for nickels, dimes, and certain other series. Soon, Whitman bought the rights and issued these and other panels, as well as, later, folders and albums.

In this era, Texas dealer B. Max Mehl extensively promoted interest in coins by running radio programs and print ads suggesting that those who learned about valuable issues by ordering his *Star Rare Coin Encyclopedia* could profit handsomely if they found a 1913 Liberty Head nickel, 1894-S dime, or other rarity.

In 1935 and 1936 there was a great boom in the market for old and new commemorative coins. In 1935 Lee F. Hewitt published the first issue of the *Numismatic Scrapbook Magazine*, which soon became immensely popular.

With all of the above activity and excitement, during the Depression the hobby of numismatics was not only alive and well, it was *dynamic*.

Next on the agenda for a major change was the nickel five-cent piece, which in 1938 observed its 25th anniversary. A nationwide competition was held to replace the Indian and "buffalo" design, 390 artists competed, and a Jefferson head by Felix O. Schlag was selected for the obverse, but his reverse was not accepted. Schlag was directed to redo it, which he did, although Chief Engraver John R. Sinnock may have helped.

During World War II, which America entered in December 1941, copper and nickel were viewed as strategic metals. Partway through 1942 the composition of the

Jefferson nickel was changed to eliminate nickel, and silver was used as a main element. These silver-content pieces, constituting a different variety for inclusion in a type set, were made through 1945. In 1943, copper was eliminated from the Lincoln cent, and zinc-coated steel was used. However, in 1944 the coinage reverted to bronze.

The Coins of Recent Generations

President Franklin D. Roosevelt, inaugurated in 1933, was subsequently elected to an unprecedented four terms in office. After his death in 1945, the same year that World War II ended, it was decided to redesign the dime to feature his portrait. Crippled with partial paralysis and confined to a wheelchair, Roosevelt had been active in the March of Dimes campaign to raise money to combat polio, and thus this denomination was a natural choice to honor him. The Roosevelt dime, designed by chief engraver John R. Sinnock, was introduced in 1946 and has been made ever since, with some modifications of metal content and portrait size.

The Liberty Walking half dollar was last struck in 1947, and in 1948 was replaced by the Franklin half dollar, also by Sinnock, from a bust by French sculptor Jean Antoine Houdon. Numismatists did not care much for the new design and generally ignored it. When I first became a coin collector in 1952, Franklin halves were very unpopular, and most in the hobby did not seek to form sets. As often happens in numismatics, yesterday's frog is tomorrow's prince, and today Franklin halves are widely collected and admired.

Changes and evolution continued. In 1959 the reverse of the Lincoln cent, formerly featuring two wheat stalks, was changed to illustrate the Lincoln Memorial building, the design being the work of assistant engraver Frank Gasparro.

In 1964, following the assassination of President John F. Kennedy in November 1963, the half dollar was changed. The obverse portrait was done by Gilroy Roberts, then the chief engraver. The reverse, a heraldic eagle motif, was the work of Frank Gasparro. Not long afterward, Joseph Segel formed the General Numismatics Corporation (name later changed to The Franklin Mint), and hired Roberts as an officer of the new company. Frank Gasparro became chief engraver at the U.S. Mint, remaining in the post until his retirement in 1981.

By 1964 the price of silver was rising on world markets. The Treasury discontinued the use of 90% silver and 10% copper alloy in circulating coins, replacing it with various copper-nickel compositions, although in later years silver coins were struck at the San Francisco Mint for collectors. To provide coins for gaming tables in Las Vegas and elsewhere, and to answer a small call for metallic dollars after silver was abandoned for regular coins, the Treasury Department issued the Eisenhower dollar, by chief engraver Gasparro, in 1971. Such coins were made through 1978.

To observe the bicentennial of American independence, three new reverse motifs were used on the 1976 quarter, half dollar, and dollar, respectively. From 1979 to 1981, a "mini" metal dollar was made, the Susan B. Anthony design by Frank Gasparro. Despite much hoopla to promote it for use to save on printing paper dollar bills, the coin was a failure, although more of the same design were made in 1999, for reasons relating to Y2K and the potential for increased public demand for coinage.

Gasparro's successor as chief engraver in 1981 was Elizabeth Jones, the first and only woman to occupy the post. She left the Mint in 1991, and the Treasury Department did not see fit to name a replacement. Jones demonstrated incredible talent and can be numbered among the great artists who were chief engravers, a list also including Joseph Wright and Christian Gobrecht. However, Jones also has the unfortunate distinction of being the only chief engraver who did not create a motif for circulating coinage—her work focused on commemoratives.

In 1982 bronze was discontinued for use in making cent planchets, and a copper-coated zinc standard was adopted, creating a new type. Among other modern coin changes and modifications reflected in the formation of a type set, the series of five different distinctive reverse designs each year, one for each state, introduced for the Washington quarter in 1999, has been notable. The State quarters were followed by similar coinage programs celebrating the District of Columbia and the five U.S. territories, and national parks, forests, waterways, and various historic sites. In the meantime, the classic portrait of Washington was "improved" at the Mint, by William Cousins, who added all sorts of raised hair squiggles. I called the United States Mint about this, and was told that this was done to eliminate complaints that the coins were not sharply struck! The spokesperson with whom I conversed had no clue that the portrait was inspired by Houdon, and that the original had no such squiggles! I could not help but muse that if the Franklin half dollar had been a current coin, it, too, would have been "improved" by giving him a head of hair!

The Sacagawea "golden dollar," a new version of a mini-coin in that denomination, was first produced in 2000. History repeated itself, and the Anthony dollar's challenges were replayed—the new dollars were used to some extent in circulation, mainly in Post Office vending machines and some mass-transit systems, but they failed to replace the paper dollar as currency. Congress has since initiated other golden dollar programs, but after 2011 the coins have been limited to numismatic sales (in sets, bags, rolls, and the like), rather than regular bank distribution and widespread circulation. All of these dollars are numismatically interesting and attractive, and they deserve a place in your type set.

As we go to press, the latest changes include the concluding panorama of America the Beautiful quarters and the newly dawning American Innovation dollars. Coin designs continue to make news headlines, with collectors and the public alike following the latest review sessions of the U.S. Commission of Fine Arts and the Citizens Coinage Advisory Committee. The Mint continues to innovate with surprises such as the 2017 Lincoln cent with Philadelphia's P mintmark, and circulating 2019 quarter dollars with West Point's W mintmark.

A collection of United States coins by design types from the 1790s to the present day forms a *living* exhibit. Who knows what congressional legislation will surprise us all next year or a few years hence, changing the designs once again? Nothing is constant except change, it is said, and in the preceding narrative of coinage history, you have seen more changes than can be easily accounted for—except by systematically building a type set!

2
Building a High-Quality Type Set

Creating a Fine Collection

Creating a fine type set can be a wonderful experience, a challenge and venture that will yield much pleasure. And, it is well known that a fine type set, if purchased carefully and held for the long term, has traditionally been a wonderful financial investment. The figures quoted herein, including from past editions of *A Guide Book of United States Coins*, show this dramatically. You can have all the fun of collecting, and, if you buy wisely and assuming the market remains strong, you may find it is one of the best investments you've ever made.

Here is what I would like you to do:

Take your time. Savor the experience. Proceed slowly, buy the easy coins first, and along the way, let your ideas develop. If you are an experienced numismatist, you may want to go faster and buy rarities at the outset. However, if you are relatively new to what has been called the world's greatest hobby, be assured that there are plenty of coins on the market, and you will not miss much by taking a few weeks to survey the territory and do some reading.

Become condition-conscious. By this I do *not* mean buying the highest grade you can find on a slabbed coin. What I mean is that within any given grade—perhaps VF-20 for your 1793 to 1796 Liberty Cap cent type, MS-65 for your 1892 to 1916 Barber dime—make sure that you get a *superb* specimen at that grade level. This means a coin that is well struck, has no defects, is on a good planchet, and has outstanding eye appeal. The numerical grade is only *part* of this equation.

You will soon find that in the numismatic world around you, only a small percentage of buyers strive for *superb quality*. Just about everybody seeks *high grade*, but that is something else entirely. A coin can be certified as MS-67 and be ugly, or MS-63 and be beautiful. It will pay you to be particular. There is no hurry, no need to rush to completion.

Ideally, you will spend several years building your type set. You may start with a subset, say of twentieth-century coins, then go backward to acquire nineteenth-century issues. Or, you may elect to get all of the copper and nickel coins and then go to other metals.

Along the way, when you acquire a coin take the time to look at it—the basic design, the rusticity of the diecutting (if it is an early issue), any illogical features it may have (the weird appearance of a word as "oF," with a lower-case o and upper case F, on the reverse of the 1959 cent; Frank Gasparro told me that he thought it was sort of cute—as John Sinnock had used this style on the 1948 Franklin half dollar), the initials of the designer if they are present (sometimes obvious, as on the 1909 V.D.B. cent, sometimes on both sides, as on the Morgan dollar, sometimes hard to find, as on certain gold dollars), and other aspects.

MANY OPTIONS BECKON TO YOU

Ideally, it would be wonderful for you to have a type set consisting of one of each major coin design from the half cent to the double eagle, in gem Mint State or Proof preservation. In practice, this cannot be done. Certain types are nearly or completely impossible to obtain in true gem grades, such a list including the 1796 and 1797 Draped Bust obverse Small Eagle reverse half dollar, 1839 Gobrecht silver dollar (original, not restrike), and 1808 quarter eagle.

Reality intervenes—the reality of how much you want to spend and also the reality of the availability of certain types. Contrasting this, thanks to the delightful flood of new Washington quarter types and all of the new issues of the past generation, at low expense you can acquire much of your type set—the issues from the 1930s until now—in gem grade for prices ranging from modest to trivial!

In the pages to follow, you will find listings for all of the *major* types of United States coins, these per conventional wisdom and hobby tradition to which I have added a measure of personal opinion. There is no scientific consistency in this arrangement or in any other that has ever reached print. For example, half dimes of the scarce 1796 and 1797 Draped Bust obverse Small Eagle reverse type exist with 13, 15, or 16 stars, and yet just about every type set ever formed, even the most expensive, has included just one coin to illustrate that design.

As to other examples, certain early Liberty Seated silver half dimes to half dollars circa 1838 to 1840, with stars on the obverse, have no drapery at Miss Liberty's elbow, but some collectors have not sought examples as a distinct type. Nor has the 1921 high-relief Peace dollar (all 1921 Peace dollars are in high relief) been listed as a separate type, but it has been included as the general class of Peace dollars 1921 to 1935. The drapery variations and the 1921 high-relief Peace dollar are separately studied here, but it is up to you to decide whether to add them to your collection.

Mint records show that 300 examples of the 1839 Gobrecht silver dollar, the only year combining the Liberty Seated with stars obverse with the flying eagle without stars reverse, were struck for circulation. However, over a long period of years, only a few type-set collectors have opted to include it. I do describe it here.

The best way to determine what you want to include in your type set is to read each section for the different types. As there are many opportunities to add sub-types or other variations, read the introduction to each denomination for further ideas. Also check *A Guide Book of United States Coins* or the deluxe *Mega Red..*

An important part of your decision-making process will be the funds you have available. I divide the famous 1793 Chain cent into two types—with AMERI. spelling on the reverse and with AMERICA. However, you might decide to include just one. If so, you will be in good company—probably 90% of people who form type sets opt for just a single example of the Chain issue.

Also, within a given type, you often have the possibility of selecting a single favorite coin, several, or even a large number of date and mintmark varieties. As an example, Barber half dollars were minted from 1892 to 1915 inclusive, across 73 different dates and mintmark varieties. Do you want the commonest of all? Or do you want to select a coin with an added aspect of interest—such as an 1892 (first year of issue), or 1906-D (the year the Denver Mint opened for business), or perhaps a coin with an O or S mintmark?

For the types that are not rarities per se, but which can be expensive in high grades, there are other decisions to make. It is an easy call to add a gem MS-65 silver-content Jefferson nickel of the 1942 to 1945 years to your type set, for this issue is available and affordable in such preservation. Ditto for most other types made in the past half century. However, when it comes to selecting an 1801 to 1807 half dollar of the Draped Bust obverse Heraldic Eagle reverse type, you may find that a nice VF-20 may be quite affordable, but that an MS-63 costs more than you want to pay, and an MS-65 is priced far beyond your limits.

Your type set will be your own expression of individuality. No one else in numismatic history will have obtained precisely the same grades you acquire and the same coins. This is quite unlike standard series by date and mintmark, such as the situation in which thousands of collectors have assembled complete sets of choice or gem Mint State Roosevelt dimes from 1946 to date, scarcely differing from one collection to another.

Below I list some ideas and options that have been popular. Perhaps one is just right for you. The beauty part of any option is that you can always expand an abbreviated or niche type set to include more coins, building on what you have already acquired.

Type Set Options to Consider

One of Everything

On the grandest scale, your type set could include one of each major type that is featured in this book, perhaps with a few sub-types added. Such a display would be a virtual panorama of American coinage from the earliest days to present.

Along the way, you would have specimens from each of the major engravers, examples of each denomination, and all of the different design variations. You could flip through the pages of any reference book, and upon seeing a picture of a type say, "I have one of those!"

In contemplating what you would like to do, this is one of the possibilities. Within the parameters of a full type set are many options for grades and price. Building a full set *except* for a handful of rarities is quite do-able for just about anyone.

Except for Gold

Quite a few type-set collectors have limited their acquisitions to the copper, nickel, and silver series, but not gold. Perhaps no more than one in a half dozen numismatists who desires to acquire all the types from the 1790s onward will include the gold, simply because the early gold types (before 1834) are all rare and expensive. If you decide to do this, and later want to collect gold, you have lost not a thing—the gold will simply be added to what you already have. This aspect is true of all other limited type sets—they can always be fleshed out.

Only Gold

Gold has a special allure, and quite a few enthusiasts have specialized only in gold, and have not cared at all to own a 1793 Chain AMERI. cent or a 1796 silver quarter.

Gold type sets can be formed in several ways:

One of the most popular methods is to begin with the Classic Head coinage of the 1834 type, this being the sharp dividing point between early gold (of higher authorized weight, of different designs, and all scarce to rare and expensive) and later gold (lower-weight and nearly all quite affordable). A set of gold designs of the 1834 to 1933 span comprises many interesting issues, including three distinct types of gold dollars, the $3 gold piece, and six major types of double eagles, among other coins.

A shorter version of the above is to collect just the twentieth-century gold coin types, consisting of only four denominations, the $2.50, $5, $10, and $20, each existing in from two to four types.

To expand on just one of the preceding examples, a type set of six different double eagles makes a spectacular display—as these are the largest and heaviest of the American gold issues. A full type set includes one each of these major designs:

1850–1866: Liberty Head Without Motto

1866–1876: Liberty Head With Motto and with denomination as TWENTY D.

1877–1907: As preceding but with denomination as TWENTY DOLLARS

MCMVII (1907): Saint-Gaudens High Relief

1907–1908: Saint-Gaudens Without Motto

1908–1933: Saint-Gaudens With Motto

Yet another idea is to collect one gold coin of each regular denomination, your choice of dates and types within that denomination:

$1: 1849–1889

$2.50: 1796–1929

$3: 1854–1889

$5: 1795–1929

$10: 1795–1933

$20: 1850–1933

Collecting a full type set of gold coins from 1795 to 1933 is not for the fainthearted, but if you can afford it, you will have the pleasure of contemplating rarity after rarity among the early 1795 to 1834 issues.

Unlike copper and silver coins, for which early issues are often collected in well-worn grades from G-4 on up, as a general rule there is not much interest in gold coins, early or late, in grades below VF. For gold types of the late nineteenth century onward, Mint State grade is the order of the day.

Twentieth-Century Type Set

This is a very popular format, usually comprising one each of the copper, nickel, and silver coins (not often the gold, but, of course, gold can be included). Among the denominations from the cent to the silver dollar none are rarities, and each can be obtained without difficulty.

In *high-quality* gem Mint State, several of the types become scarce, this being true of the Barber quarter and half dollar in particular. The 1916 and 1917 Type I Standing Liberty quarter is scarce in relation to the demand for it, but when you find a 1917 Type I (the most plentiful variety within the type), the chances are excellent that it will be of high quality—with sharply struck head of Miss Liberty and full rivets in the shield. On the other hand, the 1917 to 1930 Type II Standing Liberty quarter will be a challenge to find if you want a really sharp one.

Not even halfway in, a *twenty-first* century type set will include many different issues. Already there are many dozens, a combination of standard designs plus the regularly appearing new designs of quarters and dollars.

First Year of Issue

Within either a full type set from 1793 to date, or a twentieth-century type set, or another specialty, you might want to acquire examples of the first year of issue of the design. Under this arrangement, you would have an 1864 bronze Indian Head cent, a 1916 Mercury dime, a 1932 Washington quarter, and so on.

While many first-year-of-issue coins were hoarded due to their novelty with the public, this is not true of certain designs. Such coins as the 1839 Liberty Seated half dollar and the 1840 Liberty Seated silver dollar are very rare in choice Mint State, despite their first-year-of-issue status. On the other hand, the 1883 without CENTS Liberty Head nickel, the 1909 V.D.B. Lincoln cent, and 1913 Type I Buffalo nickel are common in this preservation.

A Favorite Design or Denomination

Liberty Seated coins, designed by Christian Gobrecht in 1836 and later modified by him and others, are a popular series with many collectors. Many different Liberty Seated types were made of the half dime, dime, twenty-cent piece, half dollar, and silver dollar, and even William Barber's 1873 to 1885 trade dollar, although not inspired by Gobrecht, is usually included.

One-cent pieces are a popular denomination to collect by types and a lineup of the different motifs used over the years is very impressive. Ditto for silver dollars. Many other denominations can be collected in this manner, although there would be no point in doing this with either two-cent pieces, nickel three-cent coins, twenty-cent pieces, trade dollars, or $3 gold pieces as each is of just a single design.

Mint State and/or Proof Coins

Most numismatists who have built type sets have aspired to acquire circulation strikes rather than Proofs. However, it is not uncommon to mix Proofs with Mint State coins. I have never seen anyone specialize only in Proofs, but it would be easy enough to do for the types from about 1858 to date, except for the gold.

There are several areas in which sharply struck choice and gem Proofs are more readily available than are choice or gem Mint State coins. Examples include the 1854 to 1858 Type III silver three-cent piece (Proofs are very rare, and when seen are usually dated 1858, but *sharply struck* Mint State coins are rarer yet), several types of Liberty Seated silver coins (the 1873 and 1874 With Arrows issues being examples), and Barber quarters and half dollars. Proofs were sold at a premium to numismatists and were meant to be saved, and, accordingly, the larger part of the various Proof mintages still survive. In the field of Liberty Seated dollars, gem Proofs of both the 1840 to 1865 type and the 1866 to 1873 type are more available than are gem Mint State specimens.

It is not practical to acquire certain early coins in Mint State. Accordingly, you might want to establish an informal threshold for acquiring Mint State pieces, say from circa 1807 and the Capped Bust coinage, or from the late 1830s when the Liberty Seated designs were inaugurated, or beginning in the twentieth century.

WHAT DETERMINES MARKET VALUE?

Several Factors

The current market value of a type coin depends on several factors, and I discuss each of them here. Curiously, what I consider to be one of the most important factors, *high quality within a given grade*, is not important to most buyers in the present scheme of things. In other words, most of your competitors in the marketplace do not care. This gives you an inside advantage—at little or no extra charge!

Absolute Rarity

The term *rare* is ubiquitous in numismatics. A person is said to be a collector of *rare* coins, even if he or she saves only Lincoln cents with the Memorial reverse (1959 to 2008) or modern State quarters.

As to rarity, it is measured either as the number of specimens known or, alternatively, their availability on the market in relation to the demand for them. By way of illustration, among rare dates of half eagles the earlier-mentioned 1822 is highly acclaimed, and only three are known to exist. Two of them are in the Smithsonian Institution, leaving just one in the private sector, and that piece is tightly held. For all practical purposes the 1822 half eagle is unique in the marketplace and impossible to buy.

On the other hand, it was generally thought among specialists that there are just four or five specimens in existence of the 1873-CC quarter dollar without arrows at the date, three Mint State and one worn piece, certainly a rare variety. However, two or three of the Mint State coins have kept reappearing on the market, jumping from one auction appearance to another, without finding solid buyers at the time. Although a Mint State 1873-CC No Arrows quarter is almost as rare as an 1822 half eagle, it is not in the same league; for the 1873-CC is *available*, and the 1822 is not.

Often the term *rare* is confused with *valuable.* In 1885, in an era in which the title of a book could be nearly as long as the book itself, a *Visitor's Guide and History of the United States Mint, Philadelphia, Elaborately Illustrating Each Department, the Business Routine, all Scientific and Mechanical Operations in every Stage of the Work, the Wonderful Machinery and Curios in the Cabinet,* was published by A.M. Smith. Concerning two particular coins on display, he had this to say:

> The rarest United States coin is the double eagle of 1849, of which there is only one in existence and belongs to the U.S. Mint Cabinet. The next in rarity is the half eagle of 1815, of this date there are only seven specimens known to exist.

What he should have said about the 1815 is, "The next in *value* is the half eagle of 1815, of this date there are only seven specimens known to exist." At the time, the 1815 half eagle was considered to be the Holy Grail of early $5 coins, and the rarer 1822, of which the Mint also had a specimen, attracted little notice, as its great rarity was not recognized until years later.

Within most types of United States coins, there are some scarce-to-rare dates and varieties. Such rarities are not of particular concern to you if others of the type are plentiful. Accordingly, in the Draped Bust cent series from 1796 to 1807, the 1799 is a very rare date and the 1804 is elusive as well, but such dates as 1801, 1802, 1803, 1805, 1806, and 1807 can be found easily enough. While an EF-45 1799 cent might command the best part of $150,000 at auction, and a generation might pass between appearances, an EF-45 1803 can be bought for a tiny fraction of that, and at any given time there are apt to be several on the market. For type-set purposes, you can ignore the 1799 and concentrate on an 1803 or other plentiful issue.

Rarity as a Design Type

In the formation of a type set, you are concerned with rarity of the *type*, not of a date or variety within that type. Fortunately, for most series that do include rarities, there are also common pieces. When you acquire an example of the 1864 to 1909 bronze Indian Head cent for your collection, you can find a gem MS-65 example of a twentieth-century date, such as 1907, rather inexpensively, whereas a gem of a rare date such as 1871, 1872, or in particular 1877, would run into the thousands of dollars.

Among the designs needed for a full type set (as described in the following pages), certain of the especially scarce and rare issues, with fewer than 7,500 pieces known all across numismatics, are given below. Those of which fewer than 1,000 are known, more or less, are indicated by an asterisk.

These coins are among the most valuable in the type set series, not because of their absolute rarity, but because of their rarity as a type. As many thousands of people enjoy collecting coins by designs, a coin of which fewer than several thousand are known will command a great deal of attention in the marketplace regardless of its grade.

Notable copper rarities among type coins:

1793 half cent.*

1794 half cent.

1793 Chain Reverse, AMERI. cent.*

1793 Chain Reverse, AMERICA cent.*

1793 Wreath Reverse cent.

Notable silver rarities among type coins:

1794–1795 Flowing Hair half dime.

1796–1797 Draped Bust, Small Eagle Reverse half dime.

1800–1805 Draped Bust, Heraldic Eagle Reverse half dime.

1796–1797 Draped Bust, Small Eagle Reverse dime.

1796 Draped Bust, Small Eagle Reverse quarter dollar.*

1794–1795 Flowing Hair half dollar.

1796–1797 Draped Bust, Small Eagle Reverse half dollar.*

1836 No Stars Obverse, With Stars Reverse Gobrecht silver dollar.*

1839 With Stars Obverse, No Stars Reverse Gobrecht silver dollar.*

Notable gold rarities among type coins:

1796 No Stars, Heraldic Eagle Reverse quarter eagle.*

1796–1807 With Stars, Heraldic Eagle Reverse quarter eagle.*

1808 Draped Bust to Left quarter eagle.*

1821–1834 Capped Head to Left quarter eagle.*

1795–1798 Small Eagle reverse half eagle.

1795–1807 Heraldic Eagle reverse half eagle.

1807–1812 Draped Bust to Left half eagle.

1813–1829 Capped Head to Left, Large Diameter half eagle.*

1829–1834 Capped Head to Left, Small Diameter half eagle.*

1795–1797 Small Eagle Reverse eagle*

1797–1804 Large Eagle Reverse eagle.

It is seen from the above list that in the early gold series there are many formidable rarities. For this reason, some collectors choose not to collect gold by type, or if they do, to collect issues of 1834 to 1933 for which all types are readily available (the most elusive being the MCMVII $20 of 1907 for which 6,000 or so are estimated to exist).

Condition Rarity

All across numismatics—type coins as well as scarce individual varieties—some issues can be plentiful in lower grades but very rare in choice or gem Mint State.

Among type coins, the 1794 to 1795 Flowing Hair half dimes, half dollars, and silver dollars are scarce but still readily available in such grades as VF or even EF, but in gem Mint State each is incredibly rare. The same can be said for most other early copper and silver issues.

Among later issues, scattered types are elusive in Mint State but common to just slightly scarce in worn grades. A short list from many examples includes all half cent types before 1809 and all cent types before 1816, 1854 to 1858 Type II silver three cents, 1866 and 1867 Shield nickels With Rays, all half dime types before 1829, all dimes and quarter types before 1838, half dollars before 1807, 1836 to 1838 Capped

Bust reeded edge half dollars with 50 CENTS reverse, the 1838 and the 1839 Capped Bust half dollars with HALF DOL. reverse, all early silver dollars and Liberty Seated dollars, and many different types of large-denomination gold coins before about 1875.

All types of copper, nickel, and silver coins of the twentieth century to date are readily available in Mint State. The most elusive are the Liberty Head nickel, the Barber silver coins, and the 1916 and 1917 Type I Standing Liberty quarters, but these are hardly *rare.*

All Proofs of the 1858 to 1916 era range from scarce to rare, and most earlier Proofs are extremely rare.

To determine the availability of a given type of *fairly valuable coin* in higher grades, the population reports issued by ANACS, the Numismatic Guaranty Corporation of America (NGC), and the Professional Coin Grading Service (PCGS) are very useful. The reports are not of much value in learning the rarity of worn common coins, as the cost of certification is such that few are submitted. Accordingly, a 1907 Indian Head cent (commonest date of that type) in G-4 grade will appear to be a great rarity in report listings, as the coins are worth only a couple of dollars and it does not pay to certify them. Well over 100,000 exist. Conversely, an MCMVII (1907) High Relief $20 will seem to be common, as so many have been certified. However, only about 6,000 exist. Each of these MCMVII coins is so much in demand that even a low-grade example is worth into the thousands of dollars, so the cost of certification is not important.

Regarding market price, the higher the grade, the higher the value. If a type coin is at once rare and valuable (such as a 1796 and 1797 Draped Bust obverse Small Eagle reverse half dollar) in *any grade* and thus is a key to the series, then all bets are off when a gem comes up for auction competition!

Fads and Cycles

Certain elements of the rare-coin market have followed price cycles. At any given time, the market does not move all at once. In 1989 the market for certain coins was extremely strong, as huge numbers of investors rushed to buy, including those who bought into rare-coin funds. The story given to many investors was that "investment quality" was defined as a silver or gold (but not copper) coin in at least MS-65 or PF-65 grade. All of a sudden, the demand for these grades multiplied, and coins that were selling for $500 went to $2,000 or more. A year or two later, the investors left *en masse* to seek new opportunities, and the prices of many "investment grade" coins plummeted.

When any market is composed of people who are primarily buying for *investment* and not for *private collections,* prices will rise, and as the presence of such investors in the market is *always temporary* (not a single exception in the past two centuries), prices will fall when the investors retreat. However, the next time that these series catch on with investors, chances are good that the new highs in the market will outdistance the old highs. As many years may pass in the meantime, this may not fit the strategy of most who are buying for investment only. Right now there are many different MS-65 and PF-65 coins that are selling for considerably less than they did in 1989.

Here are a few *investment fad cycles* from numismatic history and the hottest items in those markets. Each subsided and took years to recover. However most all did recover in time:

1859 to early 1860s: Tokens and medals depicting George Washington. Articles, a book (by James Ross Snowden, former director of the Mint), and auction-listing hype, plus the knowledge that the Mint Collection would trade rarities (restrikes mostly) for Washington pieces it needed, fueled interest. ***Aftermath:*** Prices dropped and did not recover for many years. However, in time the slump was forgotten. The market for early Washington coins, tokens, and medals is very strong today, and prices are significantly higher than they were years ago.

1935–1936: Commemoratives were all the rage, and some issues multiplied in value overnight. ***Aftermath:*** The market did not recover until years later in the 1940s, after which it went on to new highs.

1956–1957: Modern Proof sets 1936 onward, including recently released issues, led the investment market; "bid" and "ask" prices were posted on blackboards at conventions, and sets zoomed in value. ***Aftermath:*** The market crashed, investors disappeared, and modern Proofs remained a drug on the market for years. Today, all such Proofs are higher in value.

1960–1964: Bank-wrapped rolls were all the rage as were 1960 Small Date cents. A roll of 40 1950-D nickels crossed the $1,200 mark. ***Aftermath:*** The market crashed, the 1950-D nickel roll went down to about $300, and today, more than a generation later, it has not recovered. However, most other coins have risen far beyond their 1964 highs.

1971–1972: Gold coins, krugerrands (remember them?), and other gold items were hot. ***Aftermath:*** The market crashed, and by 1975 few buyers were in sight. Prices recovered later.

1970s: Franklin Mint medals, mostly struck in silver, were dynamic, and over 250,000 people belonged to the Franklin Mint Collectors Society (about 10 times the membership of the American Numismatic Association). ***Aftermath:*** The market collapsed, and most such medals today are worth little more than their melt-down value.

1978–1979: The Hunt brothers endeavored to get a corner on the silver market, the gasoline shortage and the rise of Japanese industry made many feel that the American dollar would soon become of little value, "hard money" lecturers told of investing in bulk silver and gold, and by early 1980 silver was worth over $35 per ounce and gold nearly $850. "Investment quality" rare coins of these metals rose as well. ***Aftermath:*** The Hunt brothers lost their collective shirts, prices of bullion slumped, and the market was slow for years afterward. However, most (but not all) prices have recovered in the meantime.

1988–1989: The "Wall Street" investor market saw "investment quality" coins zoom in value. Merrill Lynch and some others set up investment funds. ***Aftermath:*** The market bubble burst. Many such coins have not yet recovered.

2000s: Ultra-high-grade certified examples of otherwise common coins have been in the limelight. Action is still intense.

The above list could be expanded, but you get the idea. The majority of coins needed for a typical type set have not been affected one way or another by investment fads, as nearly all type sets are assembled by *collectors*. However, certain very high-grade silver and gold coins have been caught up in fads and have suffered. Perfectly desirable (in my opinion) MS-63 and MS-64 coins, not being of "investment" grade, have not been adversely affected to any significant extent.

In response to the most recent fad, that of ultra-high-grade but otherwise common coins, I urge caution if you contemplate paying a high price in some grades above MS-65 or MS-66, perhaps far above, for coins that are not rare in lower Mint State ranges.

Advice for Solid Value

A handy rule is that if a market is composed mainly of *serious numismatists*—collectors who study the history and science behind coins—seeking single examples of given coins for their collections, the market will probably be strong.

Investment fads and cycles are not all that bad, inasmuch as if you buy in a down time in the cycle you can get good values.

Also, *basic rarity* has never gone out of style. Chances are good that a modern coin that is common and inexpensive in grades up through, say, MS-63 or MS-65, but is rare if certified MS-69 or MS-70, is less likely to hold its value than a key date or rare type that is rare in lower grades as well.

Before buying an expensive coin today—any coin—it will pay you to investigate the price history of that coin. See how it has performed. If today a price is *multiples* of what it was just a few years ago, then use great caution when buying.

Take the time to "cherrypick" MS coins when you can, rather than relying only on the grades written on their holders. Cherrypicking is a close examination to find an attribute or feature that is not immediately obvious, but which can lend interest or value. Focus on coins that are above average in eye appeal.

3
Aspects of Coin Grading

Grading by the Numbers

Grading coins is a never-ending topic for discussion. As there are few hard conclusions to be made, and as scientific procedure yields a distant second place to opinion, there are few "rights" or "wrongs." When you make a purchase, you pay your money, and you receive a coin. Many people are perfectly happy with *anything* they buy in the marketplace and blindly assume that all dealers and collectors are offering the same quality. Reality is quite different, in my opinion.

The ANA Grading System

The grade assigned to a coin, reflecting the amount of contact or wear the coin has received, is an important element in determining its value. To some it is the *only* element, especially if marked on a certified coin holder.[7]

Per the American Numismatic Association Grading System, Mint State (also known as *Uncirculated*) coins are graded from MS-60 or the lowest level, up to a theoretical MS-70, or absolute perfection. Intermediate steps are designated MS-61, MS-62, and so on, with the MS-63 having the adjectival equivalent of "choice," and MS-65 or better, "gem." While numbers give the appearance of being precise, they are simply shorthand for someone's opinion. They are not scientific.

The seemingly curious use of 1 to 70, rather than 1 to 10 or 1 to 100, lies in a market formula for large copper cents of the 1793 to 1814 years, delineated in 1949 by Dr. William H. Sheldon in *Early American Cents.* At that time, the market for cents was far different from what it is now, and an MS-60 coin was worth just twice as much as a VF-30 one. By assigning a *Basal Value* (another Sheldon concept) to a cent, say a Basal Value of $2, then you could calculate that a VF-30 coin was worth $2 x 30 or $60, an EF-40 coin was worth $2 x 40 or $80, and an MS-60 coin was worth $2 x 60 or $120, and so on. Today, there is a huge difference between VF-30 and MS-60, and the system is completely useless. In fact, it lasted only a few years before it was recognized as being pseudo-science and invalid. However, the concept of using numbers lived on, and today we have them. Today, a Sheldon-system calculation that an MS-60 coin is worth twice the price of a VF-30 coin would be viewed as ludicrous for most series.

Years later, the American Numismatic Association set up a Grading Committee and in 1977 published *The Official ANA Grading Standards for United States Coins*, largely supervised by dealer Abe Kosoff, and compiled by Kenneth E. Bressett. At first, the ANA grading system mirrored the Sheldon system, more or less, but in successive editions, intermediate grades were added, such as AU-55, MS-63, and MS-67, among others, and then the full range of Mint State possibilities, including MS-61, MS-62, plus additions in lower categories as well. Today, in the AU range, we have AU-50, 53, 55, and 58. Perhaps someday we will also have AU-51, 52, 54, 56, 57, and 59. Who knows?

Here is the ANA Official Grading System for certain double eagles. This is a sample of the listings, varying in their content, available for all other types from half cents forward:[8]

Official ANA Grading Standards

Liberty Head Double Eagles 1850-1907 (adapted)

MINT STATE Absolutely no trace of wear.

MS-70 Uncirculated • A flawless coin exactly as it was minted, with no trace of wear or injury. Must have full mint luster and brilliance. Any unusual die or planchet traits must be described. • Contact marks: None show under magnification. • Hairlines: None show under magnification. • Luster: Very attractive, fully original. • Eye appeal: Outstanding.

MS-69 Uncirculated • Contact marks: 1 or 2 minuscule, none in prime focal areas. • Hairlines: None visible. • Luster: Very attractive, fully original. • Eye appeal: Exceptional.

MS-68 Uncirculated • Contact marks: 3 or 4 minuscule, none in prime focal areas. • Hairlines: None visible. • Luster: Attractive, fully original. • Eye appeal: Exceptional.

MS-67 Uncirculated • Virtually flawless but with very minor imperfections. • Contact marks: 3 or 4 minuscule, 1 or 2 may be in prime focal areas. • Hairlines: None visible without magnification. • Luster: Above average, fully original. • Eye appeal: Exceptional.

MS-66 Uncirculated • Contact marks: Several small, a few may be in prime focal areas. • Hairlines: None visible without magnification. • Luster: Above average, fully original. • Eye appeal: Above average.

MS-65 Uncirculated • No trace of wear; nearly as perfect as MS-67 except for some additional small blemish. Has full mint luster and brilliance but may show slight discoloration. A few minute bagmarks and surface abrasions are usually present. • Contact marks: Light and scattered without major distracting marks in prime focal areas. • Hairlines: May have a few scattered. • Luster: Fully original. • Eye appeal: Very pleasing.

MS-64 Uncirculated • Contact marks: May have light scattered marks, a few may be in prime focal areas. • Hairlines: May have a few scattered or small patch in secondary areas. • Luster: Average, full original. • Eye appeal: Pleasing.

MS-63 Uncirculated • A Mint State coin with attractive mint luster, but noticeable detracting contact marks or minor blemishes. • Contact marks: May have distracting marks in prime focal areas. • Hairlines: May have a few scattered or small patch. • Luster: May be original or slightly impaired. • Eye appeal: Rather attractive.

MS-62 Uncirculated • Contact marks: May have distracting marks in prime focal and/or secondary areas. • Hairlines: May have a few scattered to noticeable patch. • Luster: May be original or impaired. • Eye appeal: Generally acceptable.

MS-61 Uncirculated • Contact marks: May have a few heavy (or numerous light) marks in prime focal and/or secondary areas. • Hairlines: May have noticeable patch or continuous hairlining over surfaces. • Luster: May be original or impaired. • Eye appeal: Unattractive.

MS-60 Uncirculated • A strictly Uncirculated coin with no trace of wear, but with blemishes more obvious than for MS-63. Has full mint luster but may lack brilliance. Surface is usually lightly marred by minor bagmarks and abrasions. • Contact marks: May have heavy marks in all areas. • Hairlines: May have noticeable patch or continuous hairlining throughout. • Luster: May be original or impaired. • Eye appeal: Poor.

ABOUT UNCIRCULATED Small trace of wear visible on highest points.
AU-58 Very Choice • Has some signs of wear; hair, coronet; eagle's neck and wing, top of shield

AU-55 Choice • Obverse: There is a trace of wear on hair. • Reverse: Trace of wear visible on wing tips and neck. • Three-quarters of the mint luster is still present.

AU-50 Typical • Obverse: There is a trace of wear on hair at top and over eye, and on coronet. • Reverse: Trace of wear visible on wingtips, neck, and at top of shield. Half of the mint luster is still present.

EXTREMELY FINE Light wear on only the highest points.
EF-45 Choice • Obverse: There is light wear on hair and coronet prongs. • Reverse: Light wear shows on edges and tips of wings, head and neck, and on horizontal shield lines. • Part of the mint luster is still present.

EF-40 Typical • Obverse: Light wear shows on hair, coronet prongs and cheek. • Reverse: Light wear visible on wings, head, neck, horizontal shield lines and tail. • Traces of mint luster will show.

VERY FINE Light to moderate even wear. All major features are sharp.
VF-30 Choice • Obverse: About one-quarter of hair detail below coronet visible; half the detail shows above coronet. Cheek and some coronet prongs worn. Stars show wear but all details visible. • Reverse: Most of wing details visible. Top part of shield shows moderate wear. About half the detail in tail visible.

VF-20 Typical • Obverse: Less than half detail above coronet visible. About half the coronet prongs are considerably worn. Stars are flat but show most details. LIBERTY shows wear but is very clear. • Reverse: Some wing details visible. Shield shows very little detail at top. Tail is worn with very little detail.

FINE Moderate to heavy even wear. Entire design clear and bold.
F-12 • Obverse: All hair lines well worn with very little detail visible. About one-quarter of details within coronet visible. Stars show little detail. LIBERTY readable. • Reverse: Wings show very little detail. Head and neck smooth. Eye visible. Tail and top of shield smooth.

Notes: Coins of this type are seldom collected in grades lower than Fine. The hair curl under the ear is sometimes weakly struck. In the group between 1866 and 1876, the reverse motto is sometimes weakly struck. Pieces made at the Carson City Mint are usually found weakly struck and heavily bagmarked. Most of the New Orleans pieces are not fully struck up. Philadelphia coins that are rarely seen fully struck include 1878, 1888, 1902, 1905 and 1906. Double eagles dated before 1866 lack detail or relief because of the design rather than striking inadequacies.

What Grading Numbers Mean

Grading numbers are shorthand for the rating that one person, group of people, or commercial certification service assigns to a particular coin at a particular time. The system is not scientific, but is highly subjective. The preceding comment may seem curious or even improbable to a newcomer to the hobby, for it seems to indicate that one of the basic foundations of market values, *grading*, lacks a system. However, it is true.

Is this lack of consistency a problem? The answer is that it is only if you let it be. Over a long period of years, grading has been the bugbear and frustration for many casual buyers who expect precision. Such consistency did not exist in the numismatic marketplace in 1859 when Augustus Sage was the leading coin-auction cataloger, it did not exist in the 1880s when the famed Chapman brothers were in their ascendancy in the rare-coin business, it did not exist during the entire career of dealer B. Max Mehl from about 1900 to 1957, it did not exist from 1925 to 1950 when Louis E. Eliasberg Sr., assembled the only complete collection of United States coins, and it does not exist now.

Somehow, famous numismatists of the past really *enjoyed* collecting coins without all of the grading steps we have today. I never heard a peep of complaint from Louis Eliasberg, John J. Pittman, Amon Carter, Emery May Holden Norweb, Harry Bass, or any other legendary numismatist of a generation or more ago. They all knew grading by personal study and experience, evaluated coins offered to them, rejected overpriced and overgraded coins (of which they were offered many), and went on to acquire what they did want. Similarly, hundreds of thousands of collectors during the past century have enjoyed coin collecting, this before the advent of the grading systems we know today.

I suggest that you view grading numbers simply as someone's opinion of a coin's grade. Numbers are quite handy as a shortcut. Certainly, even a newcomer can instantly understand that a coin graded as "40" (EF-40) is in a lesser grade than one designated as "65" (MS-65). Also, while the use of adjectives has much tradition, not everyone can readily understand that in numismatic lingo "Fair" does not mean acceptable, desirable, or about average, but really means a coin that is worn nearly smooth. Nor can everyone understand that an "About Uncirculated" (AU-50 to AU-58) coin is far better than the same coin described as "Good" (G-4).

DIFFERENCES WITHIN A SPECIFIC GRADE

Now that we have a mind-set to accept numbers, there comes another aspect—to me and, hopefully, to you, a very important one: that of *quality* within a specific grade, a situation I discuss many times throughout this book. Not only is this important, to me it is *absolutely essential.*

The beauty part is that "out there," in the vast and wonderful marketplace for rare coins, relatively few people care about quality! In fact, hardly any certified coin holders mention quality at all, but simply list "MS-60," "MS-64," or whatever. For you this offers a fantastic opportunity to review numerically graded coins and pick ones of high quality. More than just a few professional numismatists make a lot of money doing this, just as in the securities market an arbitrager can spot differences and advantages among financial numbers, and make profits.

In just about everything I've written in the rare-coin field, including in the present Whitman Publishing Bowers Series, I have endeavored to give my readers an inside advantage. Of course, this is good only for people who are willing to spend some time learning what quality means.

In the field of copper half cents and large cents, the name of William C. Noyes is one of the most familiar. He has worked with countless thousands of coins, ranging from the Ted Naftzger Collection (the finest-ever assembled of early large cents) to pieces seen at conventions and dealers' stocks. In his publication, *Penny Prices: A Price Guide for 1793–1857 Half Cents and Large Cents*, Noyes has this to say (excerpted):

> My personal criteria for buying have always been to pay a premium to get choice large cents that grade F-12 to MS-60+; to buy average coins when priced correctly or when they fit into my collection; and to never buy scudzy pieces unless they are very cheap or very rare. For example, I might pay $75 for a choice VF-20 middle date with exceptional color and problem-free surfaces, but only $40 for an average VF-20, and only $5 for a scudzy VF-20. If you doubt the validity of the above, check a few major auctions and/or price lists—you'll find many people agree when it comes to buying and not just talking.
>
> Before you buy a coin:
>
> 1) You must have done your homework. Know what you are collecting; what grade ranges you are looking for; and what they are worth. Look at enough coins to have a clear idea of which problems bother you, and which ones do not.
>
> 2) You should closely examine the coin on both the macro and micro level.
>
> 3) If it is a choice coin and one you need or want, do not be overly concerned by price, if within reason.
>
> 4) Do not trust anyone with your money! You must learn about grading and rarity for yourself and not rely upon other peoples' opinions. Ask questions and seek advice, but do not spend your money until you know what you are buying.
>
> 5) Most importantly, enjoy your coins. They are really miniature works of art. Take them out of the bank—look at them, study them, and read about them. Spending a quiet evening with a box of large cents is a most pleasant experience.

4

Secrets of Being a Smart Buyer

Guidelines for Success

Step No. 1: Setting the Numerical Grade

Look at the grade of a coin offered, or if you are familiar with grading, assign your own number. Immediately, you can see if it qualifies *for further consideration.* For example, if you are seeking an EF-40 coin to illustrate the 1796 to 1807 Draped Bust large copper cent for your collection, and if you are at a coin show, ask to see pieces in the EF category. Except for information or educational purposes, do not waste time looking at coins in significantly lower or higher grades.

Many of the scarcer and more expensive coins you need will be certified by one or another of the grading services. There are vast differences in the quality and reputation of the various services. Ask around and get some ideas.

The existence of certified coins vastly simplifies the buying of most coins, especially in a series in which large numbers of pieces have been encapsulated. If you are seeking a choice trade dollar of the 1870s for your type set, just ask, "What do you have in MS-63 to MS-65 trade dollars," and you may be handed a little pile of "slabs" containing such pieces. While you and I might think that a certain coin graded MS-63 falls short of the mark or, conversely, is undergraded, at least the group of coins will be in the ballpark *for further consideration.*

As to which grades to ask for, that depends on what you have already selected as a general guideline, typically based on market prices. Of course, instead of an EF-40 Draped Bust cent of 1796 to 1807, you would like to have a gem MS-65, but reality intervenes, and for now you are looking for an EF. On the other hand, for the fascinating but readily available 1883 Liberty Head nickel without CENTS on the reverse, you might ask to review a group in the MS-64 to MS-66 grades.

Within any given grade, reject any that seem to you to be overgraded. This will come with some experience. If at a convention you look through 100 Morgan dollars classified as MS-65, you'll soon enough see which ones seem to be on target and which seem to be below par.

Step No. 2: Judging Eye Appeal at First Glance

Take a quick glance at the coin. Is the toning (if present) attractive, or is it dark or blotchy? Is the coin stained? If it is brilliant, is it attractively lustrous, or is it dull and lifeless?

For nearly all coins you will be considering for your type set, there are many opportunities in the marketplace. It is not at all necessary in any instance to compromise on eye appeal! If it is not attractive, then reject it and go on to look at another. The price is not important (remember Bill Noyes's comments quoted at the end of chapter 3). An ugly coin graded as MS-65 is still ugly, and if it were my decision, I would not buy it for *half* of the current market price! Avoid price-bargains, because many if not most are "scudzy" coins (as Bill Noyes and others have called them).

If the coin is attractive to your eye, then in some distant future year when time comes to sell it, the piece will be attractive to other buyers, an important consideration. Now, with an attractive coin in hand, it is a candidate *for further consideration.*

Step No. 3: Evaluating Sharpness and Related Features

At this point, you have a coin that you believe to be more or less in the numerical grade assigned, and one with excellent eye appeal. The next step is to take out a magnifying glass or loupe and evaluate the coin's sharpness. Here, one rule does not fit all. It will be useful if you consult the information I give for each type later in the book. For some types, you can expect to find a sharp specimen. For some other types, in the distinct minority, this will range from difficult to nearly impossible.

For starters, for every type from the middle of the nineteenth century, say 1850, to date, you can set as a goal the finding of a *sharply detailed* coin. You are completely on your own in this quest, as certified holders are useful *for further consideration*, but are not definitive.

For some series, there are guidelines used by certification services and others (as discussed in detail in the appropriate sections in later pages). For example, the 1916 to 1930 Standing Liberty quarter dollar, if with the full hair and facial details of Miss Liberty present, is designated "FH," for Full Head. However, a little secret is that a coin certified as FH can be weakly struck in *other* areas! Often, the details of the shield rivets on the obverse of Standing Liberty quarters are blurred or weak, even though the head is sharp. Similarly, the reverse of a 1916 to 1945 Mercury dime can have Full Bands (FB), but the obverse rim can be poorly struck. Most buyers are not aware of these things. Perhaps someday FD (Full Details) or a similar designation will be more useful.

For sharpness, it pays to know the territory, and for each issue, early and late, common and rare, learn what to look for—and then find a sharply struck specimen. You may have to compromise slightly on some issues, such as Draped Bust obverse, Heraldic Eagle reverse half dimes, dimes, quarters, and half dollars of the early nineteenth century (not a complete list of such possibilities), but such instances are in the minority.

As part of Step 3, look at the planchet and surface quality. For *early* silver and gold coins, especially those of the 1790s through about 1810, Mint-caused *adjustment marks* are common. During the planchet preparation process, planchets found to be slightly overweight were filed down to the legal requirement. At the Mint, many people were kept busy in a special room doing this task. It was easier to make a planchet slightly overweight and to adjust it, than to make it underweight and have to return it to the melting pot for recycling. Adjustment marks are usually seen on the rim and/or the higher parts of the design. Your search for a coin without adjustment marks may be long and arduous for the larger silver and gold denominations of the 1790s, but stay the course and, eventually, you will be rewarded with success.

In other instances, coins were struck from "tired" dies that had been used in some instances to strike over 100,000 pieces. Such dies often became grainy or streaked—common on Morgan silver dollars 1878 to 1921, or somewhat bulged and uneven (common on the reverse of many Lincoln cents, especially of the era from 1916 to 1958).

Beyond this, some planchets were made of imperfect strips, with granularity, or the inclusion of carbon or dark spots and flecks, or bits of copper (causing copper stains on gold coins). In other instances, bits of thread, human hair, or debris clung to the surface of a die, causing recessed *lint marks* on the finished coins, this being quite common on some Proofs.

Examine your prospective coin carefully, and reject it if there are *any* problems with the surface or planchet. No compromise need be made. Once again, certified coin labels make no mention of the above, and few buyers even know about the possibilities.

If the coin you are considering buying has passed the preceding tests, it is ready *for further consideration.*

Step No. 4: Establishing a Fair Market Price

Now, you have a very nice coin at hand! Next comes the evaluation of its price.

For starters, use one or several handy market guides for a ballpark estimate. Few coins you are seeking, especially those dating before 1950, have precise market values. It is perfectly normal for one guide to suggest $300 as the value for a certain coin and grade, and another to list $275, and a third to post $320. If you look at the prices of coins sold at auction, you will find even wider variances, even among the same varieties certified by the same grading service and sold in the same month. However, from the above, you will get an idea of the approximate value of a coin in a given grade.

Now comes the fun part: if the coin is common enough in a given grade, with sharp strike, with fine planchet quality, and with good eye appeal, then the market price is very relevant, as you can shop around. If a coin is common in the grade you want, and with all other desired features, and you have ascertained that the market price level is about $300, then there is no sense paying $400 or $500. Wait until you find one at or near $300. On the other hand, chances are good that you will not find a problem-free coin for, say, $200 or $250. Generally, if something is offered to you for *below wholesale*, this simply means that any dealer wanting to buy a choice coin will not buy *this* one—and, accordingly, it is available for less!

For many of the types you need, high-quality coins are no problem at all. As an example, nearly all 1881-S Morgan silver dollars, the most common of all nineteenth-century Morgan dollars in gem MS-65 grade, are well struck, on nice planchets, and have great eye appeal. Most silver-content "wartime" Jefferson nickels of 1942 to 1945 are similarly choice. Other examples can be mentioned.

However, for some early issues the finding of a truly choice coin, fully passing the steps 1 through 3 above, can be extremely difficult. I use again the example of silver half dimes, dimes, quarters, and half dollars of the Draped Bust obverse, Heraldic Eagle reverse, of the early nineteenth century. If I were offered, say, an MS-63 specimen of any one of these, and it was needle-sharp and gorgeous, in my opinion, it would be a great buy at double or triple the current market price! And, I believe that you will agree.

In Step 4, that of pricing, you need to combine current market levels with the true rarity and availability of really choice examples, which for some early series can be a very important factor.

There is a very good possibility—another beautiful part of this process—that when you do find a sharply struck coin it will simply be certified in a given grade, and you can buy it for little more than you might pay for an ordinary example. Here, knowledge is king.

If you do find a long-sought rarity in terms of sharpness and eye appeal, don't be picayune about the price—step right up and buy it!

PROOF COINS FOR YOUR TYPE SET

Introduction

For inclusion in type sets, the majority of early United States issues—those before the 1850s—are usually collected in circulation-strike form. This is by necessity, as for many types no Proofs were struck. For other early types, Proofs are either very rare, or unsatisfactory, or extremely expensive, or a combination of all these factors. Details are given below.

For certain types, Proofs dated from the late 1850s and onward are more readily available in gem preservation (PF-65 or higher) than are circulation strikes (MS-65 or higher). Examples include the 1874 With Arrows dime, quarter, and half dollar, the 1873 to 1885 trade dollar, and the 1866 to 1876 $20 gold double eagle (although gem Proofs of this double eagle type are exceedingly rare, true gem circulation strikes are even more elusive!).

In building a type set, you can mix and match, adding Proofs here and there, often a way to acquire *sharply struck* examples of types that are not easily found this way in circulation-strike form. As is the case throughout the type-set collecting field, there is no right or wrong way to proceed, and the choice is up to you.

Early Proofs

Proof coins have been produced especially for numismatists for a long time, dating back to at least the second decade of the nineteenth century. All such pieces were struck at the Philadelphia Mint (it was not until generations later, with the 1968-S set, that Proofs were routinely made in San Francisco).

As many coins of 1796 (in particular) are highly prooflike, some collectors have called these *Proofs*. Similarly, quite a few other early coins have been attributed as Proofs, although many are simply circulation strikes with prooflike surfaces. For many Proofs dated before 1858 (the first year Proofs were widely sold to the public), the attribution of Proof format is in the eye of the beholder. The late Walter Breen (1930 to 1993) took a very liberal view of what was Proof and what was not, in his opinion at least, and issued many letters and certificates stating that this or that coin was a Proof. Today, many specialists consider some of these to be prooflike circulation strikes. In a word, be *careful* when buying any pre-1858 "Proof," certified or not, this being especially true of Proofs dated prior to 1854. Also, avoid "Proofs" that are very deeply toned—so toned, in fact, that it is nearly impossible to ascertain the true nature of the surfaces.

That said, among the unquestioned pre-1858 Proofs are many copper and silver issues from the 1820s to 1857 that are very attractive, and with full mirror fields—not at all different from the Proofs of 1858 and later except that they were not sold in quantity. For some reason, in the year 1853 no Proof sets at all were made, although a few scattered denominations were produced in this format. Years later, when the Mint was secretly restriking Proofs and patterns for collectors (mainly from spring 1859 to the mid-1870s), it was realized that no Proof dollars had been struck for the year 1853, and the deficiency was attended to forthwith, by making some from newly prepared Proof dies. About the same time the rare silver dollars of 1851 (no Proofs known to have been made originally) and 1852 (a few were made) were also restruck.

Although the field of early Proofs is not exactly *terra incognita*, there are many traps for the unwary, and all across American numismatics just a handful of collectors and professionals have studied the field carefully. However, there are experts available, and it may pay you to consult them.

Proofs from 1858 to the Early Twentieth Century

The hobby of numismatics took a giant stride forward in 1857 with the discontinuation of the large copper cent and the advent of the new, small Flying Eagle cent in copper-nickel. In the next year, 1858, Proof coins were first sold to collectors on a widespread basis. In that year it is believed that 210 silver Proof sets were sold (comprising the trime, dime, half dime, quarter, half dollar, and silver dollar), plus a larger number of individual Proof Flying Eagle cents, plus a very small number of gold coins. The gold issues, from $1 to $20, were available singly. Based upon surviving examples it seems that most were made of the gold dollar, $2.50 and $3, but relatively few of the higher values. The Proof 1858 $5, $10, and $20 are so rare that decades can elapse between offerings. In fact, a number of years ago when Ed Trompeter, the California numismatist, spent three decades in the quest to acquire one of each Proof gold coin from the $1 to the $20, 1858 to 1915, the only coin he was not able to find was the 1858 $20.

In general, Proofs of the 1858 to early twentieth-century era were struck with care, using a medal press rather than a high-speed steam-powered production press. Although there are many exceptions, Proofs of various denominations usually show excellent detail, including on such features as the centers of the stars, the hair of Miss Liberty, the leaves on the wreath, the dentils (toothlike projections around the inner rim), and other features of whatever the particular design may be. However, there are many exceptions, and it will pay to look for a sharp example of any type you are seeking.

It was the general practice until 1902 to give the fields of Proof dies a high mirror finish and to have the lettering and design parts be matte or frosted. Although use of terminology is not consistent in numismatics today, since the 1990s it has been popular to call frosted Proofs "cameo," "deep cameo," or some related nomenclature, indicating this feature. In practice, whether or not a coin is so labeled, it is a general rule that within a given date or variety of early Proof coins, all pieces are either "cameo" or they are not. As random examples, *all* Proof 1864 $20 pieces (a great rarity) have cameo surfaces. On the other hand, *nearly all* 1878 Shield nickels were made from imperfectly polished dies, are rather lustrous in appearance, and look more like circulation strikes than Proofs—hardly "cameo."

Beginning in 1902, and continuing for several years after, some seemingly misguided person at the Mint began polishing the portraits and other design features, in addition to the field. The resulting coins have "shiny" or non-cameo features. Within a given issue nearly all are this way. For example, if you look at a Proof Morgan silver dollar of 1903, you will see that it has a polished portrait. I have never seen one otherwise. On the other hand, Proof Morgan dollars of the 1880s generally have cameo or frosted portraits.

Sand Blast, Satin Finish, and Matte Proofs

Beginning in 1907, and continuing in a significant way from 1908 through 1915, the Mint experimented with different types of Proof finishes. In general, Proof gold denominations from the $2.50 to $20 were made in Sand Blast Proof finish in 1908 and again from 1911 through 1915. Such pieces were struck carefully on a medal press from ordinary dies, then subjected to blasting by a fine stream of sand particles, giving them a matte or sandpaper-like finish. The Mint considered this to be quite artistic, and earlier had used the process on many different types of medals, taking their cue from the Paris Mint, which had made sand blast Proofs for a long time. Incidentally, the term *Sand Blast Proof* is what such pieces were called in their day, although in modern times some have called them "matte," a confusing term when applied to gold issues.

In 1909 and 1910 a special satiny surface was used on gold coins (but not others), quite attractive, yielding Satin Finish Proofs.

Among other denominations, the early Proofs of the Lincoln cent beginning in 1909 and the Buffalo nickel beginning in 1913 are what are correctly called Matte Proof pieces, struck from dies having lightly pickled surfaces, yielding a satiny matte-like finish. Except that such pieces usually are extremely well struck, they are often difficult to distinguish from regular circulation strikes. Accordingly, in their time they were not very popular with collectors, and after 1916 their production was discontinued completely.

A Few Words About Striking

Among Proofs of all denominations from the late 1850s to the early twentieth century, the Mint sometimes was careless or sloppy in its production methods. Sometimes pieces of thread, human hair, or other particles were left on die surfaces, creating on coins what are called *lint marks* today. Quite a few 1858 Proof quarter dollars are this way, but Proof dollars of the same year are not. Certain Proofs of the 1870s and 1880s can lack details, with Liberty Seated coins having weakness of strike on certain obverse and reverse features. Points to check include the details of the figure on the obverse, and, on the reverse, the wreath leaf details or the eagle details (particularly toward the bottom, and also the leaves and arrows). Also, some issues, particularly the dimes, have the Liberty Seated figure less than fully frosty. Such Proofs need to be examined on an issue-by-issue basis.

When first struck, copper and bronze Proof coins were brilliant, perhaps correctly called *orange*, but now for some reason called *red*, although this makes no particular sense.

In time, copper, being a chemically active metal, toned through shades of light brown and then rich leather brown. Proof coins from "red" through brown are very desirable to own, provided that the surfaces are attractive, and that the toning, if present, is evenly distributed. I strongly recommend that stained, blotched Proofs be avoided. Also, more than just a few Proofs have been dipped and retoned. The entire area is one that requires much care, and often a certified holder will only tell part of the story, and some coins in high grades such as PF-64 and upward are, to my eye, not at all appealing. Relevant to Proof coins, bronze two-cent pieces are very difficult to find in original gem preservation. Extreme care is advised if you want quality!

Somehow, in the wide world of rare-coin investment, it became a precept that "red" Proofs are desirable among copper coins, but that red and brown Proofs or brown Proofs should be avoided. This is wonderful news for serious numismatists, as such coins, if carefully selected, can be very beautiful and very desirable to own. Often, gem Proofs with brown surfaces, such as for Indian Head cents in the 1880s, can be more attractive than fully bright ones—this being my opinion.

Proofs from 1936 to Date

After 1916 no Proofs were struck for numismatists until 1936. From that year, continuing to 1942, Proofs of the cent, nickel, dime, quarter, and half dollar were sold individually (no requirement that a full set be purchased) by the Philadelphia Mint. Production was then stopped due to the exigencies of World War II.

In 1950 Proof coinage was resumed, offered only as complete sets. Mintage continued through 1964, after which numismatists were unfairly blamed for creating a nationwide coin shortage, and the Mint stopped making Proofs.

In 1968 Proof coinage was resumed, at the San Francisco Mint, with coins in Proof sets bearing S mintmarks for the first time. In recent years, the Proofs have been of truly superb quality, neatly satisfying those who want pieces graded as PF-68 to PF-70.

However, Proofs of the early dates, especially 1936 through 1942, do vary in their quality today, as many have been cleaned or mishandled. Certain early Proofs have frosted or cameo surfaces and others do not, even within the same year. Finding a frosted one for "type" will not be difficult, as so many possibilities exist. However, the specialist collector wanting ones of each date will find that certain issues are more available than others.

For Proofs from 1950 onward, there has been much interest in "cameo" Proofs, and the certification services have noted such on certain of their holders. Certain issues of the 1950s and early 1960s can be elusive with frosty devices, for most have polished-die features for the portrait and designs.

Steps to Buying High-Quality Proof Coins

Proof coins of all eras were virtually perfection when first minted, without any hairlines, and usually without much in the way of marks (unless some marks from the original planchet were present).

Over a period of time, most pieces of 1916 and earlier years have been dipped, cleaned, or otherwise handled, yielding what are called hairlines in the field. If this seems to be surprising to you, consider that some numismatic publications often recommended or included articles suggesting that collectors brighten their coins by dipping them and rubbing them with paste or powder, or otherwise "improving" them. The curators of the National Numismatic Collection cleaned their coins several times, with the result that nearly all the nineteenth-century silver coins in the Mint Collection have extensive hairlines today. If it is any satisfaction to you, if you acquire a gem Proof Liberty Seated silver coin, you can probably say with truth, "My coin is finer than that in the Mint Collection."

David W. Lange's *Guide Book of Modern United States Proof Coin Sets*. The Mint sells Proof versions of circulating coins.

Proof coins are less forgiving to marks and handling than are circulation strikes, for often the lustrous surface of a circulation strike will absorb a few nicks and abrasions. Moreover, the hairlines from cleaning are often lost in the luster of a circulation strike, while they are painfully obvious in the mirror surface of Proofs.

The rules for buying Proofs are the same as for circulation strikes—go through a step-by-step process, beginning with seeking pieces in the general grade level wanted. However, the early test of eye appeal will be more difficult in Proofs, and more pieces will be eliminated at this stage. In general, striking and planchet quality will be no problem.

Unlike circulation strikes, the survival of which is a matter of chance—ranging from large hoards to scarcely any at all for certain dates and varieties—Proofs were typically saved in generous proportion to the numbers minted. Thus, if 1,000 Proofs were minted of a given variety a century ago, probably 600 or 800 survive today, as they were sold at a premium at the time and were preserved by numismatists. Accordingly, your search may be easier, except for eye appeal. As mentioned earlier, finding truly choice early bronze Proofs (such as a two-cent piece to illustrate the 1864 to 1873 design) will be a challenge—but challenges are what numismatics is all about!

5
How to Use This Book

On the pages that follow, each major design type of United States coin from 1792 to the present day is described. Chapters are arranged by denomination, beginning with half cents (1793 to 1857). Within each chapter will be found a general overview of the denomination, a general guide to collecting the different types, and a discussion of "Beyond a Type Set," the last for possible interest if you wish to specialize in or learn more about a given series.

For most coins, specific information is then given as follows:

Circulation Strike Mintage: Total number of coins minted for use in circulation or commerce, generally from the *Annual Report of the Director of the Mint*, but sometimes estimated (and identified as such).

Proof Mintage: Total number of Proofs minted for collectors, per the *Annual Report*, or, if not known (as with nearly all minor coins prior to 1878 and silver and gold coins before the 1860s), then estimated.

As a general rule of thumb, circulation-strike coins were spent, used, melted, or otherwise employed in commerce, with the result that for most early issues only a small percentage of each issue survives today. On the other hand, as Proofs were especially meant to be saved, most still exist.

Designer: The Mint employee or other artist who designed the coin.

Composition: Metallic composition of the coin.

Diameter: Expressed in millimeters.

Weight: Expressed in grams.

Edge: Treatment of the edge—plain, reeded, lettered, or otherwise.

Key to Collecting: Introduces each type and discusses the availability of the type in circulated grades from Good to AU and Mint State grades of MS-60 and higher.

Aspects of Striking and Appearance: Comments about the sharpness of striking, details, and luster.

Proof Coins: Information on availability, quality, and other details about the Proof coins of the type.

Notes: Various notes for additional information (given for some but not all types).

Most coin types feature a set of charts providing information on the current market values of typical circulated, Mint State, and Proof coins within each coin type, and the history of its market value over the past 70 years or so.

Market values are estimated using information from multiple sources. They are provided simply as an opinion and guide at the time of compilation, in 2019. Certain transactions might take place at higher or lower prices.

Market Value: Circulation Strikes—For most coin types, estimated market values are given for various grades of circulation strikes (those coins struck for commercial use, and not as Proofs for collectors or presentation). These might include circulated grades (AG to AU), and/or Mint State grades (MS-60 to MS-70).

Market Value: Proof Strikes—Many coin types feature a chart for estimated market values of Proof pieces. These can range from PF-60 to PF-70, depending on the coin's detail, surface quality, and other factors of preservation and visual appeal. Designations lower than 60 are for impaired Proofs—those that have been damaged or worn, possibly after entering circulation (an unusual situation, but one known to have happened at times) or from improper storage or handling.

Field Populations (Circulated, Mint State, and Proofs)—These are the number of coins estimated to exist today, for circulation strikes (in circulated grades and in Mint State) and for Proofs. These estimates include both certified and non-certified coins.

Factual information is difficult or impossible to find in some instances. For example, according to Treasury Department records, no half cents of 1793 to 1857 were ever redeemed, and *all* are outstanding. Of course, only a fraction of the mintage exists today, and an estimate has been made of the quantities still in existence. For Proofs of known mintage, the estimates are most reliable, as these were sold at a premium to buyers who, for the most part, kept them and took good care of them. For modern issues and certain others that exist in huge quantities, either from original production numbers or from their ongoing production today, such adjectives as "plentiful" and "many billions" are used.

Retail Price Trends: This consists of a listing of prices over a period of years, mostly based upon editions of *A Guide Book of United States Coins*, when such listings are available. The earliest data are from 1946 (the first edition, with a 1947 cover date), with additional data from decades after that, up to the 2020 edition. Prices are for a typical common or "type" issue. In early years of the *Red Book*, listings of certain coins were simply for Fine, Very Fine, Uncirculated, Proof, or some other grade, verbally descriptive but without numbers attached. Also, Uncirculated and Proof were not divided into levels—it was just *Uncirculated* and just *Proof*, period. For use in the present text, I have adapted the old "Fine" listing to be given here as "F-12," "Very Fine" as "VF-20," and older "Uncirculated" listings to be equal to "MS-60" to "MS-65," depending on the coin series, and "Proof" to be "PF-63" to "PF-65," these being estimated typical grades a quality-minded numismatist might have obtained.

For early copper half cents and cents, G-4 is given as the lowest grade studied for prices, while in the Liberty Seated silver series VF-20 is generally the basic lowest grade. Prices of various early coins are estimated, in the absence of certain grade levels in the *Red Book*.

Most prices for early (pre-1858) Proofs are estimates, as few such coins have been listed in the *Guide Book* over the years.

Prices for very common modern coins, such as $0.20 for a current Lincoln cent, mostly represent a dealer's effort in handling such pieces, not an indication of the resale value of such coins.

Please note that during any era, actual transactions may have taken place at higher or lower prices than *Red Book* or other historical listings. In addition, certain select coins may have sold for higher prices and unattractive coins for lower prices. Past listings and performance figures are not necessarily representative of a continuing trend or of future performance, for market conditions change and the future is unknown. For a more comprehensive view with additional grades, review historical sources.

For coin types still being minted today—the copper-coated zinc Lincoln cent, recent Jefferson nickels, the copper-nickel Roosevelt dime, America the Beautiful quarters, the Kennedy half dollar, and various golden dollars—price history is flat, as gem Mint State examples are traditionally common and inexpensive. For this reason, their "Retail Price Trends" charts are not included.

6
Half Cents
1793-1857

Overview of the Denomination

The Mint Act of April 2, 1792, provided for the half cent as the smallest denomination in the American coinage series. Mintage of half cents commenced in July 1793 with the expectation that these coins would be very popular in commerce, circulating as readily as the copper cents. However, half cents were never popular with the public. After 1811, production was intermittent, and such pieces were scarcely ever seen in circulation. Meanwhile, copper cents were widely used.

The Coinage Act of 1857 provided for the discontinuation of the copper half cent and cent, the latter to be replaced by a new, small cent made of copper-nickel. The half cents were not missed in the channels of trade, as the current generation did not use them to any extent. However, half cents became very popular with numismatists, and ever since coin collecting became a popular pursuit in the late 1850s, these pieces have been widely sought.

Collecting a Type Set of Half Cents

Building a type set of the six different major designs in the half cent series can be a challenging and rewarding pursuit. The first design, with Liberty Head facing left with pole and cap, minted only in 1793, is scarce in all grades and will be the most difficult to locate. Here, indeed, is an American classic. However, hundreds exist, and many are fairly attractive.

The second type, with large Liberty Head facing right with pole and cap, made only in 1794, is scarce with good eye appeal. Most are dark and rough. The next type, the *small* Liberty Head facing right, with pole and cap, is scarce, but enough are on the market that you can find one without difficulty.

The Draped Bust half cents, struck from 1800 to 1808, are easily available as a type, including in higher grades. The Classic Head (1809 to 1836) and Braided Hair (1840 to 1857) half cents are plentiful as types.

For the earlier half cent types, there is ample opportunity for connoisseurship, for quality often varies widely, and every coin is apt to have a different appearance and "personality," even within the same grade.

BEYOND A TYPE SET

Collecting half cents by dates and major varieties has been a popular niche specialty for a long time. Among the key issues in the series are the 1793, 1796 with pole to cap, 1796 without pole to cap (the most famous of all the rarities), 1802, 2 Over 0, with reverse of 1800 (a single leaf at each side of the wreath apex, rare but somewhat obscure), 1831, and the Proof-only issues of 1836, 1840 through 1848, 1849 Small Date, and 1852.

As there are so many Proof varieties, and each of these is rare as well as expensive, many collectors have opted to acquire only the circulation strikes. However, the Proofs are not nearly as expensive as one might think, probably because with so many different dates and varieties needed to complete a collection the prospect is daunting to many buyers. Proofs of most dates are available in both original and restrike forms. Although this rule is not without exceptions, the original strikings of the 1840 to 1848 and 1849 Small Date half cents are usually described as having the Large Berries reverse, while restrikes are of the Small Berries reverse (within the Small Berries issues there are two dies—one with diagonal die striae below RICA and the other with doubling at the ribbon wreath).

Die varieties are especially abundant among half cents of the first several types, 1793 to 1808. The year 1804 offers a panorama of dies, some of which have been studied as to *die states,* referring to the progression of use of a die as it develops wear and cracks. Varieties of 1795 exist with and without pole to the liberty cap, the without-pole being the result of a die being relapped (reground to dress the surface), during which process the pole was removed. On the other hand, the 1796 without-pole half cent was the result of a die-engraving error—the diecutter forgot to add it. Some half cents of 1795 and 1797 were struck on planchets cut from copper tokens issued by the New York City firm of Talbot, Allum & Lee. Upon close inspection, some of the design details of the tokens can still be seen.

Several years ago, I had the opportunity to examine a 1795 half cent struck on a planchet cut down from a 1794 *pattern half dollar* in copper—a coin discovered by Chris Young and described for an American Numismatic Rarities auction by John Kraljevich, the sixth such variety known to exist. I mention this as it was the second truly major discovery Chris Young has made in recent years, the other being an entirely new variety of 1794 copper cent! This proves that there are still a lot of things "out there" just waiting for alert numismatists to discover.

One curious and readily available variety of the 1828 half cent has 12 stars instead of the standard 13. However, in choice Mint State the 12-stars issue becomes a rarity, for, unlike the 13-stars issue, none were ever found in hoards.

Early American Coppers (online at www.EACS.org) is a special-interest group emphasizing copper half cents and large cents. Its journal, *Penny-Wise,* provides much research, social, and collecting news and information. The sharing of your hobby interest with this peer group will add a lot to your enjoyment.

Liberty Cap, Head Facing Left (1793)

Circulation-Strike Mintage: 35,334

Field Population: Circulated, 500 to 1,000; Mint State, 35 to 50

Designer: Henry Voigt. **Weight:** 6.74 grams.
Composition: Copper. **Diameter:** 21.2 to 24.6 mm.
Edge: Lettered TWO HUNDRED FOR A DOLLAR. **Mint:** Philadelphia.

Key to Collecting: The 1793 half cent, the key issue of the six major half cent types, is the only year of the design with Miss Liberty facing left, with a liberty cap on pole behind her head, this being the ancient *pilaeus*, or symbol of freedom. The motif was adapted from Augustin Dupré's Libertas Americana medal created in Paris in 1782 by commission from Benjamin Franklin. Several months after these half cents were struck in 1793, the Liberty Cap design was employed on the large copper cent, but with Miss Liberty facing right. Not only is the 1793 half cent one of a kind as a design type, but also it has the further cachet of being the first year of the denomination and a key date as well—it is elusive in all grades. Accordingly, the possession of an attractive 1793 half cent has been a badge of distinction for many accomplished numismatists. The typical specimen encountered is apt to show extensive wear, most being found in grades from AG-3 to F-12. At the VF and EF levels, enough pieces are in numismatic hands that they appear at auction with some frequency, but the demand is such that there is always strong competition. Mint State pieces are exceedingly rare. When found, they are usually very pleasing in appearance with lustrous brown surfaces. No more than a few dozen exist.

Aspects of Striking and Appearance: Most specimens are of pleasing appearance, often light brown, and on fairly smooth planchets, indicating a good quality of copper used. Certain varieties are lightly defined at HALF CENT on the reverse, due to a combination of striking and shallow depth of letters in the die. This is apt to be most obvious on specimens in grades up to and including VG-8, for which these words may be absent. I recommend searching until you find one with clear lettering.

Market Value: Circulation Strikes

AG-3	G-4	VG-8	F-12	VF-20	EF-40	AU-50	MS-60BN	MS-63BN
$2,500	$3,500	$5,500	$9,000	$14,000	$22,500	$27,500	$60,000	$95,000

Retail Price Trends

Year	G-4	VF-20	MS-60
1946	$17.50	$90	$180
1950	$22.50	$100	$200
1960	$65	$225	$600
1970	$250	$1,100	$5,000
1980	$600	$2,000	$10,000

Year	G-4	VF-20	MS-60
1990	$1,300	$3,750	$17,000
2000	$1,400	$5,000	$18,000
2010	$3,000	$12,500	$65,000
2019	$3,500	$14,000	$60,000

Liberty Cap, Large Head Facing Right (1794)

Circulation-Strike Mintage: 81,600

Field Population: Circulated, 1,000 to 2,000; Mint State, 15 to 25

Designer: Robert Scot. **Weight:** 6.74 grams. **Composition:** Copper. **Diameter:** 23.5 mm. **Edge:** Lettered TWO HUNDRED FOR A DOLLAR. **Mint:** Philadelphia.

Key to Collecting: The type of 1794 with Large Liberty Head Facing Right, Liberty Cap behind head, is very distinctive. As to whether it should be considered as a basic type, as here, or simply as a sub-type to be included with the 1795 to 1797 issues is a matter of opinion, and you can make your own decision. In high grades, truly choice coins are rare—more so than the famous 1793. In this category, the 1794 Large Liberty Head is the Holy Grail of half cent types. However, you do have the market advantage that not everyone considers the 1794 to be a separate type, and, beyond that, relatively few non-specialists are aware of the rarity of pieces with good eye appeal.

Half cents of 1794 of high aesthetic quality are few and far between. Finding a choice one will be a great challenge, and it may be the case that if you are concerned about quality, you may have to examine a dozen or more before making a final selection. Because of this, do not be a slave to market values if a coin of exceptional eye appeal is found.

Aspects of Striking and Appearance: Half cents of this type usually have some areas of light striking. The planchet quality is usually poor, with porosity and darkness being the rule. There are exceptions, but not many.

Notes: Lettered edge varieties within this type give the denomination *three times:* as HALF / CENT, 1/200 on the reverse, and as TWO HUNDRED FOR A DOLLAR on the edge. The same triple-denomination feature is found on several other early copper types, including the earlier described 1793 half cent and certain of the next type.

Market Value: Circulation Strikes

AG-3	G-4	VG-8	F-12	VF-20	EF-40	AU-50	MS-60BN	MS-63BN
$350	$575	$850	$1,500	$2,250	$5,000	$12,000	$25,000	$55,000

Retail Price Trends

Year	G-4	VF-20	MS-60BN
1946	$8	$27.50	$55
1950	$8	$30	$60
1960	$25	$125	$300
1970	$80	$310	$1,800
1980	$120	$500	$3,500

Year	G-4	VF-20	MS-60BN
1990	$225	$1,200	$5,000
2000	$300	$1,400	$6,200
2010	$550	$2,000	$20,000
2019	$575	$2,250	$25,000

Liberty Cap, Small Head Facing Right (1795–1797)

Circulation-Strike Mintage: 268,920

Field Population: Circulated, 3,000 to 5,000; Mint State, 150 to 250

Designer: Possibly Robert Scot, John Smith Gardner, or other. **Weight:** 5.44 grams. **Composition:** Copper. **Diameter:** 23.5 mm. **Edge:** ***Some of 1795, some of 1797:*** Lettered TWO HUNDRED FOR A DOLLAR; ***1795, 1796, most of 1797:*** Plain; some of ***1797:*** Either gripped or lettered. **Mint:** Philadelphia.

Key to Collecting: The half cent type of 1795 to 1797 with Small Liberty Head Facing Right, Liberty Cap behind head, can be divided into subtypes, with either lettered edge or plain edge. However, most numismatists are content with a single example to illustrate the *general* style. Quality of specimens varies widely. The Mint State issues of 1795 are the most fertile field for quality, as most are on smooth light-brown planchets and are very attractive, virtual paradigms of numismatic excellence. Half cents of 1796 (with and without pole to cap) are major rarities and are thus beyond consideration for type-set purposes. Those dated 1797 are more readily available, although in smaller numbers than 1795, and usually with dark or rough surfaces (although there are some notable exceptions). Indeed, the half cents of 1797 are quite curious for their primitive appearance, quite unlike the beauty that is generally seen for the two earlier dates. In contrast to 1795, coins of trophy quality are hardly to be found.

Aspects of Striking and Appearance: Half cents of this type are often struck somewhat off center. Like as not, a given half cent of the 1795 to 1797 years will have indistinct definition of hair details and some lightness of a few leaf details in the wreath. The border denticles (toothlike projections) are often very prominent on certain varieties of 1795 and 1797. Half cents of 1797 are usually seen in low grades and often on unsatisfactory planchets.

Market Value: Circulation Strikes

AG-3	G-4	VG-8	F-12	VF-20	EF-40	AU-50	MS-60BN	MS-63BN
$220	$500	$675	$1,250	$2,000	$4,750	$8,500	$14,000	$25,000

Retail Price Trends

Year	G-4	VF-20	MS-60BN
1946	$6.50	$25	$50
1950	$7.50	$30	$60
1960	$17.50	$120	$250
1970	$60	$260	$1,500
1980	$95	$380	$3,000
1990	$165	$875	$4,500
2000	$200	$1,000	$5,000
2010	$550	$2,500	$20,000
2019	$575	$2,500	$25,000

Draped Bust (1800–1808)

Circulation-Strike Mintage: 3,416,950

Field Population: Circulated, 30,000 to 40,000; Mint State, 1,750 to 2,500

Designer: Robert Scot. **Weight:** 5.44 grams. **Composition:** Copper. **Diameter:** 23.5 mm. **Edge:** Plain. **Mint:** Philadelphia.

Key to Collecting: The Draped Bust half cent is readily available in most any desired grade, up through and including Mint State, the latter being somewhat elusive in proportion to the demand for them. Mint State examples from old-time hoards are sometimes available of 1800 and 1806, especially the latter date. High-quality circulation-strike examples are readily available in grades such as VF, EF, and AU. The most obtainable dates are 1800, 1803 (less so), 1804, 1805, and 1806. 1802, 2 Over 0, is a rarity. 1807 and 1808 are often with porous surfaces. These are usually highly lustrous, attractive, and have original mint orange blended with natural light-brown toning. The reverses typically have areas of light striking, particularly on the upper leaves.

Aspects of Striking and Appearance: Generally struck on high-quality planchets (for 1800, 1803 to 1806 dates). Planchets for the rare 1802, 2 Over 0, are apt to be rough. Detail varies, but sharp pieces are available. Points of observation include hair and leaf features.

Market Value: Circulation Strikes

AG-3	G-4	VG-8	F-12	VF-20	EF-40	AU-50	MS-60BN	MS-63BN	MS-63RB	MS-65BN
$40	$85	$125	$145	$175	$325	$675	$1,200	$2,900	$3,800	$7,750

Retail Price Trends

Year	VF-20	MS-60BN
1946	$4	$8
1950	$4	$8
1960	$2.50	$9
1970	$30	$100
1980	$60	$300

Year	VF-20	MS-60BN
1990	$70	$350
2000	$30	$550
2010	$190	$1,200
2019	$175	$1,200

Classic Head (1809–1836)

Circulation-Strike Mintage: 3,517,912

Proof Mintage: *150–175* *(mostly restrikes)*

Field Population: Circulated, 35,000 to 45,000; Mint State, 5,000 to 8,000; Proof, 90 to 120

Designer: John Reich. **Weight:** 5.44 grams. **Composition:** Copper. **Diameter:** 23.5 mm. **Edge:** Plain. **Mint:** Philadelphia.

Key to Collecting: Attractive circulation-strike specimens are found easily enough in grades from VF to AU. Mint State coins, mostly from old hoards, are often spotted and require care when buying. There are many retoned and artificially colored pieces on the market, including ones in certified holders. Cherrypicking is strongly recommended, and you may have to consider several or more possibilities before finding one with excellent aesthetic appeal.

Aspects of Striking and Appearance: As a general rule, the earlier dates of this type, including the high-mintage 1809, are usually seen lightly struck in areas, particularly on the portrait details. Half cents of the 1820s and 1830s are usually well struck. Points to check include the star centers, hair details, and leaf details.

Proof Coins: Proofs were struck of various years in the 1820s and 1830s, with 1831 and 1836 being great rarities (these dates were also restruck at the Mint circa 1859 and later). Some prooflike coins (especially of the 1833 date) have been sold as Proofs. Finding a choice Proof with excellent appeal is a daunting task.

Market Value: Circulation Strikes

VG-8	F-12	VF-20	EF-40	AU-50	MS-60BN	MS-63BN	MS-63RB	MS-65BN	MS-65RB	MS-65RD
$65	$90	$110	$125	$200	$325	$450	$750	$1,250	$3,500	$8,500

Retail Price Trends

Year	VF-20	MS-64RB	PF-64RB
1946	$2	$4.50	$110
1950	$2.50	$7.50	$120
1960	$8	$25	$170
1970	$20	$95	$200
1980	$38	$245	$500

Year	VF-20	MS-64RB	PF-64RB
1990	$45	$600	$1,000
2000	$50	$700	$3,000
2010	$90	$1,200	$9,000
2019	$110	$1,200	$9,000

Braided Hair (1840–1857)

Circulation-Strike Mintage: 544,510

Proof Mintage: Fewer than 1,500, combined originals and restrikes

Field Population: Circulated, 30,000 to 45,000; Mint State, 6,000 to 9,000; Proof, 1,000 to 1,200

Designer: Christian Gobrecht. **Weight:** 5.44 grams. **Composition:** Copper. **Diameter:** 23 mm. **Edge:** Plain. **Mint:** Philadelphia.

Key to Collecting: Today, most Braided Hair circulation-strike half cents on the market are of pleasing appearance. Grades range from VF upward. Full bright Mint State orange examples can be found for 1850, 1851, 1854, 1855, and 1857. The 1849 Large Date and the 1853 are usually seen toned, possibly due to the nature of the copper used in these years. Half cents of 1857 are usually red or brown. Many recolored pieces are on the market, and others have spots. Connoisseurship is needed to acquire choice examples, and it is worthwhile to pay a premium for such.

Aspects of Striking and Appearance: Most Braided Hair half cents are well struck, but there are numerous exceptions. Points to look for are sharp details on the denticles, star centers, hair, and leaves.

Proof Coins: For the issues of 1840 to 1848, 1849 Small Date, and 1852, only Proofs were made, without related examples for circulation. As these are basically rare *as dates*, they are expensive. All were restruck at the Mint. Today, such pieces form an interesting study in themselves. Proofs of 1854 to 1857 were made to the extent of up to a hundred or so of each date and can be found with some searching.

Market Value: Circulation Strikes

VG-8	F-12	VF-20	EF-40	AU-50	MS-60BN	MS-63BN	MS-63RB	MS-65BN	MS-65RB
$60	$75	$90	$100	$165	$275	$550	$650	$1,000	$1,600

Market Value: Proof Strikes

PF-60BN	PF-63BN	PF-63RB	PF-65BN	PF-65RB
$3,500	$4,500	$7,500	$8,000	$13,500

Retail Price Trends

Year	VF-20	MS-64RB	PF-64RB
1946	$2	$6	$12.50
1950	$2.50	$7	$45
1960	$6	$17.50	$100
1970	$22	$90	$300
1980	$39	$245	$750

Year	VF-20	MS-64RB	PF-64RB
1990	$50	$360	$1,000
2000	$50	$900	$3,000
2010	$80	$1,200	$10,000
2019	$90	$1,300	$11,000

7
Large Cents
1793-1857

Overview of the Large Cent Series

Large copper cents are what American numismatics is all about. Production of these large, heavy cents was discontinued in January 1857 (*officially* by the Act of February 21, 1857, a few weeks later), and the small-diameter Flying Eagle cent became the new standard, and there was a wave of nostalgia. A scramble ensued, and thousands of citizens endeavored to find one each of as many different dates as possible. Most who were dedicated could put together a sequence dating back to 1816, possibly excepting the rare 1823. Earlier issues from 1793 to 1814 (no cents were struck in 1815) could be found here and there, but usually very worn, sometimes to virtual smoothness.

Authorized by the Mint Act of April 2, 1792, the first copper cents were struck at the Philadelphia Mint in February 1793. Walter Breen states that Henry Voigt, chief coiner at the Mint, cut the dies, but as he did not have appropriate skills, "his designs were kept simple."[9] The initial design featured the head of Miss Liberty on the obverse, facing right, while on the reverse was a chain of 15 links, one for each state in the Union. Soon afterward, the motif was extensively modified, and soon a new copper cent of 1793 made its appearance, with Miss Liberty restyled and, on the reverse, a wreath.

In late summer 1793, the Liberty Cap style made its debut, the *chef d'oeuvre* of talented artist Joseph Wright, the recently hired engraver at the Mint. His tenure was all too brief and was cut short by his death on September 12 or 13 of the same year, a victim of yellow fever.

In 1796 the Draped Bust design replaced the Liberty Cap style, the work of Robert Scot, engraver at the Mint following the passing of Wright. In 1808 the Classic Head motif, by John Reich, was introduced, and continued through 1814. In 1816 cents of a new design, now called the *Matron Head*, became the standard, a motif continued to the mid-1830s. From 1835 to 1839, Mint engraver Christian Gobrecht experimented with several different portraits, finally settling on the Braided Hair style, employed with modifications through 1857.

At the Philadelphia Mint, silver and gold coins were produced at the specific request of banks, merchants, and other depositors of precious metal, often in the form of foreign coins. A charge was levied for refining, assaying, and coining the metal, but this barely covered expenses. On the other hand, copper half cents and cents were produced specifically for the Mint's own account, and the Mint retained any profit derived therefrom. Accordingly, if it cost the Mint $6 to produce $10 in face value in copper cents (1,000 coins), a profit of $4 was registered. The making of copper cents was *very important* to the economy of the Mint, and for that reason, production was typically in large quantity and continuous. In 1816 cents were the only denomination made there!

Beginning in 1850, the Mint sought to replace the traditional large copper cent with a smaller version, to increase profits and to provide a coin more convenient to handle. The price of copper was trending upward, and profits were being diminished. Patterns were made during the next few years, until in 1856 a new alloy, copper-nickel, was decided upon for a new small-diameter cent, the work of James B. Longacre, who had been appointed chief engraver at the Mint in 1844.

The Mint Act of February 21, 1857, provided for the new small cents and, at the same time, the discontinuation of the copper half cent and cent. Certain foreign gold and silver coins that had been legal tender for many years had this status revoked, effective in two years (later given a six-month extension).

After an extensive coinage of 1856 pattern Flying Eagle cents, coins of the new format were struck for circulation in 1857 and released on May 25 of that year. The new Flying Eagle cents proved to be immensely popular with the public, and by the time the Civil War began, in April 1861, large copper cents were hardly ever seen in commercial transactions. In the meantime, numismatic interest in the series remained very intense.

COLLECTING A TYPE SET OF LARGE CENTS

Collecting one each of the major types of 1793 to 1857 copper cents can be a fascinating challenge. Early varieties were struck from hand-engraved dies, often on planchets of uncertain quality. It was not until 1836 that steam power was used to run coining presses at the Mint. All earlier issues were made by hand, by two men tugging on the weighted lever arm of a small screw-type press. As might be expected, this resulted in many variations of striking quality.

The following listings comprise major types. There is no single right or wrong way to devise a list of what to include, as there are a number of variations that can or cannot be called types, depending upon your opinion. As an example, I list two types of the 1793 Chain cent, one with the reverse bearing the abbreviation AMERI., and the other with full spelling as AMERICA. You might want to collect just one for the Chain type, in view of the rarity and cost of such pieces, this being the procedure followed by most numismatists over the years.

Wreath cents of 1793 occur with the edge displaying a vine and bars motif and also with lettering ONE HUNDRED FOR A DOLLAR. I have combined these as a single Wreath cent type. Liberty Cap cents of the years 1793 to 1796 have lettered edges (ONE HUNDRED FOR A DOLLAR) used in 1793, 1794, and part of 1795, and plain edges for most 1795 coins and all of 1796. I have listed just a single Liberty Cap type, but you might want to own one of each edge style. In today's world, in which many early cents are encapsulated in holders, the edges are not visible, and interest in such variations is diminished.

The nine different types I list can be condensed to eight by combining the two Chain reverse styles or can be expanded by considering variations in edge styles. Eight or nine different ones will probably fill the bill for most readers. Buying copper large cents for your type set is an experience that should be *savored,* as there are endlessly fascinating varieties and surface colors and characteristics available. Even if you can buy a given type instantly, I recommend taking your time to find one that is just right.

Beyond a Type Set

For the enjoyment of copper cents of 1793 to 1857, it is possible to go *far* beyond a type set. Over a long period of years, many prominent numismatists have made such coins the centerpoint of their hobby interest.

Today, varieties of the 1793 to 1814 cents are generally collected by Sheldon numbers (S-1, S-2, etc.) first given in *Early American Cents,* 1949, and its revision, *Penny Whimsy,* 1958. Building upon this foundation, *Walter Breen's Encyclopedia of Early United States Large Cents 1793 to 1814,* edited by Mark Borckardt, gives more information than available in any other single source.

Among dates and major varieties in the early range of the series, the 1793 Chain AMERI., Chain AMERICA, Wreath, and Liberty Cap issues, the 1799 (far and away the rarest date in the series), and the 1804 are key issues, each a part of an extensive series of more than 300 die varieties through and including 1814.

Dr. Sheldon devised the interesting concept of designating certain rare die varieties as "Non-Collectible," listing them as NC-1, NC-2, and so further, with the thought that a collection can be "complete" by including just the regular Sheldon (S-1 and others) numbers and ignoring the NCs. However, similar to certain other Sheldon notions (including the numerical grading / market formula for pricing), it was defective. Additional specimens of certain NC varieties were discovered, making some NC issues more available than certain varieties among the S numbers!

The most popular way to collect early copper cents is by basic *Red Book* varieties, mainly dates, overdates, and major varieties. Sometimes, a particular date is selected as a specialty for collecting die varieties by Sheldon numbers, 1794 being a favorite in this regard.

Flowing Hair, Chain Reverse, AMERI. in Legend (1793)

Circulation-Strike Mintage: *5,000–10,000*

Field Population: Circulated, 200 to 300; Mint State, 2 to 4

Designer: Henry Voigt. **Weight:** 13.48 grams. **Composition:** Copper. **Diameter:** Average 26 to 27 mm. **Edge:** Vine and bars design. **Mint:** Philadelphia.

Key to Collecting: The first cents for circulation were struck at the Mint from February 27 through March 12, 1793. These were of the Chain motif and were made to the extent of 36,103 pieces. The first of these issues bore the abbreviated inscription UNITED STATES OF AMERI. (today designated as the Sheldon-1 variety). Perhaps 5,000 to 10,000 were of this style, judging from the ratio of surviving examples. The rest of the 36,103 pieces were of the AMERICA type. Chain AMERI. cents are rare in all grades. As noted in the introduction, many type-set collectors combine this and the next in an endeavor to obtain just one Chain cent. Most circulated issues are in lower grades. Specimens in Fair and AG grades can sometimes be identified, as the central chain device is usually visible even if the date is worn away. Mint State coins are essentially unobtainable, for only a few exist.

Aspects of Striking and Appearance: The details of Miss Liberty's hair are often indistinct or missing, including on many higher-grade specimens. For all grades, the reverse is often sharper than the obverse. Hence, if split grading were popular today (as it once was), a Chain AMERI. cent might be correctly graded as VG-8/F-12, or similarly.

Market Value: Circulation Strikes

AG-3	G-4	VG-8	F-12	VF-20	EF-40	AU-50	MS-60BN
$5,750	$10,000	$18,000	$27,000	$42,500	$77,500	$150,000	$170,000

Retail Price Trends

Year	G-4	VF-20	MS-60BN
1946	$45	$175	$350
1950	$50	$200	$400
1960	$90	$300	$600
1970	$350	$1,600	$5,800
1980	$800	$4,500	$40,000

Year	G-4	VF-20	MS-60BN
1990	$2,000	$7,000	$80,000
2000	$3,000	$12,000	$100,000
2010	$10,000	$45,000	$195,000
2019	$10,000	$42,500	$170,000

Flowing Hair, Chain Reverse, AMERICA in Legend (1793)

Circulation-Strike Mintage: 36,103 *(less an estimated 5,000–10,000 of the AMERI. variety)*

Field Population: Circulated, 500 to 800; Mint State, 12 to 15

Designer: Henry Voigt. **Weight:** 13.48 grams. **Composition:** Copper. **Diameter:** Average 26 to 27 mm. **Edge:** Vine and bars design. **Mint:** Philadelphia.

Key to Collecting: This is the second type within the Chain design. The majority of surviving 1793 Chain cents are of this type. Most specimens known today are well worn. Most are in lower grades from Fair through VG-8 and F-12, although VF coins come on the market with some frequency. Some exceedingly worn specimens are smooth save for traces of the chain device, which serves adequately to identify them as cents of this year and general type. Mint State coins are exceedingly rare.

Aspects of Striking and Appearance: Similar to the preceding type, the obverse portrait details are often weak, although less so than on the Chain AMERI. variety. On circulated examples, the reverse is typically a grade or two higher than the obverse.

Market Value: Circulation Strikes

AG-3	G-4	VG-8	F-12	VF-20	EF-40	AU-50	MS-60BN
$4,750	$7,500	$14,000	$19,500	$32,000	$60,000	$100,000	$180,000

Retail Price Trends

Year	G-4	VF-20	MS-60BN
1946	$35	$150	$350
1950	$35	$200	$400
1960	$75	$500	$3,000
1970	$285	$1,300	$4,700
1980	$600	$3,900	$35,000
1990	$1,750	$6,250	$45,000
2000	$2,500	$11,000	$60,000
2010	$10,000	$45,000	$195,000
2019	$7,500	$32,000	$180,000

Flowing Hair, Wreath Reverse (1793)

Circulation-Strike Mintage: 563,353

Field Population: Circulated, 2,000 to 3,000; Mint State, 80 to 110

Designer: Henry Voigt. **Weight:** 13.48 grams. **Composition:** Copper. **Diameter:** 26 to 28 mm. **Edge:** Vine and bars design, or lettered ONE HUNDRED FOR A DOLLAR followed by either a single or a double leaf. **Mint:** Philadelphia.

Key to Collecting: The Wreath cent, named for the reverse, reflected a great change in the cent motif—now with a restyled portrait in high relief and with the reverse chain eliminated. Both obverse and reverse were given a beaded border, at once protective and attractive. At least seven pairs of dies were used to accomplish the coinage. Early examples have the vine-and-bars edge treatment, while later (scarcer) ones are lettered ONE HUNDRED FOR A DOLLAR. Today, Wreath cents are at once rare and popular, serving as foundation stones in American numismatics. Such coins are in continual demand, and there has never been a time in which the market for them has been slow. Circulated coins are rare in all grades. Typical grades are G to F, although VF and even EF pieces come on the market with regularity, especially when important collections are dispersed. Many pieces have problems, and cherrypicking is needed to find one that is just right. Mint State coins are extremely rare, but more available than the other types of this year.

Aspects of Striking and Appearance: Usually fairly well struck, although high-grade pieces may exhibit some weakness on the highest hair tresses and on the leaf details. On lower-grade pieces, these areas are worn, so the point is moot. Specimens are often grainy or porous, but choice examples can be found with searching.

Market Value: Circulation Strikes

AG-3	G-4	VG-8	F-12	VF-20	EF-40	AU-50	MS-60BN	MS-63BN
$1,600	$3,250	$4,700	$7,500	$13,000	$21,000	$35,000	$55,000	$100,000

Retail Price Trends

Year	G-4	VF-20	MS-63RB	Year	G-4	VF-20	MS-63RB
1946	$27.50	$120	$350	1990	$750	$2,800	$25,000
1950	$27.50	$120	$350	2000	$850	$3,500	$32,000
1960	$65	$400	$1,500	2010	$2,150	$7,250	$150,000
1970	$220	$1,050	$6,500	2019	$3,250	$13,000	$180,000
1980	$300	$1,750	$20,000				

Liberty Cap (1793–1796)

Circulation-Strike Mintage: 1,577,902

Field Population: Circulated, 14,000 to 18,000; Mint State, 400 to 700

Designer: ***1793–1795, thick planchet:*** Probably Joseph Wright; ***1795–1796, thin planchet:*** John Smith Gardner. **Weight:** ***1793–1795, thick planchet:*** 13.48 grams; ***1795–1796, thin planchet:*** 10.89 grams. **Composition:** Copper. **Diameter:** Average 29 mm. **Edge:** ***1793–1795, thick planchet:*** Lettered ONE HUNDRED FOR A DOLLAR; ***1795–1796, thin planchet:*** Plain. **Mint:** Philadelphia.

Key to Collecting: The Liberty Cap cent was created in the summer of 1793 by Joseph Wright, an accomplished artist, who also engraved some earlier dies for the Mint, including the 1792 eagle-on-globe pattern. The motif of the cent followed the obverse design of Augustin Dupré's Libertas Americana medal produced in Paris in 1782 at the suggestion of Benjamin Franklin, except that on the cent the head faces to the right rather than to the left. This was the second use of the motif at the Mint, as in July half cents were made of the Liberty Cap design (with Miss Liberty facing to the left, as on Dupré's original). While Liberty Cap cents dated 1793 are major rarities, this was the standard design for 1794, 1795, and part of 1796, during which period well over a million were made, thus offering an affordable example for a type set. Those of 1794 and some of 1795 have the edge lettered ONE HUNDRED FOR A DOLLAR, while those made later in 1795 and in 1796 are on thinner planchets and have a plain edge. The type is sufficiently plentiful in just about any grade desired but most numerous in preservations from G to F or so. VF coins are offered frequently, and EF and AU pieces less often. Those dated 1795 are the most often seen. Mint State coins are very rare and are usually available only when specialized collections are sold. In Mint State, 1795 is the date most often encountered.

Aspects of Striking and Appearance: Vary depending upon the variety. Points to look for are hair details, leaf details, and sharpness of the border denticles.

Notes: The earlier varieties, those minted in 1794 and in early 1795, with lettered edge give the denomination three times: as ONE / CENT, 1/100 on the reverse, and as ONE HUNDRED FOR A DOLLAR on the edge. The same triple-denomination feature is found on several other early copper types.

Market Value: Circulation Strikes

AG-3	G-4	VG-8	F-12	VF-20	EF-40	AU-50	MS-60BN	MS-63BN
$200	$375	$600	$1,000	$1,800	$3,300	$6,000	$8,500	$20,000

Retail Price Trends

Year	G-4	VF-20	MS-63RB
1946	$3	$6	$17.50
1950	$3.50	$7	$20
1960	$9	$45	$225
1970	$30	$125	$675
1980	$47.50	$250	$3,000
1990	$100	$550	$5,000
2000	$140	$650	$5,000
2010	$325	$1,350	$25,000
2019	$375	$1,800	$25,000

Draped Bust (1796-1807)

Circulation-Strike Mintage: 16,069,270

Field Population: Circulated, 100,000 to 200,000; Mint State, 1,000 to 1,600

Designer: Robert Scot. **Weight:** 10.89 grams. **Composition:** Copper. **Diameter:** Average 29 mm. **Edge:** Plain. **Mint:** Philadelphia.

Key to Collecting: The Draped Bust cent made its debut in 1796, following a coinage of Liberty Cap cents the same year. The motif, from a drawing by Gilbert Stuart, was first employed on certain silver dollars of 1795. The new design proved to be very durable and was used through and including 1807. While the 1799 is a classic rarity and the 1804 is elusive, enough exist of most other dates that finding a choice one will be no problem. Plentiful in all lower grades, but most range from G to F. Mint State coins, however, are very scarce, and are generally in lower grades, MS-60 to MS-63, with brown surfaces.

Aspects of Striking and Appearance: Often lightly struck in some areas of the denticles. Also check for hair-strand detail and leaf detail on higher-grade specimens. Planchet quality is generally good, but many rough and porous pieces exist. Careful selection is recommended.

Market Value: Circulation Strikes

AG-3	G-4	VG-8	F-12	VF-20	EF-40	AU-50	MS-60BN	MS-63BN	MS-63RB	MS-65BN
$65	$125	$150	$325	$800	$1,800	$4,000	$10,000	$20,000	$32,000	$65,000

Retail Price Trends

Year	G-4	VF-20	MS-63RB
1946	$1	$5	$12
1950	$1	$6	$18
1960	$3	$20	$200
1970	$9	$45	$900
1980	$12	$85	$1,200
1990	$20	$200	$2,000
2000	$30	$250	$5,000
2010	$55	$400	$16,000
2019	$125	$800	$32,000

Classic Head (1808–1814)

Circulation-Strike Mintage: 4,757,722

Field Population: Circulated, 20,000 to 50,000; Mint State, 500 to 800

Designer: John Reich. **Weight:** 10.89 grams. **Composition:** Copper. **Diameter:** Average 29 mm. **Edge:** Plain. **Mint:** Philadelphia.

Key to Collecting: Today, all dates are available, with no major rarities, although those of 1809 are considered to be scarcer than the others. When found, an ideal piece will probably not cost much more than an average specimen of its date and grade, for most buyers are not oriented toward seeking quality. Grading numbers alone suffice for all but dedicated specialists. Mint State coins are exceedingly rare. Most are in lower grade ranges such as MS-60 to MS-63.

Aspects of Striking and Appearance: Striking sharpness varies. Generally, the earlier dates in the type are less well defined than are 1813 and 1814. They are seen on light brown planchets and are somewhat casually struck, with many design details weak or absent. Points to look for include sharpness of the denticles, star centers, hair details, and leaf details. Cents of 1814 are sometimes dark and porous due to the copper stock used. Finding a sharply struck Classic Head cent with smooth, attractive fields will be a great challenge involving inspecting many coins.

Market Value: Circulation Strikes

AG-3	G-4	VG-8	F-12	VF-20	EF-40	AU-50	MS-60BN	MS-63BN
$60	$100	$200	$400	$700	$1,700	$3,000	$6,000	$12,500

Retail Price Trends

Year	G-4	VF-20	MS-63RB
1946	$1	$6	$18
1950	$1.50	$8	$24
1960	$3.50	$30	$300
1970	$12	$57.50	$800
1980	$20	$140	$2,000
1990	$22.50	$225	$2,000
2000	$33	$450	$5,000
2010	$50	$550	$10,000
2019	$100	$700	$13,000

Matron Head (1816-1835)

Circulation-Strike Mintage: 45,654,912

Proof Mintage: 150 Proofs at most

Field Population: Circulated, 350,000 to 500,000; Mint State, 10,000 to 15,000

Designer: Possibly Robert Scot or John Birch. **Weight:** 10.89 grams. **Composition:** Copper. **Diameter:** 28 to 29 mm. **Edge:** Plain. **Mint:** Philadelphia.

Key to Collecting: The term *Matron Head* to describe cents of 1816 to 1835 (no cents were struck in 1815) seems to have been popularized by Kenneth E. Bressett as a heading for listings in the *Red Book*, possibly after use of the term by members of the Early American Coppers Club. The same general portrait was in use from 1816 to 1835, after which it went through several modifications of neck and hair style (see following 1836 to 1839 type). Many collectors of type coins choose to ignore the modifications and include the Matron Head as extending from 1816 to 1839. Those of 1816 to 1820 (particularly 1818 and 1820) are readily available in Mint State from the famous Randall Hoard. Otherwise, Mint State coins are generally scarce in the type, although those of the 1830s are more available than those of the 1820s. Circulated examples exist in approximate relationship to their mintages.

Aspects of Striking and Appearance: Vary widely. Points to look for include denticles on both sides, star centers, hair details, and leaf details.

Proof Coins: Proofs were made of most dates from about 1817 onward. A few "expertised" as Proofs are simply circulation strikes with somewhat prooflike surfaces, sometimes so deeply toned that little can be ascertained about the true character of the surface. Opinions vary widely, and I suggest that you bide your time until you find a deeply reflective fully mirrorlike example that has been reviewed by a trusted dealer or other expert.

Market Value: Circulation Strikes

G-4	VG-8	F-12	VF-20	EF-40	AU-50	MS-60BN	MS-63BN	MS-63RB	MS-65BN	MS-65RB
$25	$30	$45	$85	$175	$300	$400	$650	$900	$1,800	$2,500

Market Value: Proof Strikes

PF-60BN	PF-63BN	PF-64BN	PF-65BN
$10,000	$15,000	$21,000	$40,000

Retail Price Trends

Year	VF-20	MS-64RB	PF-64RB
1946	$2.50	$5.25	$50
1950	$3	$15	$150
1960	$5	$22.50	$250
1970	$13.50	$157.50	$1,000
1980	$17.50	$350	$3,000

Year	VF-20	MS-64RB	PF-64RB
1990	$35	$750	$9,000
2000	$55	$800	$12,000
2010	$65	$1,200	$31,000
2019	$85	$1,400	$32,000

Matron Head Modified (1835–1839)

Circulation-Strike Mintage: 17,168,161 (less some 1839 Braided Hair cents, less than a million)

Proof Mintage: Fewer than 100

Field Population: Circulated, 90,000 to 120,000; Mint State, 2,000 to 3,000; Proof, 35 to 55

Designer: Christian Gobrecht. **Weight:** 10.89 grams. **Composition:** Copper. **Diameter:** 27.5 mm. **Edge:** Plain. **Mint:** Philadelphia.

Key to Collecting: The modified Matron Head era 1836 to 1839 includes different portrait styles by Christian Gobrecht, who seems to have been experimenting. In 1837 a beaded hair cord was introduced to tie the bun in Miss Liberty's hair. Other variations include the facial and head appearances and shape of the neck truncation as well as hair-strand placement. Distinctive names such as *Booby Head* and *Silly Head* have been given to some of the 1839 varieties. Enough cents of the 1836 to 1839 era exist that examples are readily available in all circulated grades, although those of 1839 are more elusive than others. Mint State coins are scarce, but come on the market with regularity. Grades range from MS-60 and upward, generally with brown or red-and-brown surfaces. Many have been cleaned and retoned. However, choice pieces do exist, and some have outstanding eye appeal.

Aspects of Striking and Appearance: Generally quite good. However, check for denticles, star centers, hair details, and leaf denticles.

Proof Coins: Exceedingly rare.

Market Value: Circulation Strikes

G-4	VG-8	F-12	VF-20	EF-40	AU-50	MS-60BN	MS-63BN	MS-63RB	MS-65BN	MS-65RB
$20	$25	$35	$50	$110	$200	$325	$500	$775	$1,200	$1,900

Market Value: Proof Strikes

PF-60BN	PF-63BN	PF-64BN	PF-65BN
$10,500	$14,000	$20,000	$38,000

Retail Price Trends

Year	VF-20	MS-64RB	PF-64RB
1946	$2	$7.50	$50
1950	$3	$9	$150
1960	$5	$17.50	$200
1970	$13	$127.50	$900
1980	$17.50	$250	$2,750

Year	VF-20	MS-64RB	PF-64RB
1990	$35	$700	$4,500
2000	$40	$900	$6,000
2010	$50	$1,300	$35,000
2019	$50	$1,200	$30,000

Braided Hair (1839–1857)

Circulation-Strike Mintage: 70,916,893 (plus somewhat less than a million dated 1839)

Proof Mintage: Fewer than 1,200, mostly dated 1854 to 1857

Field Population: Circulated, 500,000 to 700,000; Mint State, 25,000 to 35,000; Proof, 700 to 900

Designer: Christian Gobrecht. **Weight:** 10.89 grams. **Composition:** Copper. **Diameter:** 27.5 mm. **Edge:** Plain. **Mint:** Philadelphia.

Key to Collecting: Examples are plentiful in all circulated grades. Mint State specimens range from scarce to very scarce for the earlier dates, but in the context of such coins being plentiful from 1850 onward, those of 1850 to 1856 are particularly so. However, those of 1839 through the early 1840s are quite scarce. Cents of 1843 to 1849 are found in lustrous brown Mint State, but are very rare with *original* bright orange ("red") surfaces. Cents of all dates 1850 to 1856 are generally available in nearly full mint red, but often with flecks or spots, these coins tracing their origin to hoards of long ago. Cents of 1857 are scarce and are hardly ever seen full mint red.

Aspects of Striking and Appearance: Check the denticles, star centers, and leaf details. Some are struck on "flaky" (laminated) planchets.

Proof Coins: Very rare for issues prior to 1854. Those of 1854 to 1857 were made up to the extent of a hundred or so of each date.

Market Value: Circulation Strikes

G-4	VG-8	F-12	VF-20	EF-40	AU-50	MS-60BN	MS-63BN	MS-63RB	MS-65BN	MS-65RB
$20	$25	$35	$40	$65	$125	$180	$230	$350	$635	$1,150

Market Value: Proof Strikes

PF-60BN	PF-63BN	PF-64BN	PF-65BN
$4,000	$6,000	$9,500	$18,500

Retail Price Trends

Year	EF-40	MS-65RB	PF-65RB
1946	$1.50	$5.75	$50
1950	$2	$5	$150
1960	$4	$14	$200
1970	$16	$75	$900
1980	$25	$200	$2,750

Year	EF-40	MS-65RB	PF-65RB
1990	$50	$750	$4,500
2000	$45	$800	$6,000
2010	$1,100	$11,000	$9,200
2019	$1,150	$17,000	$9,200

8
Small Cents
1856 to Date

Overview of the Denomination

The Mint Act of February 21, 1857, abolished the old copper large cent and provided for its replacement by a small-diameter cent made of copper-nickel (88% copper and 12% nickel), weighing 72 grains. Chief Engraver James B. Longacre created a new motif by taking the flying eagle used by Christian Gobrecht on the reverse of the 1836 silver dollar and combining it with the "agricultural" wreath Longacre had devised in 1854 for the Type II gold dollar and the new three-dollar denomination. The motifs of this new cent were not new at all!

In 1856 and early 1857, nearly 1,000 patterns were made of the Flying Eagle cent, dated 1856, for distribution to congressmen, newspaper editors, and others of influence to acquaint them with the forthcoming design, as the copper cents of childhood and later days were to be replaced with the smaller, lightweight style.

On May 25, 1857, distribution of the copper-nickel Flying Eagle cents began. The new coins were well received, and soon the old large cents nearly disappeared. However, problems developed in striking the Flying Eagle cents properly, as the head and tail of the eagle were opposite on the dies (when in the coining press) from the heavy details on the wreath, and it was difficult for the metal to fill deep die recesses in each direction. Accordingly, in 1858 extensive experimentation was done to revise the motif, to either a small "skinny" eagle as seen on certain patterns or, as eventually adopted, an Indian Head motif.

Flying Eagle cents were produced for circulation only in 1857 and 1858. The Indian Head cents of 1859 had a laurel or olive (the Mint used both terms) wreath on the reverse. In 1860 this was changed to an oak wreath and shield motif.

Copper-nickel remained the alloy for cents until spring 1864, when bronze (95% copper and 5% tin and zinc; also called "French bronze") became the standard and was afterward used through the end of the series. Cents from that time onward were on thinner planchets weighing 48 grains. In the autumn of 1864, the tiny initial L was added to the headdress ribbon of the Indian, signifying Longacre, the engraver. However, for most numismatists, this does not constitute a major new type.

On August 2, 1909, the Lincoln motif cent by Victor D. Brenner was released into circulation, continuing the recent policy of having coin motifs made by artists other than Mint employees, the work of Chief Engraver Charles Barber being heavily criticized. In 1907 and 1908 the gold coinage had been redesigned, and in 1909 the Lincoln cent was the next step. The earliest issues had the initials of the engraver, V.D.B., on the reverse. There was some public complaint about this, and the letters were removed later in the same month, creating a distinct type. Curiously, numismatic tradition has it that Longacre's added L on the 1864 Indian Head cent does not constitute new *type*, but the V.D.B. on the Lincoln cent qualifies. Inconsistencies abound in what is a type and what is not, all contributing to the challenge of numismatics.

The Lincoln cent without V.D.B. on the reverse was produced continuously through 1958. In 1918 the V.D.B. initials were restored to the cent, this time in tiny letters on the obverse, on Lincoln's shoulder. This modification, again per numismatic tradition, does not constitute a new type. In 1943 the cents were made of zinc-coated steel to conserve copper for the war effort. From 1944 to 1946, cents were made of metal from discarded cartridge-shell cases, these being 95% copper and 5% zinc (instead of the earlier and later mixture of 95% copper and the remaining 5% being a mixture of tin and zinc). Some collectors consider this to be a separate type, but most do not (and it is not designated separately in the present text). In 1947 the standard bronze was resumed.

In 1959 the Lincoln Memorial reverse was introduced, the designer being Frank Gasparro, an engraver on the Mint staff (who would later become chief engraver). The new motif was not particularly well received. In 1962 the alloy was changed to 95% copper and 5% zinc (eliminating tin), which was continued part way through 1982. Since that latter time, the composition for circulating coins has been copper-plated zinc.

Although there have been many discussions in Congress and among the general public that the "penny" is obsolete in today's world of higher prices, the Lincoln cent continues to be popular; and from 1793 to the present time, cents have been minted continuously except for the year 1815. The year 2009 marked the 200th anniversary of Abraham Lincoln's birth, and with it the circulation of four new reverse designs on the 100-year-old Lincoln cent. A new "Union Shield" design followed.

Collecting a Type Set of Small Cents

Forming a type set of small cents is easy enough, although the first two issues, the 1857 and 1858 Flying Eagle cent and the 1859 Indian Head with laurel wreath reverse, can be expensive in higher grades. Striking quality is a consideration for all small cents 1857 to the end of the Indian Head series in 1909, but enough exist that finding a needle-sharp piece is simply a matter of time. Lincoln cents can be obtained without difficulty.

Every now and then someone building a type set spices up the more common issues by adding a rare date or mintmark, such as a "story" coin, the 1909-S V.D.B. Lincoln being a prime example. However, most stay with the more plentiful issues.

BEYOND A TYPE SET

Flying Eagle and Indian Head cents are usually collected together by specialists, who often aspire to add the pattern 1856 Flying Eagle to the series. A full run of dates and major varieties includes:

Flying Eagle cents: 1856 (pattern); 1857; 1858, 8 Over 7; 1858, Large Letters; and 1858, Small Letters.

Indian Head cents: 1859, with laurel wreath reverse; 1860–1864, with oak wreath and shield reverse, struck in copper-nickel; 1864, bronze; 1864, bronze with L on ribbon; and one of each date to 1909, plus 1908-S and 1909-S. Significant varieties after 1864 include 1873, Doubled LIBERTY; 1873, Close 3; 1873, Open 3; 1886, early hub with last feather pointing between the I and C in AMERICA; 1886, late hub with last feather pointing between C and A; 1888, 8 Over 7; and 1894, repunched date.

Proof Flying Eagle and Indian Head cents form a separate specialty and are widely collected.

The collecting of 1909 to date Lincoln cents is a foundation of American numismatics. It can be fun to look through pocket change to see how many different varieties can be obtained. Today, in the early twenty-first century, such a search might go back to 1959, the first year of the Lincoln Memorial reverse, before which time pieces even of high-mintage issues are hardly ever seen. A generation ago it was possible to find cents from 1909 onward. However, key issues such as 1909-S V.D.B. (the most famous of all "popular rarities" in the United States series), 1914-D, 1924-D, 1926-S, 1931-S, and 1955 Doubled Die Obverse eluded most enthusiasts.

Lincoln cents can be collected casually, or a specialty can be made of them. A dedicated enthusiast may want to secure one each in a grade such as MS-65, also taking care that each is sharply struck. There are quite a few issues, including Denver and San Francisco varieties from about 1916 to the late 1920s, that are plentiful *except* if sharply struck (with full hair detail on the Lincoln portrait, no tiny marks on Lincoln's shoulder, and sharp details and a smooth field on the reverse).

By collecting the types described here or by striving to build a full set, you will find the series to be very interesting.

Flying Eagle (1856–1858)

Circulation-Strike Mintage: 42,050,000

Proof Mintage: Fewer than 2,000

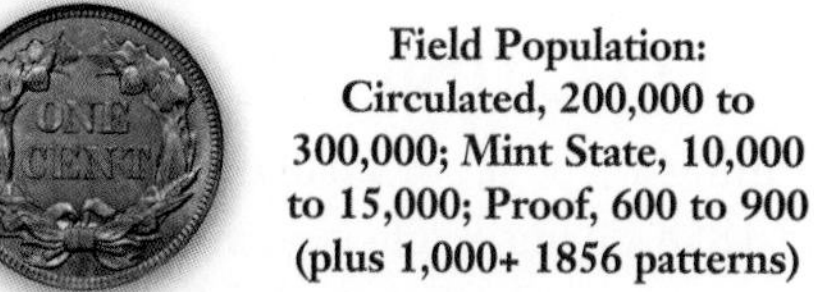

Field Population: Circulated, 200,000 to 300,000; Mint State, 10,000 to 15,000; Proof, 600 to 900 (plus 1,000+ 1856 patterns)

Designer: James B. Longacre. **Weight:** 4.67 grams. **Composition:** .880 copper, .120 nickel. **Diameter:** 19 mm. **Edge:** Plain. **Mint:** Philadelphia.

Key to Collecting: The Flying Eagle cents first appeared in circulation on May 25, 1857. Within a year, most old copper "large" cents had disappeared, and the new small cents were standard in the channels of commerce. These were struck in quantity for the remainder of 1857 and in 1858, after which the design was abandoned, as problems resulted in striking. Examples are easy to obtain today. Most are in worn grades from G to F or better. Mint State pieces are plentiful in the marketplace, but within any assigned grading number, quality is apt to vary widely. Cherrypicking for a choice example is highly advised.

Aspects of Striking and Appearance: Striking is usually fairly good. However, some are weak on the eagle's head and tail feathers and, sometimes, in the lettering on the obverse. The reverse tends to be better struck, but weakness can occur on the higher areas of the wreath. Most Mint State coins are lustrous.

Proof Coins: Proof coins of the 1856 *pattern* are plentiful, with over 1,500 believed to have been made, most as restrikes. Among regular issues, Proofs of 1857 are very rare and those of 1858 are quite rare but not in the league of the 1857.

Market Value: Circulation Strikes

G-4	VG-8	F-12	VF-20	EF-40	AU-50	MS-60	MS-63	MS-64	MS-65
$25	$40	$50	$60	$140	$215	$450	$1,000	$1,500	$3,500

Market Value: Proof Strikes

PF-60	PF-63	PF-64	PF-65	PF-65CAM
$5,000	$8,000	$11,000	$25,000	$27,500

Retail Price Trends

Year	VF-20	MS-65	PF-65
1946	$1.75	$7.50	$55
1950	$2	$10	$65
1960	$7	$37.50	$250
1970	$14	$200	$2,000
1980	$24	$2,000	$5,000
1990	$25	$2,500	$6,000
2000	$36	$3,000	$16,000
2010	$60	$3,750	$25,000
2019	$60	$3,500	$23,500

Indian Head, Copper-Nickel, Laurel Wreath Reverse (1859)

Circulation-Strike Mintage: 36,400,000

Proof Mintage: *800*

Field Population: Circulated, 100,000 to 200,000; Mint State, 6,000 to 9,000; Proof, 450 to 600

Designer: James B. Longacre. **Weight:** 4.67 grams. **Composition:** .880 copper, .120 nickel. **Diameter:** 19 mm. **Edge:** Plain. **Mint:** Philadelphia.

Key to Collecting: The 1859 Indian Head cent is the only year with the laurel wreath reverse. Circulated coins are plentiful in all grades. Mint State coins exist across a wide range of numerical designations. Surface quality varies but is usually good. Finding one with excellent aesthetic appeal will be no problem.

Aspects of Striking and Appearance: Usually well struck. Look for details at the feather tips, on the diamonds on the ribbon of the portrait, and on the leaves on the reverse.

Proof Coins: Fairly scarce, but enough remain from the estimated mintage of 800 coins that they appear on the market with regularity. Quality is an entirely different matter, and coins with deep mirror fields and excellent eye appeal are rare. Fortunately for you, most buyers simply read the labels on holders and do not care about aesthetic appeal—this being a story that is repeated for most types of United States coins. Accordingly, when you find a special piece, the premium for it will not be great.

Market Value: Circulation Strikes

G-4	VG-8	F-12	VF-20	EF-40	AU-50	MS-60BN	MS-63BN	MS-64BN	MS-65
$15	$20	$25	$55	$110	$200	$285	$700	$1,250	$2,800

Market Value: Proof Strikes

PF-63	PF-64	PF-65	PF-66
$1,650	$2,500	$4,500	$7,000

Retail Price Trends

Year	VF-20	MS-65	PF-65
1946	$1.75	$6.75	$15
1950	$2	$8	$16
1960	$5	$45	$95
1970	$11	$1,000	$1,200
1980	$22	$1,650	$2,000
1990	$23	$1,700	$2,700
2000	$35	$1,800	$4,600
2010	$60	$3,500	$5,000
2019	$55	$2,800	$4,500

Indian Head, Copper-Nickel, Oak Wreath With Shield Reverse (1860–1864)

Circulation-Strike Mintage: 122,321,000

Proof Mintage: Fewer than 5,000

Field Population: Circulated, 400,000 to 600,000; Mint State, 20,000 to 30,000; Proof, 1,500 to 1,900

Designer: James B. Longacre. **Weight:** 4.67 grams. **Composition:** .880 copper, .120 nickel. **Diameter:** 19 mm. **Edge:** Plain. **Mint:** Philadelphia.

Key to Collecting: For reasons that are not clear today, Mint Director James Ross Snowden found the laurel wreath reverse of the 1859 cent to be unsatisfactory and directed that patterns be made for a new style. In 1860 this new style became the standard. The new motif, popularly called the "oak wreath and shield," was adopted and was continued in use for the remainder of the Indian Head cent series. Today, examples exist in all grades. However, finding a sharply struck one can be a challenge. The lowest-mintage date of this type, the 1861, is also the date usually found with the best strike. Mint State coins are very plentiful, especially in grades from MS-60 to MS-63. Most often seen are those dated 1862 and 1863.

Aspects of Striking and Appearance: Usually weakly struck on the obverse, especially at the tips of the feathers and the ribbon on the headdress, although other points should be checked as well. Probably not one coin in ten is a sharp strike, if indeed even that many.

Proof Coins: Scarce. These exist in proportion to their mintages. Truly choice pieces with deep mirror surfaces and without flecks or problems are very rare, but as such things are not widely noticed by most buyers, you can quietly search until you find one.

Market Value: Circulation Strikes

G-4	VG-8	F-12	VF-20	EF-40	AU-50	MS-60	MS-63	MS-64	MS-65
$10	$15	$20	$30	$50	$75	$110	$200	$375	$1,000

Market Value: Proof Strikes

PF-63	PF-64	PF-65	PF-66
$850	$1,250	$2,500	$4,000

Retail Price Trends

Year	VF-20	MS-65	PF-65
1946	$0.70	$1.50	$15
1950	$0.70	$1.50	$15
1960	$2	$7.50	$50
1970	$5.25	$200	$600
1980	$10	$700	$2,900

Year	VF-20	MS-65	PF-65
1990	$8	$1,000	$2,500
2000	$12	$700	$1,850
2010	$25	$1,000	$2,750
2019	$30	$1,000	$2,500

Indian Head, Bronze (1864–1909)

Circulation-Strike Mintage: 1,690,839,937

Proof Mintage: *100,000*

Field Population: Circulated, 5,000,000 to 10,000,000; Mint State, 125,000 to 175,000; Proof, 50,000 to 70,000

Weight: 3.11 grams. **Composition:** .950 copper, .050 tin and zinc. **Diameter:** 19 mm. **Edge:** Plain. **Mints:** Philadelphia, San Francisco.

Key to Collecting: Today, examples for type-set purposes are readily available in all grades. Despite the common nature of even gem Mint State coins, high-quality examples are in the minority. Certain dates and mintmarks are elusive. Most often encountered are dates from 1879 through 1909. Lustrous brown or red-and-brown coins offer exceptional value as most investors are urged to buy only "red" coins, accordingly raising the prices for those. However, among pieces certified as mint red, relatively few, including those in such ranges as MS-65 to MS-67, are completely without spots or flecks. Many have been recolored. Although gem cents of this type seem easy enough to find, it will pay you to seek out high quality.

Aspects of Striking and Appearance: Vary widely, but generally quite good. Points to look for include sharp feather, ribbon, wreath, and shield details.

Proof Coins: Plentiful as a type. Gems without flecks or spots can be hard to find, but as few buyers seem to care, you will have the advantage of being an educated buyer and will be able to find one for little added premium. Choice brown and red and brown coins offer good values in my opinion.

Market Value: Circulation Strikes

G-4	VG-8	F-12	VF-20	EF-40	AU-50
$2	$3	$5	$6	$10	$20
MS-60BN	**MS-63BN**	**MS-64RB**	**MS-64RD**	**MS-65RB**	**MS-65RD**
$40	$60	$100	$185	$165	$450

Market Value: Proof Strikes

PF-63BN	PF-63RB	PF-64RB	PF-64RD	PF-65RD	PF-66RD
$150	$215	$325	$550	$1,200	$2,300

Retail Price Trends

Year	VF-20	MS-65RD	PF-65RD
1946	$0.30	$1.25	$4
1950	$0.30	$1.25	$4.50
1960	$1	$5	$14
1970	$1.50	$225	$350
1980	$2.30	$445	$400
1990	$2.30	$160	$900
2000	$2.15	$150	$350
2010	$6	$200	$425
2019	$6	$450	$1,200

Lincoln, Wheat Ears Reverse, Bronze, V.D.B. (1909)

Circulation-Strike Mintage: 28,479,000

Matte Proof Mintage: 420

Field Population: Circulated, 300,000 to 400,000; Mint State, 100,000 to 200,000; Proof, 250 to 325

Designer: Victor D. Brenner. **Weight:** 3.11 grams. **Composition:** .950 copper, .050 tin and zinc. **Diameter:** 19 mm. **Edge:** Plain. **Mints:** Philadelphia, San Francisco.

Key to Collecting: The first issues had the initials V.D.B. on the reverse. However, many people suggested that as Brenner was simply contracted by the Mint, he should not be personally "advertised" by having his initials placed on the coin. This was illogical, as other artists and engravers had been so recognized. The initials were soon removed, isolating the 1909 V.D.B. cent as a short-lived type. Today, the 1909 V.D.B. cent is readily available in all grades from well worn to gem Mint State. This is one of America's most historic coins. Just think of it: you can find a gem inexpensively.

Aspects of Striking and Appearance: Usually well struck in all areas. Points to check include the hair details on the portrait and the absence of tiny marks on Lincoln's shoulder.

Matte Proof Coins: These Proofs, of a new style, have minutely matte or pebbled surfaces caused by special treatment of the dies. The rims are square and sharp. Such pieces cannot easily be told from certain circulation strikes with similar borders. Most are brown or brown with tinges of red. Nearly all full "red" coins have been dipped or recolored.

Market Value: Circulation Strikes

G-4	VG-8	F-12	VF-20	EF-40	AU-50
$15	$16	$17	$18	$19	$20
MS-60BN	**MS-63BN**	**MS-64BN**	**MS-64RB**	**MS-64RD**	**MS-65RD**
$25	$30	$50	$70	$100	$165

Market Value: Proof Strikes

PF-63BN	PF-63RB	PF-64RB	PF-65RB
$8,500	$11,500	$22,500	$37,500

Retail Price Trends

Year	EF-40	MS-65RD	Matte PF-65RB
1946	$0.10	$0.30	$9
1950	$0.15	$0.35	$10
1960	$0.50	$2.25	$75
1970	$2.15	$10	$700
1980	$3.50	$17.50	$1,000

Year	VF-20	MS-65RD	Matte PF-65RB
1990	$4	$60	$1,700
2000	$4	$70	$2,500
2010	$16	$100	$12,500
2019	$18	$165	$37,500

Lincoln, Wheat Ears Reverse, Bronze (1909–1942; 1944–1958)

Circulation-Strike Mintage: 24,499,202,552

Proof Mintage:
Matte Proofs, 1909–1916: **15,314**
Mirror-Finish Proofs, 1936–1942 and 1950–1958: **3,836,869**

Field Population:
Circulated, billions;
Mint State, many millions;
Proof, 8,000 to 11,000 Matte;
2,500,000 to 3,000,000 Mirror

Designer: Victor D. Brenner. **Weight:** 3.11 grams. **Composition:** ***1909–1942 and 1947–1958:*** .950 copper, .050 tin and zinc; ***1944–1946:*** .950 copper, .050 zinc. **Diameter:** 19 mm. **Edge:** Plain. **Mints:** Philadelphia, Denver, San Francisco.

Key to Collecting: So many were made of this type, and over such a long period of time, that finding a suitable specimen for a type set will be easy and inexpensive.

Aspects of Striking and Appearance: Some Denver and San Francisco issues of the 1916 to 1929 era are lightly struck. Striking of most other issues is fairly good, but many variations occur. Check hair details on the portrait and for absence of marks on the shoulder. Seek smooth fields, and examine other areas for sharpness.

Proof Coins: Matte Proofs are nearly always superbly struck. Most are brown or brown with tinges of red. Most fully red coins have been cleaned or recolored, but there are exceptions. Proofs of the 1936 to 1942 and 1950 to 1958 eras are mostly with dies polished overall, although some later issues have frosted ("cameo") portraits.

Market Value: Circulation Strikes

VF-20	EF-40	AU-50	MS-63RB	MS-64RB	MS-64RD	MS-65RB	MS-65RD
$0.10	$0.12	$0.15	$0.30	$0.50	$1	$1.25	$1.50

Market Value: Proof Strikes

PF-65RD	PF-66RD	PF-67RD
$8	$20	$30

Retail Price Trends

Year	MS-65RD	Mirror-Finish PF-65
1960	$0.50	$2
1970	$0.60	$2.50
1980	$0.20	$3
1990	$1.10	$3.25

Year	MS-65RD	Mirror-Finish PF-65
2000	$0.15	$3.50
2010	$0.50	$4.00
2019	$1.50	$8.00

Lincoln, Wheat Ears Reverse, Steel (1943)

Circulation-Strike Mintage: 1,093,838,670

Field Population: Circulated, many millions; Mint State, several million

Designer: Victor D. Brenner. **Weight:** 2.70 grams. **Composition:** Steel, coated with zinc. **Diameter:** 19 mm. **Edge:** Plain. **Mints:** Philadelphia, Denver, San Francisco.

Key to Collecting: To conserve copper for wartime munitions and products, in 1943 cents were made of zinc-coated steel. Production in quantity took place at all three mints. Although there were no particular problems with the production of such pieces, in 1944 copper was used once again. Circulated coins are common. They are usually rather blotchy and unattractive unless processed to become bright. (Tarnished circulated steel cents are sometimes processed to make them shiny again, for souvenir sets. However, cleaning and otherwise treating coins is not considered a good numismatic practice. MS examples with original luster are plentiful enough that you can easily find an inexpensive example for your type set.) Mint State coins are common through and including gem levels.

Aspects of Striking and Appearance: Usually very well struck, which seems unusual due to the hardness of the planchet!

Market Value: Circulation Strikes

F-12	VF-20	EF-40	AU-50	MS-63	MS-65	MS-66	MS-67	MS-68
$0.30	$0.35	$0.40	$0.50	$2.50	$8	$35	$175	$2,500

Retail Price Trends

Year	EF-40	MS-60	MS-65
1960	$0.20	$0.50	$0.75
1970	$0.30	$0.55	$0.80
1980	$0.30	$0.60	$1.75
1990	$0.30	$0.50	$3

Year	EF-40	MS-60	MS-65
2000	$0.40	$0.75	$4
2010	$0.40	$1.25	$8.00
2019	$0.40	$1.25	$8.00

Lincoln, Memorial Reverse, Bronze (1959–1982)

Circulation-Strike Mintage: 158,121,942,417 (including 1982 copper-plated zinc)

Proof Mintage: 65,103,802

Field Population: Circulated, many billions; Mint State, billions; Proof, 45,000,000 to 60,000,000

Designer: ***Obverse:*** Victor D. Brenner; ***Reverse:*** Frank Gasparro. **Weight:** 3.11 grams. **Composition:** ***1959–1962:*** .950 copper, .050 tin and zinc; ***1962–1982:*** .950 copper, .050 zinc. **Diameter:** 19 mm. **Edge:** Plain. **Mints:** Philadelphia, Denver, San Francisco.

Key to Collecting: In 1959 the reverse of the cent was redesigned to feature a plan view of the Lincoln Memorial building. The design seems to fit uncomfortably, rendering an effect that at least to the casual observer seems to be bottom-heavy, rather than balanced. However, for 50 years it was the standard. Not much needs to be said about this type.

Aspects of Striking and Appearance: Striking sharpness varies. You will need to look through quite a few pieces to find one that has excellent strike on both sides. On the obverse, look for sharp hair details in the portrait and an absence of tiny marks on the shoulder. On the reverse, look for full details of the building steps and the tiny Lincoln statue. Such sharp pieces, though in the minority, are still plentiful.

Proof Coins: Common and usually well struck.

Market Value: Circulation Strikes

MS-63RB	MS-65RD	MS-66RD	MS-67RD
$0.15	$0.30	$20	$35

Market Value: Proof Strikes

PF-65RD	PF-67RD	PF-67Cam	PF-68DC
1.00	13.00	16.00	30.00

Retail Price Trends

Year	MS-65RD	PF-65RD
1990	$0.10	$1
2000	$0.10	$1
2010	$0.20	$1
2019	$0.30	$1

Lincoln, Memorial Reverse, Copper-Plated Zinc (1982–2008)

Circulation-Strike Mintage: more than 270 billion

Proof Mintage: *81,845,239*

Field Population: Circulated, many billions; Mint State, billions; Proof, 75,000,000 or more

Designer: ***Obverse:*** Victor D. Brenner; ***Reverse:*** Frank Gasparro. **Weight:** 2.5 grams. **Composition:** copper-plated zinc (core: .992 zinc, .008 copper, with a plating of pure copper; total content .975 zinc, .025 copper). **Diameter:** 19 mm. **Edge:** Plain. **Mints:** Philadelphia, Denver, San Francisco.

Key to Collecting: In the 1970s and 1980s, Treasury Department officials were concerned with the rising price of copper and feared that cents might be hoarded for their metallic content. Partway through 1982, a change was made to a planchet consisting of zinc coated with copper available at a lower cost than bronze. These coins are common in circulation and Mint State grades. For type-set purposes, you are home free, or almost free, with this coin. Admittedly, you do have to pay face value, or perhaps even the 20¢ suggested by the *Red Book* if you buy one from a dealer (handling and packaging, you know—still not much profit there). You can indulge yourself and keep looking until you find a superb gem MS-70.

Although it seems like only yesterday that this type made its appearance, it was over three decades ago. From 1982 until the Memorial Reverse's exit from the numismatic stage in 2008, many different dates, mintmarks, and curious varieties were produced. Indeed, a full set of everything listed in the *Red Book* would comprise nearly 100 coins! Among these, we have the 1982 Large Date and Small Date; the interesting Proof 1990, which should have had an S mintmark, but someone forgot to put it on the die; several dies with doubling; and varieties that differ from each other in the spacing between the A and M in AMERICA.

Aspects of Striking and Appearance: On the obverse, look for sharp hair details in the portrait and an absence of tiny marks on the shoulder. On the reverse, look for full details of the building steps and the tiny Lincoln statue.

Proof Coins: Common. Usually well struck.

Market Value: Circulation Strikes

MS-63RB	MS-65RD	MS-66RD	MS-67RD
$0.15	$0.30	$11	$15

Market Value: Proof Strikes

PF-65RD	PF-67RD	PF-67Cam	PF-68DC
$3	$10	$11	$15

Lincoln, Bicentennial Reverses (2009)

Circulation-Strike Mintage: 380,409,228

Proof Mintage: 2,995,615

Circulation-Strike Mintage: 741,169,228

Proof Mintage: 2,995,615

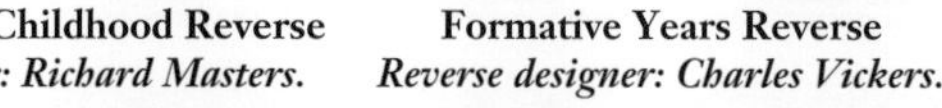

Birth and Early Childhood Reverse
Reverse designer: Richard Masters.

Formative Years Reverse
Reverse designer: Charles Vickers.

Circulation-Strike Mintage: 653,569,228

Proof Mintage: 2,995,615

Circulation-Strike Mintage: 329,169,228

Proof Mintage: 2,995,615

Professional Life Reverse
Reverse designer: Joel Iskowitz.

Presidency Reverse
Reverse designer: Susan Gamble.

Field Population, all designs:
Circulated, hundreds of millions;
Mint State, tens or hundreds of millions; Proof, millions

Designer: ***Obverse:*** Victor D. Brenner; ***Reverse:*** See image captions for reverse designers. **Weight:** ***Regular-issue Coins:*** 2.5 grams; ***Special Coins Included in Collector Sets:*** 3.1 grams. **Composition:** ***Regular-issue Coins:*** copper-plated zinc (core: .992 zinc, .008 copper, with a plating of pure copper; total content .975 zinc, .025 copper); ***Special Coins Included in Collector Sets:*** .950 copper, .050 tin and zinc. **Diameter:** 19 mm. **Edge:** Plain. **Mints:** Philadelphia, Denver, San Francisco.

Key to Collecting: The one-cent coins issued during 2009 pay unique tribute to President Abraham Lincoln, commemorating the bicentennial of his birth and the 100th anniversary of the first issuance of the Lincoln cent. Four different reverse designs were issued by the U.S. Mint, each representing a major aspect of Lincoln's life. The obverse retained the traditional profile portrait of previous years.

The coins issued for general circulation were made of the exact same copper-plated composition used in the cent since 1982. Special versions struck for inclusion in collector sets were made of the same alloy as the first Lincoln cents of 1909—95 parts copper and 5 parts tin and zinc—and with a Satin finish.

Cents of this year were minted in quantities that, while large, were much smaller than for previous years (in the hundreds of millions, rather than multiple billions), if each of the four designs is considered individually. They are readily available in the numismatic marketplace, and are starting to be seen more frequently in circulation.

Several die varieties (both circulation-strike and Proof) exist with minor doubling in the Formative Years reverse. Their values, which vary generally according to the severity of the doubling, are not yet firmly established with an active buy-and-sell market.

Aspects of Striking and Appearance: Striking is generally sharp. The quality of the fields can vary. Some 2009 cents, even from original rolls and bags, have surface marks that look like water spots.

Proof Coins: High-quality Proofs (PF-69 and 70) are common in the secondary market. All Proof Lincoln Bicentennial cents are mirror Proofs, usually with cameo or frosted contrast between the devices and the fields.

Market Value: Circulation Strikes

MS-63RB	MS-65RD	MS-66RD	MS-67RD
$0.15	$0.30	$12	$20

Market Value: Proof Strikes

PF-65RD	PF-67RD	PF-67Cam	PF-68DC
$4	$7	$8	$10

Lincoln, Shield Reverse (2010 to Date)

Circulation-Strike Mintage: Tens of billions, still being minted

Proof Mintage: Tens of millions, still being minted

Field Population: Circulated, many billions; Mint State, billions; Proof, tens of millions

Designer: ***Obverse:*** Victor D. Brenner; ***Reverse:*** Lyndall Bass. **Weight:** 2.5 grams. **Composition:** Copper-plated zinc (core: .992 zinc, .008 copper, with a plating of pure copper; total content .975 zinc, .025 copper). **Diameter:** 19 mm. **Edge:** Plain. **Mints:** Philadelphia, Denver, San Francisco, West Point.

Key to Collecting: Symbolically capping the life story told by the Lincoln Bicentennial cents of 2009, today's cents feature a reverse design "emblematic of President Lincoln's preservation of the United States as a single and united country." The shield motif was designed by U.S. Mint Artistic Infusion Program Associate Designer Lyndall Bass, and engraved by Mint medallic sculptor (now chief engraver) Joseph Menna. In addition to a new reverse design, the Shield Reverse cents feature a modern update of Victor David Brenner's original portrait for the 1909 Lincoln cent.

Circulation-strike cents minted in Philadelphia in 2017 bear a P mintmark in honor of the 225th anniversary of coinage there. In 2019 some special cents were minted at West Point for collectors.

Cents of this design are minted in large quantities. They are readily available in the numismatic marketplace, and have successfully entered circulation through normal distribution channels.

Aspects of Striking and Appearance: Striking is generally sharp.

Proof Coins: High-quality Proofs (PF-69 and 70) are common in the secondary market. All Proof Lincoln, Shield Reverse, cents are mirror Proofs, usually with cameo or frosted contrast between the devices and the fields. Cents with other special formats, such as an Enhanced Uncirculated finish, have been made for collectors.

Market Value: Circulation Strikes

MS-63RB	MS-65RD	MS-66RD	MS-67RD
$0.15	$0.30	$10	$15

Market Value: Proof Strikes

PF-65RD	PF-67RD	PF-67Cam	PF-68DC
$4	$7	$8	$10

9

Two-Cent Pieces
1864–1873

Overview of the Denomination

The two-cent denomination, struck in bronze, made its debut in 1864 under the authorization of the Mint Act of that year, which also provided that Indian Head cents be made of bronze. At the time, there were no silver or gold coins in circulation in the East or Midwest. The need for small change was met by Indian Head cents, paper Fractional Currency notes (of denominations from 3¢ to 50¢), and a wide variety of privately issued Civil War tokens (as they are called today), paper scrip, and encased postage stamps. The two-cent denomination was hardly a new idea, and in 1836 some interesting patterns were made to test the proposal, but no circulating coinage resulted at the time. The 1864 two-cent piece represents the first appearance of the motto IN GOD WE TRUST on a circulating coin.

It was anticipated that the two-cent piece would be popular, and in the first year 19,847,500 were struck, which proved to be the all-time high figure. In the following year, 1865, the nickel three-cent denomination was introduced and took much interest away from the two-cent piece. Then followed the nickel five-cent piece in 1866, further reducing the need for the two-cent denomination. The two-cent coin was viewed as redundant, mintages fell precipitously, and just 65,000 were made for circulation in 1872, this being the final year of regular coinage. In 1873 an estimated 1,500 or so Proofs were made for collectors. The far-ranging Coinage Act of 1873 abolished the denomination.

Selecting a Coin for Your Type Set

A full "type set" of the two-cent piece consists of but a single coin. Most available in Mint State are the issues of 1864 and 1865, often seen with original mint orange color, fading to natural brown. Proofs are available for all years.

Circulation strikes as well as Proofs must be selected with care, for the number of truly choice "original" (unprocessed, undipped, not retoned) coins is but a small percentage of the whole. Many coins can be called, but few will be chosen by connoisseurs. However, on an absolute basis, there are enough around that this will not be among your type set nemeses.

BEYOND A TYPE SET

Two-cent pieces can be collected advantageously by date and variety. A basic display consists of an 1864 Large Motto, 1864 Small Motto (rare), 1873 Close 3, and 1873 Open 3, the last two being available only in Proof format. Some specialists opt to include just one of the 1873 varieties.

Several specialized studies of two-cent pieces have been published over a long span of years, the first of significance being "Two-Cent Pieces of the United States," by S.W. Freeman, published in *The Numismatist*, June 1954. In its time, *The Two-Cent Piece and Varieties*, by Myron ("Mike") Kliman, 1977, was popular. Frank Leone's *Longacre's Two-Cent Piece Die Varieties & Errors*, 1991, has useful information as well.

Two-Cent Pieces (1864–1873)

Circulation-Strike Mintage: **45,601,000**

Proof Mintage: **15,000**

Field Population: **Circulated, 200,000 to 300,000; Mint State, 20,000 to 35,000; Proof, 7,000 to 10,000**

Designer: James B. Longacre. **Weight:** 6.22 grams. **Composition:** .950 copper, .050 tin and zinc. **Diameter:** 23 mm. **Edge:** Plain. **Mint:** Philadelphia.

Key to Collecting: Examples are readily available in nearly all grades. The first several years of the series can be purchased in such grades as VF, EF, and AU. Most have light brown surfaces and are quite attractive. Gems with excellent aesthetic appeal are elusive. Most Mint State coins seen in the marketplace are of the first several years, particularly 1864 Large Motto and 1865. Attractive pieces can be purchased with brown, red and brown, or red surfaces. Many full red (*orange* is a more appropriate description) coins are flecked or spotted. Quality coins are elusive.

Aspects of Striking and Appearance: Points to check for sharpness include the leaves and horizontal shield lines on the obverse, and, on the reverse, the wreath details and the border letters.

Proof Coins: Proofs were made of all years 1864 to 1873. The mintages are not recorded, but probably were larger toward the end of the series. Among varieties, the 1864 Small Motto Proof is a major rarity with probably fewer than two dozen known. The majority of Proofs of the various dates, even those classified in high grades, have problems of one sort or another—such as spotting or staining, or retoning. To put together a high-quality set of one of each date of Proofs would take several years or more. However, as you will be seeking just a single coin, the search will be less arduous.

Do not overlook the many nice brown and red-and-brown pieces on the market ("investment" advisors often suggest that only "red" copper is worth buying, leaving many great values among other coins!).

Market Value: Circulation Strikes

G-4	F-12	VF-20	EF-40	AU-50	MS-60BN
$15	$25	$30	$50	$80	$110
MS-63BN	**MS-63RB**	**MS-64BN**	**MS-64RD**	**MS-65RB**	**MS-65RD**
$175	$185	$200	$650	$600	$1,150

Market Value: Proof Strikes

PF-20	PF-40	PF-63BN	PF-64BN	PF-64RB	PF-65RB
$1,500	$1,650	$3,200	$3,500	$3,750	$4,750

Retail Price Trends

Year	VF-20	MS-65RD
1946	$0.50	$1.50
1950	$0.50	$1.50
1960	$2.75	$10
1970	$10.50	$200
1980	$14	$350

Year	VF-20	MS-65RD
1990	$12	$440
2000	$20	$450
2010	$35	$600
2019	$30	$1,150

10
Silver Three-Cent Pieces
1851-1873

Overview of the Denomination

After the discovery of gold in California in 1848 and the influx of large quantities of bullion into the Eastern markets in 1849, gold became "common" in relation to silver. Traditionally, gold was considered to be worth about 16 times the value of silver, in that one ounce of gold was worth about 16 ounces of silver. Now, the ratio was disturbed. Beginning in 1850, currently existing silver coins from the half dime to the dollar became worth more in melt-down value than in face value. Accordingly, the coinage of additional pieces was no longer efficient. Mintage quantities dropped sharply. Silver coins disappeared from circulation. There were no coins in commerce other than copper cents (half cents were not popular) and gold.

To remedy this, the Act of March 3, 1851, provided for a new denomination: a silver three-cent piece. This legislation became effective on June 30, 1851. The alloy, not earlier used in American coinage, was set at 75% silver and 25% copper instead of the 90% silver and 10% copper used in other silver denominations. It was hoped that this would permit the new three-cent coins to be struck in large quantities and to circulate effectively, as there would be no financial incentive to melt them. The new three-cent piece also facilitated the purchase of 3¢ postage stamps. These three-cent pieces were called *trimes* in Treasury Department records, but the nomenclature was not popular either with the public or, in time, with numismatists—until the late twentieth century when collectors began to revive its use.

The first trimes, popularly called Type I issues by numismatists today, were minted from 1851 to 1853. Each has a six-pointed star on the obverse, with a shield at its center, with inscription surrounding. The reverse bears a C-shaped ornament and the Roman numeral III. All trimes of this and later types were struck at the Philadelphia Mint with the solitary exception of the 1851-O, made in New Orleans.

The Type I trimes served their purpose well, circulated widely, and were appreciated for their utility, although their small diameter of 14 mm (unchanged for the life of the denomination) made them somewhat inconvenient to handle.

The Coinage Act of February 21, 1853, sounded the death knell of the trime, for it lowered the authorized weights of the half dime, dime, quarter dollar, and half dollar (but not the dollar). Soon, these other denominations reappeared in circulation in quantity, and silver three-cent pieces became redundant.

In 1854 the trime design was changed considerably, creating the Type II. The alloy was modified to the regular standard for other issues, 90% silver and 10% copper, and the overall weight was lightened from 12.375 grains to 11.52 grains. A raised border was added to the obverse star plus three line frames around it, and on the reverse, an olive branch was placed above the III denomination and a bundle of arrows below it. The new motif proved to be very difficult to strike up properly, and most examples seen today are rather miserable from the aspect of sharpness (see details on page 86).

In 1859 the design was modified again; one of the line frames around the star was dropped, and the lettering was made more delicate. Specimens of the new configuration, known as Type III issues today, are for the most part struck up properly. Demand for the trime continued to be small, and after 1862, very few were made for circulation, as silver coins were hoarded by the public and began to trade at a premium. Proofs were made each year for collectors.

Under the Coinage Act of 1873, the trime was discontinued. In that year, only Proofs were made, with no related circulation strikes.

Collecting a Type Set of Trimes

Of the three types of trimes, the Type II is at once the scarcest and, by far, the most difficult to find with a sharp strike. In fact, not one in fifty Type II coins is needle sharp. Curiously, when such pieces are found, they are likely to be dated 1855, the lowest-mintage issue of the type (reminding one that among copper-nickel Indian Head cents of the 1860 to 1864 type, the sharpest pieces are often dated 1861, the lowest mintage for that type). Trimes of the 1851 to 1853 Type I design vary widely in striking, but can be found sharp. Type III coins are often sharp.

Mint State coins are readily found for Type I (1851 to 1853) and are usually in grades from MS-60 to MS-63 or so, although quite a few gems are around with attractive luster. Sharply struck gems are another matter and require some searching to find. Certification services do not note whether pieces are sharply detailed. Mint State Type II trimes are all rare and when seen are apt to be miserably struck and in lower grades. A *sharply struck* gem is an item that will make a connoisseur jump with glee! Type III coins are readily found in Mint State, including in gem preservation.

Proofs were made of all years, but not in quantity until 1858, when an estimated 210 were struck. For all dates after 1862, high-grade Proofs are much more available today than are Mint State coins.

Circulated examples are available of all three types. While extensively worn coins of Type I are available, most Type II coins are Fine or better and most Type III pieces are VF or better, reflecting that such coins did not circulate extensively after the summer of 1862.

BEYOND A TYPE SET

Trimes constitute an American series that covers a fairly long span of years, in this instance 1851 to 1873, that embraces three design types, but which has no "impossible" rarities. Accordingly, it is realistic to collect one of each Philadelphia Mint coin from 1851 to 1873 plus the 1851-O. There are two overdates in the series: an 1862, 2 Over 1 (which is distinct and occurs only in circulation-strike format) and an 1863, 3 Over 2 (only Proofs, and not boldly defined), which some specialists collect and others ignore. A curious variety of 1852 has the first digit of the date over an inverted 2.

Typically, a high-grade set includes Mint State examples of all issues 1851 through 1857 and Proofs after that date. As noted, Type II trimes of 1854 to 1858 usually are very poorly struck, save the occasionally encountered sharp 1855. As an example, if I were a specialist in the series and found an 1856 with needle-sharp details, at three times the regular market price, I would run to buy it! After 1862, Mint State coins are rare for most dates. I have never seen a full set of Mint State pieces. The formation of a choice Mint State set 1851 through 1872 plus a Proof 1873 (this year was struck only in Proof format) would be a formidable challenge and would take years to complete!

A set of circulated coins can be gathered through and including 1862, after which such pieces become very rare. Most later dates will have to be acquired on a catch-as-catch-can basis, perhaps by acquiring impaired Proofs for certain of the years.

Trimes in themselves have not formed the one and only specialty for any numismatists I have known, but are collected along with other series. For additional information, see *Walter Breen's Complete Encyclopedia of U.S. and Colonial Coins*.

Trimes, No Outline to Star (1851–1853)

Circulation-Strike Mintage: 47,396

Proof Mintage: Fewer than 15

Field population: Circulated, 150,000 to 170,000; Mint State, 20,000 to 30,000; Proof, fewer than 15

Designer: James B. Longacre. **Weight:** 0.80 gram. **Composition:** .750 silver, .250 copper. **Diameter:** 14 mm. **Edge:** Plain. **Mints:** Philadelphia, New Orleans.

Key to Collecting: Today, examples are plentiful in circulated grades. On the numismatic market, Mint State coins are seen with frequency, although gems are scarce. The only mintmark in the series, the 1851-O, is of this type. Most high-grade 1851-O trimes are very attractive. Such a coin might be of interest if you are looking for something special to include in your type set.

Aspects of Striking and Appearance: Often lacking certain details of the shield. Check this feature carefully and also the strength of the III. Finding a truly sharp coin will take some doing.

Proof Coins: A few were made, but today they are unobtainable for all intents and purposes. Some prooflike circulation strikes have been expertised as "Proof." *Caveat emptor.*

Market Value: Circulation Strikes

G-4	VG-8	F-12	VF-20	EF-40	AU-50	MS-60	MS-63	MS-64	MS-65	MS-66
$30	$45	$50	$65	$80	$165	$200	$275	$450	$675	$1,200

Retail Price Trends

Year	VF-20	MS-65
1946	$1.50	$4.50
1950	$1.50	$4.50
1960	$5	$14
1970	$14	$150
1980	$25	$300
1990	$27.50	$450
2000	$27.50	$500
2010	$50	$575
2019	$65	$675

Trimes, Three Outlines to Star (1854–1858)

Circulation-Strike Mintage: 4,914,100

Proof Mintage: Fewer than 600 (including 210 of 1858)

Field population: Circulated, 8,000 to 12,000; Mint State, 3,000 to 5,000; Proof, 400 to 500

Designer: James B. Longacre. **Weight:** 0.75 gram. **Composition:** .900 silver, .100 copper. **Diameter:** 14 mm. **Edge:** Plain. **Mint:** Philadelphia.

Key to Collecting: Type II trimes are much scarcer than are those of Type I and Type III. Most are very poorly struck, except for the scarce date 1855. Generally, 1854 trimes are poorly struck, and those dated from 1856 to 1858 are worse yet. Save for those dated 1855, probably no more than one trime in fifty in the Type II series is sharply struck on all features. The beauty part is that when you do find a sharply struck coin, the added premium will probably be modest. It might be twice the price, but will be quite worthwhile.

Aspects of Striking and Appearance: Usually miserably struck with some or all of these characteristics: obverse lettering weak in places, frames around the star of inconsistent strength or missing in certain areas, and shield weak in places; reverse stars are irregular and poorly formed, olive branch and arrows are weak in areas; weak or irregular rims.

Proof Coins: Proofs exist of all Type II dates, but the most often seen is 1858. When found, these are usually well struck.

Market Value: Circulation Strikes

G-4	VG-8	F-12	VF-20	EF-40	AU-50	MS-60	MS-63	MS-64	MS-65	MS-66
$40	$45	$50	$70	$120	$235	$360	$700	$1,250	$2,250	$4,500

Market Value: Proof Strikes

PF-63	PF-64	PF-65	PF-65CAM
$2,500	$4,500	$6,500	$10,000

Retail Price Trends

Year	VF-20	MS-65	PF-65
1946	$2.50	$3.75	$18
1950	$3	$6	$20
1960	$7	$17	$160
1970	$22.50	$1,000	$3,000
1980	$35	$2,000	$6,100

Year	VF-20	MS-65	PF-65
1990	$35	$3,000	$4,000
2000	$35	$4,000	$5,600
2010	$60	$3,900	$6,000
2019	$70	$2,250	$6,500

Trimes, Two Outlines to Star (1859–1873)

Circulation-Strike Mintage: 1,572,600

Proof Mintage: 10,840

Field Population: Circulated, 25,000 to 35,000; Mint State, 10,000 to 15,000; Proof, 6,000 to 8,000

Designer: James B. Longacre. **Weight:** 0.75 gram. **Composition:** .900 silver, .100 copper. **Diameter:** 14 mm. **Edge:** Plain. **Mint:** Philadelphia.

Key to Collecting: Circulated coins are most available for the years 1859 to 1862. Mint State coins on the market are nearly always from the early 1860s. A readily encountered year such as 1862 is a nice possibility for a type set, but rarer dates may pique your interest as they often cost only a small amount more. Some examples of the readily available 1861 and 1862 years have an especially frosty luster.

Aspects of Striking and Appearance: Striking varies. Points to look for include full outlines around the star, full shield on the star, and full leaf details on the obverse.

Proof Coins: Today, several hundred or more exist of each, and all are readily collectible. Proofs have furnished the path to forming a high-grade date run, as Mint State examples of most issues after 1862 are generally unavailable. Striking quality varies, and careful examination is recommended. Some have the top of the D in UNITED broken.

Market Value: Circulation Strikes

G-4	VG-8	F-12	VF-20	EF-40	AU-50	MS-60	MS-63	MS-64	MS-65	MS-66
$40	$45	$50	$60	$90	$175	$215	$300	$525	$875	$1,250

Market Value: Proof Strikes

PF-63	PF-64	PF-65	PF-65CAM
$750	$1,100	$1,500	$1,800

Retail Price Trends

Year	VF-20	MS-65	PF-65
1946	$1.50	$3	$9
1950	$1.50	$2.50	$11
1960	$6	$14	$32
1970	$22.50	$300	$600
1980	$32	$600	$900

Year	VF-20	MS-65	PF-65
1990	$32	$700	$900
2000	$35	$800	$1,185
2010	$55	$800	$1,250
2019	$60	$875	$1,500

11
Nickel Three-Cent Pieces
1865–1889

Overview of the Denomination

Nickel-three cent coins were launched in 1865, a time in which there were no silver or gold coins in circulation in the East or Midwest. The need for small change was mostly filled by Indian Head cents and the new (in 1864) bronze two-cent pieces, plus paper Fractional Currency notes. By 1865, the importance of privately issued Civil War tokens and encased postage stamps had faded considerably.

In the first year, 11,382,000 of the nickel three-cent pieces were made, an auspicious beginning. However, in the next year, the nickel five-cent piece was produced for the first time and took considerably from the popularity of both the two-cent and nickel three-cent coins. Production soon took a nosedive, and in 1866 just 4,801,000 were struck. Mintages declined to the point at which in 1877 and 1878 only Proofs were made. Afterward, mintages of the nickel three-cent piece remained low, except for the anomalous year of 1881 when 1,077,000 were made, although such coins were hardly needed in commerce.

In 1889 the nickel three-cent coin was discontinued along with the $1 and $3 gold denominations.

Selecting a Coin for your Type Set

Mint State coins are readily available for the early years, although many if not most have weak striking in areas or are from clashed dies. Pristine, sharp Mint State coins on the market are mostly of later years, in the 1880s, where such pieces are the rule, not the exception.

Beyond a Type Set

Nickel three-cent coins are interesting to collect by date sequence from 1865 to 1889. Varieties are provided by the 1873 Close 3 and Open 3 and the 1887, 7 Over 6, overdate. A set of Mint State coins is considerably more difficult to form than a run of

Proofs. Probably, a hand-selected set of well-struck coins MS-65 or finer would take several years to complete.

Among Proofs, the rarest year is 1865, probably followed by the "perfect date" (not overdate) 1887. Proofs of the 1860s and early 1870s are scarce in gem state with excellent strike and eye appeal. Proofs of the last decade of coinage are much more available and are usually choice.

For limited additional information, see *Walter Breen's Complete Encyclopedia of U.S. and Colonial Coins*.

Nickel Three-Cent Piece (1865–1889)

Circulation-Strike Mintage: 31,332,527

Proof Mintage: 75,000

Field Population: Circulated, 200,000 to 300,000; Mint State, 15,000 to 25,000; Proof, 35,000 to 45,000

Designer: James B. Longacre. **Weight:** 1.94 grams. **Composition:** .750 copper, .250 nickel. **Diameter:** 17.9 mm. **Edge:** Plain. **Mint:** Philadelphia.

Key to Collecting: Specimens are available in most grades. Circulated coins are generally available. Attractive VF to AU coins are readily obtainable of the early dates, with 1865 being the most often seen. Well-struck Mint State coins are easier to find of the later years, 1879 to 1889. Many are partially prooflike and may have been struck as Proofs.

Aspects of Striking and Appearance: Best-struck pieces are those toward the end of the series. Choice well-struck, lustrous examples are scarce among the years 1865 to 1876, although there is no lack of certified "gems" on the market that are not choice.

Proof Coins: An easy option for a choice piece is one dated from 1879 to 1889, a range that combines high Proof mintage figures with usually well-struck details. Proofs of the 1860s and early 1870s are difficult to find in overall high quality. The first year of issue, sometimes selected for a type set, is quite rare.

Market Value: Circulation Strikes

G-4	VG-8	F-12	VF-20	EF-40	AU-50	MS-60	MS-63	MS-64	MS-65	MS-66
$15	$20		$30	$40	$65	$100	$160	$245	$625	$1,100

Market Value: Proof Strikes

PF-20	PF-40	PF-63	PF-64	PF-65	PF-66	PF-66Cam
$350	$375	$400	$425	$625	$800	$1,000

Retail Price Trends

Year	VF-20	MS-65	PF-65
1946	$0.80	$2.25	$4.50
1950	$0.70	$2.25	$4.50
1960	$1.25	$6.75	$15
1970	$5	$100	$100
1980	$10	$300	$250

Year	VF-20	MS-65	PF-65
1990	$7	$450	$350
2000	$12	$500	$460
2010	$30	$600	$600
2019	$30	$625	$625

12
Nickel Five-Cent Pieces
1866 to Date

Overview of the Denomination

The nickel five-cent piece, commonly called a "nickel" today, was first made for circulation in 1866. The composition was set as 75% copper and 25% nickel, but the nickel gave the alloy a silver appearance. Technically, perhaps these should be called "coppers," as nickel is the minority element! However, nickels they are, even some made in *silver* for a short time in the 1940s.

In the mid-1860s, there were no silver or gold coins in circulation in the East or Midwest, and the need for small change met by the earlier-delineated bronze cents, two-cent pieces, and nickel three-cent pieces, the latter introduced in 1865. In addition, Fractional Currency bills from 3¢ to 50¢ were common in commercial transactions. Earlier, the silver half dime had circulated widely, but after spring 1862, they were hoarded. Accordingly, in 1866 the new nickel became the only coin of that denomination in popular use.

The first nickels were designed by James B. Longacre and employed a shield design on the obverse, adapted from Longacre's motif on the bronze two-cent piece introduced in 1864. The reverse depicted the large numeral 5 with stars surrounding. Between each star, a ray was inserted, creating what is today known as the Shield nickel With Rays type. Difficulties arose in striking these pieces with full detail, and in early 1867 the rays were eliminated, creating the Shield nickel Without Rays type. These were coined through and including 1883.

In 1883 a new motif was introduced, the Liberty Head by Charles E. Barber, chief engraver at the Mint. The obverse featured Miss Liberty facing to the left, stars surrounding, and the date below. On the reverse, the denomination was simply stated by the Roman numeral V, a tradition following the use of III to designate the value of the nickel and silver three-cent pieces. The word CENTS did not appear. Certain miscreants gold-plated the new nickels and passed them off as five-dollar gold coins, the diameters of the two denominations being nearly the same. Realizing the omission, Barber added the word CENTS to the reverse, ending the deception. Liberty Head nickels Without CENTS were coined only in 1883, and those With CENTS were coined from 1883 through 1912, plus a small unofficial mintage (estimated at just five coins) in 1913. Accordingly, in 1883 there were three different nickel types made: Shield, Liberty Head Without CENTS, and Liberty Head with CENTS. In 1912 nickels were struck at branch mints in Denver and San Francisco for the first time.

In 1913 the Indian Head nickel was introduced, featuring an American bison, popularly called a "buffalo," on the reverse. In popular parlance, this became known as the Buffalo nickel. Those made early in the year had the bison standing on a raised mound, these being known as Type I coins. Soon the motif was modified by placing the bison on flat ground, creating the Type II, which was used until the end of the series in 1938.

In the latter year, the Jefferson nickel, designed by Felix O. Schlag, was introduced, with the president's head on the obverse. On the reverse, Monticello, Jefferson's home in Virginia, was depicted. For part of 1942, continuing through 1945, nickel was removed from the alloy as it was needed for wartime purposes, and a silver composition was introduced. Large P (not earlier used on coinage), D, and S mintmarks were placed above the dome of Monticello, instead of the usual inconspicuous place to the right of the building. This was to facilitate the easy sorting of silver-content coins in later years when the Treasury expected to redeem them.

In 1946 the regular 75% copper and 25% nickel alloy was resumed. In 1966 the first and last initials, FS, of designer Felix O. Schlag, were added to the obverse of the coin, creating a new type. In 2004 the Monticello motif was abandoned, at least temporarily, and two new reverse designs were produced, one with a design of clasped hands borrowed from an old Indian peace medal, and the other with a keelboat, symbolizing the Lewis and Clark expedition. These "Westward Journey" themes continued with additional new designs in 2005 and 2006.

COLLECTING A TYPE SET OF FIVE-CENT PIECES

The designs of the nickel five-cent piece from 1866 to date are beautiful to behold. While Shield nickels of both types are slightly scarce in upper Mint State levels, they are within the financial reach of most collectors. Proofs are available of each type, but the 1866 and 1867 With Rays and the 1913 Buffalo Type I issues are rare.

The quality of strike presents a challenge across the various early types, most particularly with the 1866 and 1867 With Rays, for there are fewer possibilities from which to choose. Although 1913 to 1938 Type II Buffalo nickels are often poorly struck, there are enough sharp ones that finding a choice example will be no problem.

BEYOND A TYPE SET

Shield nickels of the 1866 to 1883 era are often collected by date sequence. A full set includes 1866 and 1867 Without Rays plus 1867 to 1883 With Rays. In addition, there is the 1879, 9 Over 8, overdate, which is found only in Proof format but is readily available (constituting perhaps a third or so of the Proof Mintage of 3,200 for the 1879 year) and the 1883, 3 Over 2 (scarce, and available only as a circulation strike).

Circulation strikes are available of all Shield nickel dates 1866 to 1883 except 1877 and 1878, which were made only in Proof format. A set of Proofs 1866 to 1883 can be completed except for the 1867 With Rays, which is exceedingly rare in Proof finish, with an estimated population of fewer than two dozen coins. Most 1878 Proofs are frosty and appear not much different from Mint State, but as only Proofs were made this year, they are called Proofs.

In circulated grades, Shield nickels are available in proportion to their mintage figures. The dates 1879 to 1881 had high Proof mintages (in the context of Proof figures), but low circulation-strike mintages, and thus they are key dates in the latter format. In other words, a gem Mint State 1880 Shield nickel (16,000 coined, but few were saved, as collectors acquired Proofs instead) is exceedingly rare today. In the same year, 3,955 Proofs were struck, and all were preserved by collectors and dealers. Today, the Proof 1880 is one of the most plentiful dates!

Liberty Head nickels of the 1883 Without CENTS (a.k.a. No CENTS) type are plentiful in Mint State and also in Proof finish. Later dates With CENTS, through 1912, are generally available in proportion to their mintages. The 1885 and 1886 are considered to be key dates. Proofs are readily collectible, although pristine high-quality specimens can be hard to find. The 1912-D and 1912-S are scarce, the low-mintage 1912-S being particularly so. In 1913 an estimated five Liberty Head nickels were privately made at the Philadelphia Mint, and today stand as famous rarities.

Among Buffalo nickels 1913 to 1938, the different dates and mints can be collected easily enough in circulated grades, although certain issues such as 1913-S Type II, 1921-S, and 1926-S are more scarce. An overdate, 1918-D, 8 Over 7, is a rarity at all grade levels. Curious varieties are provided by the very rare 1916 Doubled Die, the scarce 1937-D Three Legged (one of the forelegs of the bison was inadvertently filed off of the die), and the fascinating and very available 1938-D, D Over S, overmintmark.

In choice or gem Mint State, most branch mint Buffalo nickels 1914 to 1927 are fairly scarce, and some are quite rare. Most branch-mint coins of the 1920s are lightly struck in one area or another, with the 1926-D being particularly famous in this regard (most are truly miserable strikes). Sharply struck examples of such varieties are worth much more than lightly struck ones, although the grading services take no particular note of such differences. Matte Proofs of dates 1913 to 1916 were struck, and mirror-finish Proofs were made in 1936 and 1937. These exist today in proportion to their mintages.

Jefferson nickels from 1938 to date are readily collectible in Mint State and Proof format. Many otherwise common varieties can be very rare if sharply struck.

Shield, Rays Between Stars (1866–1867)

Circulation-Strike Mintage: **16,761,500**

Proof Mintage: ***500*, nearly all dated 1866**

Field Population: **Circulated, 100,000 to 125,000; Mint State, 8,000 to 12,000; Proof, 350 to 425**

Designer: James B. Longacre. **Weight:** 5 grams. **Composition:** .750 copper, .250 nickel. **Diameter:** 20.5 mm. **Edge:** Plain. **Mint:** Philadelphia.

Key to Collecting: Nickel five-cent pieces of the Shield type With Rays were made only in 1866 and early in 1867. Great problems developed with striking the design details properly, and it was thought that the rays contributed to the situation, taking metal flow that might be used to fill in the obverse shield details. Accordingly, the rays were dropped in early 1867, isolating this as a short-lived type. 1866 Shield nickels are fairly plentiful, and VF to AU coins can be found easily. Nearly all are weakly struck in one area or another. Accordingly, finding a choice one will require patience. Most are in lower grades, MS-60 to MS-63. Choice specimens of the 1867 With Rays are rare; gems are elusive, and if sharply struck with smooth, high-quality fields, are quite rare.

Aspects of Striking and Appearance: Usually with areas of light striking. Key areas for inspection include the horizontal stripes in the shield, the leaves in the wreath, and on the reverse, the centers of the stars. Coins struck from well-used dies are apt to have grainy or irregular fields. Die cracks are seen on most coins (and do not affect the value one way or the other, and in some instances can be interesting to observe).

Proof Coins: Proofs are very rare. Single Proofs were available for 10¢ each from the Mint in 1866, but it seems that little notice was taken of them. Of the 1867 With Rays, it is likely that fewer than two dozen Proofs are known—a classic rarity. Proofs are usually well struck and fairly attractive, but there are exceptions, and it will pay to study carefully any piece offered.

Market Value: Circulation Strikes

G-4	VG-8	F-12	VF-20	EF-40	AU-50	MS-60	MS-63	MS-64	MS-65	MS-66
$30	$45	$50	$100	$155	$240	$300	$425	$725	$1,600	$3,500

Market Value: Proof Strikes

PF-63	PF-64	PF-65	PF-66	PF-66Cam
$1,750	$2,000	$3,000	$3,500	$4,250

Retail Price Trends

Year	VF-20	MS-65	PF-65
1946	$10	$18	$50
1950	$6	$15	$45
1960	$8	$30	$300
1970	$20	$900	$1,700
1980	$30	$1,300	$2,200

Year	VF-20	MS-65	PF-65
1990	$30	$1,300	$2,200
2000	$60	$2,000	$3,125
2010	$90	$1,400	$2,800
2019	$100	$1,600	$3,000

Shield, Without Rays (1867–1883)

Circulation-Strike Mintage: 111,256,110

Proof Mintage: 35,000

Field population: Circulated, 500,000 to 800,000; Mint State, 75,000 to 100,000; Proof, 22,000 to 26,000

Designer: James B. Longacre. **Weight:** 5 grams. **Composition:** .750 copper, .250 nickel. **Diameter:** 20.5 mm. **Edge:** Plain. **Mint:** Philadelphia.

Key to Collecting: In early 1867, the Shield nickel motif was revised by eliminating the rays between the stars on the reverse. Afterward, the striking quality improved, as Mint officials hoped it would. However, the hard nickel-copper alloy was difficult to work with, and today it is a numismatic challenge to acquire choice pieces. Enough coins were made in circulation strike and Proof format that finding one will be no problem. However, it is important to keep an eye open for quality. Mint State coins are plentiful, especially of the last two dates in the series, 1882 and 1883.

Aspects of Striking and Appearance: The striking is generally much better than on the 1866 and 1867 With Rays style. Striking quality and aesthetic appeal are generally better for the later-dated coins. Issues of the 1860s and 1870s require special care to find quality pieces. Points to check include the horizontal shield lines and the star details. Die cracks are common among earlier dates and are sometimes a virtual network of tiny connecting lines—interesting to observe.

Proof Coins: Proofs of 1867 to 1876 are apt to vary in quality, and cherrypicking is advised. The 1877 and 1878 dates were made only in Proof format, the 1878 having a frosty surface not much different from a circulation strike in appearance. Proofs of the 1879 to 1883 years are generally of higher quality, with more mirrorlike fields and sharper details than found on earlier issues.

Market Value: Circulation Strikes

G-4	VG-8	F-12	VF-20	EF-40	AU-50	MS-60	MS-63	MS-64	MS-65	MS-66
$25	$30	$35	$45	$65	$110	$150	$225	$350	$650	$1,100

Market Value: Proof Strikes

PF-40	PF-63	PF-64	PF-65	PF-66	PF-66Cam
$1,000	$1,250	$1,350	$1,650	$2,000	$2,500

Retail Price Trends

Year	VF-20	MS-65	PF-65
1946	$1.50	$3	$5
1950	$2	$4	$6
1960	$3	$12.50	$20
1970	$12	$300	$400
1980	$18	$450	$500

Year	VF-20	MS-65	PF-65
1990	$15	$600	$700
2000	$20	$700	$520
2010	$40	$850	$2,000
2019	$45	$1,100	$1,650

Liberty Head, Without CENTS (1883)

Circulation-Strike Mintage: 5,474,000

Proof Mintage: 5,219

Field Population: Circulated, 400,000 to 600,000; Mint State, 125,000 to 250,000; Proof, 3,000 to 4,000

Designer: Charles E. Barber. **Weight:** 5 grams. **Composition:** .750 copper, .250 nickel. **Diameter:** 21.2 mm. **Edge:** Plain. **Mints:** Philadelphia, Denver, San Francisco.

Key to Collecting: In 1883 a new design was made for the nickel five-cent piece. The obverse featured an attractive head of Miss Liberty, possibly intended to represent the goddess Diana. The reverse depicted a wreath and inscriptions, including a V as the only mark of value—logical enough, as Roman numerals had served to identify the denominations for nickel three-cent pieces (introduced in 1865) and silver three-cent pieces (1851 onward). However, the diameter of the five-cent piece was about the same as a 5-dollar gold coin, and it became an infamous deception to gold-plate the new nickels and pass them off as five-dollar coins, sometimes adding reeding to aid in the caper. Word spread that the Treasury Department had made a grave error in the design and that all these coins would be recalled from circulation. A great excitement arose as speculators rushed to acquire as many as possible, aided by many advertisements from dealers offering them for sale. The result was that millions were hoarded.

Plentiful in all circulated grades. Mint State 1883 Liberty Head nickels without CENTS are the most plentiful of all Uncirculated nineteenth-century United States coins, except for certain Morgan silver dollars.

Aspects of Striking and Appearance: Many have areas of light striking. Points to check include the central star details on the obverse and the wreath details on the reverse. Die cracks are common and can lend interest.

Proof Coins: The "error" in the design created a lot of attention, resulting in record quantities of minor Proof sets (bronze cent, nickel three-cent and five-cent coins) being ordered from the Mint. Today, such pieces are plentiful, but the demand is great.

Market Value: Circulation Strikes

G-4	VG-8	F-12	VF-20	EF-40	AU-50	MS-60	MS-63	MS-64	MS-65	MS-66
$7	$8	$9	$11	$15	$20	$35	$50	$70	$225	$425

Market Value: Proof Strikes

PF-63	PF-64	PF-65	PF-66	PF-66Cam
$300	$450	$800	$1,200	$1,600

Retail Price Trends

Year	VF-20	MS-65	PF-65
1946	$0.30	$0.75	$3.50
1950	$0.40	$0.75	$4.50
1960	$1	$4.50	$17.50
1970	$3	$12	$500
1980	$5.50	$50	$750
1990	$6	$700	$1,000
2000	$7	$170	$1,125
2010	$10	$200	$900
2019	$11	$225	$800

Liberty Head, With CENTS (1883–1913)

Circulation-Strike Mintage: 596,534,050

Proof Mintage: 81,841

Field population: Circulated, 8,000,000 to 12,000,000; Mint State, 500,000 to 800,000; Proof, 50,000 to 65,000

Designer: Charles E. Barber. **Weight:** 5 grams. **Composition:** .750 copper, .250 nickel. **Diameter:** 21.2 mm. **Edge:** Plain. **Mints:** Philadelphia, Denver, San Francisco.

Key to Collecting: Produced in quantity from 1883 to 1912, the Liberty Head nickel with CENTS on the reverse was a mainstay of American commerce and entertainment during that period. Most surviving Liberty Head nickels are in worn grades, but enough Mint State examples survive that they can be systematically collected. Available for all dates 1883 to 1912, these coins are nonetheless most often seen from the late 1890s through 1912. Surfaces range from satiny to deeply frosty. Sharply struck gems with good eye appeal are very beautiful and are in the minority of extant specimens. The least expensive are those of the early twentieth century.

Aspects of Striking and Appearance: Many have areas of light striking. Points to check include the central star details on the obverse and the wreath details on the reverse. Avoid pieces with granular fields.

Proof Coins: Available of all dates 1883 to 1912, with those after the 1890s and 1900s being somewhat scarcer than those of the 1880s. Quality varies widely, even among coins certified in high grades, and careful selection is need to find a truly choice example.

Market Value: Circulation Strikes

G-4	VG-8	F-12	VF-20	EF-40	AU-50	MS-60	MS-63	MS-64	MS-65	MS-66
$2	$3	$4	$15	$30	$60	$85	$125	$200	$450	$900

Market Value: Proof Strikes

PF-63	PF-64	PF-65	PF-66	PF-66Cam
$250	$345	$550	$750	$900

Retail Price Trends

Year	VF-20	MS-65	PF-65
1946	$0.75	$3	$4.50
1950	$1.25	$4	$5
1960	$2.25	$14	$20
1970	$4	$200	$100
1980	$6	$350	$200
1990	$6	$450	$350
2000	$7	$600	$430
2010	$13	$550	$450
2019	$15	$450	$550

Indian Head or Buffalo, FIVE CENTS on Raised Ground (1913)

Circulation-Strike Mintage: 38,434,000

Proof Mintage: 1,250

Field Population: Circulated, 450,000 to 600,000; Mint State, 150,000 to 250,000; Proof, 500 to 650

Designer: James Earle Fraser. **Weight:** 5 grams. **Composition:** .750 copper, .250 nickel. **Diameter:** 21.2 mm. **Edge:** Plain. **Mints:** Philadelphia, Denver, San Francisco.

Key to Collecting: The Buffalo nickel featured on the obverse depicts an authentic portrait of a Native American, modeled as a composite from three life subjects: Iron Tail (who had bested General George Custer in his "last stand" at the Battle of Little Big Horn in Montana), John Big Tree, and Two Moons (who later toured the amusement circuit showcasing himself as the "Indian on the nickel"). The reverse was modeled from Black Diamond, a bison residing in the Central Park Zoo in New York City.

Unlike any preceding coin made for circulation, the Buffalo nickel had little in the way of open, smooth field surfaces. Instead, most areas on the obverse and reverse were filled with design elements or, especially on the reverse, an irregular background as on a bas-relief plaque. The entire ensemble, in high relief on both sides, was viewed as being very artistic, and the motif was highly acclaimed.

Upon reflection soon after the first coins were released, it was thought that the inscription FIVE CENTS, on a high area of the motif, would wear too quickly. Accordingly, ground under the bison, arranged in the form of a mound on Type I, was lowered to become flat, creating the next style (Type II).

Aspects of Striking and Appearance: Some coins have areas of light striking, particularly on the higher areas of the Indian's hair and on the upper part of the bison. However, as a general rule, Type I Buffalo nickels are much better struck than are those of Type II.

Matte Proof Coins: Probably no more than half of the original mintage still exists. Expertising is recommended, as these are difficult to distinguish from circulation strikes. All Matte Proofs have needle-sharp design details and squared rims.

Market Value: Circulation Strikes

G-4	VG-8	F-12	VF-20	EF-40	AU-50	MS-60	MS-63	MS-64	MS-65	MS-66
$12	$15	$16	$20	$25	$35	$45	$60	$75	$170	$275

Market Value: Proof Strikes

PF-63	PF-64	PF-65	PF-66	PF-67
$1,350	$2,000	$3,750	$4,750	$7,000

Retail Price Trends

Year	VF-20	MS-65	Matte PF-65
1946	$0.75	$1.25	$7
1950	$0.75	$1.23	$9.50
1960	$0.90	$4.50	$25
1970	$3	$110	$900
1980	$6.50	$50	$500
1990	$7	$100	$2,000
2000	$7.50	$125	$1,000
2010	$20	$150	$3,000
2019	$20	$170	$3,750

Indian Head or Buffalo, FIVE CENTS in Recess (1913–1938)

Circulation-Strike Mintage:
1,165,744,671

Proof Mintage:
Matte Proofs, 1913–1916:
4,439
Mirror-Finish Proofs,
***1936–1937:* 10,189**
(including some Satin Finish Proofs struck in early 1936)

Field Population:
Circulated,
15,000,000 to 30,000,000;
Mint State,
2,000,000 to 4,000,000;
Matte Proof, 2,500 to 3,200;
later Proofs, 6,000 to 8,000

Designer: James Earle Fraser. **Weight:** 5 grams. **Composition:** .750 copper, .250 nickel. **Diameter:** 21.2 mm. **Edge:** Plain. **Mints:** Philadelphia, Denver, San Francisco.

Key to Collecting: Circulated coins are readily available for common dates such as in the 1930s. Mint State coins are also plentiful for most issues in the 1930s. However, certain earlier date and mintmark varieties are scarce. Most varieties of the 1930s are highly frosty and lustrous.

Aspects of Striking and Appearance: Most Type II Buffalo nickels are poorly struck in one or more areas, and for many Denver and San Francisco issues of the 1920s, the striking is miserable. However, enough sharp strikes exist among common dates of the 1930s that one can be found with some patience.

Proof Coins: Matte Proofs of 1913 to 1916 are rare. As these are difficult to distinguish from circulation strikes, be careful when buying. Proofs of 1936 occur with a satiny surface and also with a mirror surface (in the relatively small amount of the open field available). Proofs of 1937 have mirror surface in the fields. The motifs of the 1936 and 1937 mirror Proofs are lightly polished in the die (not frosty or matte).

Market Value: Circulation Strikes

G-4	VG-8	F-12	VF-20	EF-40	AU-50	MS-60	MS-63	MS-64	MS-65	MS-66
$1	$1.50	$1.75	$3	$4	$10	$35	$45	$50	$60	$85

Market Value: Proof Strikes

PF-63	PF-64	PF-65	PF-66	PF-67
$900	$1,300	$2,000	$2,750	$4,500

Retail Price Trends

Year	VF-20	MS-65	Matte PF-65
1946	$0.15	$0.50	$7.50
1950	$0.15	$0.50	$7.50
1960	$0.10	$0.75	$10
1970	$0.10	$5	$85
1980	$0.75	$25	$650
1990	$0.75	$50	$1,200
2000	$1.25	$25	$800
2010	$2.40	$47	$2,250
2019	$3	$60	$2,000

Jefferson, Monticello Reverse, No Designer's Initials (1938–1942; 1946–1965)

Circulation-Strike Mintage: 6,981,092,900

Proof Mintage: 19,931,995

Field Population: Circulated, billions; Mint State, hundreds of millions; Proof, 14,000,000 to 17,000,000

Designer: Felix Schlag. **Weight:** 5 grams. **Composition:** .750 copper, .250 nickel. **Diameter:** 21.2 mm. **Edge:** Plain. **Mints:** Philadelphia, Denver, San Francisco.

Key to Collecting: The Treasury Department desired to replace the Buffalo nickel with a new motif and announced a nationwide competition among artists and sculptors. The obverse was to depict President Thomas Jefferson and the reverse was to illustrate Monticello, his home in Charlottesville, Virginia.

Production of the new nickels began in September, and although coin collecting was extremely popular at the time, as it had been throughout the Depression years, not much interest was paid to the new nickels, and no widespread public hoarding or speculation resulted. Accordingly, unlike the first years of issue for the Liberty Head nickel (1883) and the Buffalo nickel (1913), the first year of issue of the Jefferson nickel, while readily available, does not stand out as being common.

The Jefferson nickel obverse design was employed from 1938 until 2005, with a change to silver alloy during World War II (creating a new type, listed in the following section), and some minor modifications. In 1966, through a campaign conducted by *Numismatic News*, the initials FS were added to the obverse to recognize designer Felix O. Schlag.

Aspects of Striking and Appearance: Many pieces have weak details on the six steps of Monticello, as this section on the reverse was opposite in the dies (in the press) from the high parts of the Jefferson portrait, and metal could not effectively flow in both directions at once. Planchet weight allowance was another cause, the dies being spaced slightly too far apart.

Proof Coins: Common in the context of Proofs. Usually fairly well struck, but not always.

Market Value: Circulation Strikes

MS-60	MS-63	MS-65	MS-66	MS-67
$0.25	$0.50	$3	$40	$285

Market Value: Proof Strikes

PF-65	PF-66	PF-67	PF-68
$3	$10	$18	$25

Retail Price Trends

Year	VF-20	MS-65	PF-65
1946	$0.10	$0.10	$0.50
1950	$0.10	$0.10	$0.75
1960	$0.15	$0.20	$0.90
1970	$0.10	$0.10	$1
1980	$0.10	$0.10	$1
1990	$0.10	$0.15	$0.40
2000	$0.30	$0.50	$0.80
2010	$0.30	$1.20	$1.10
2019	$0.30	$3	$3

Jefferson, Monticello Reverse, No Designer's Initials, Wartime Silver Alloy (1942–1945)

Circulation-Strike Mintage: 869,896,100

Proof Mintage: 27,600

Field Population: Circulated, 40,000,000 to 70,000,000; Mint State, 5,000,000 to 10,000,000; Proof, 18,000 to 23,000

Designer: Felix Schlag. **Weight:** 5 grams. **Composition:** .560 copper, .350 silver, .090 manganese, with net weight .05626 oz. pure silver. **Diameter:** 21.2 mm. **Edge:** Plain. **Mints:** Philadelphia, Denver, San Francisco.

Key to Collecting: To conserve nickel metal for critical wartime use, partway through 1942, the Mint revised the alloy of the five-cent piece to eliminate this element. The so-called "wartime" or "silver" composition comprised 56% copper, 35% silver, and 9% manganese. To quickly differentiate pieces in this metal, the mintmark was placed as a large letter prominently over the dome of Monticello on the reverse (instead of a small letter to the right of the building, as earlier). For the first time, a P was used to designate Philadelphia issues.

Circulated coins are common but not usually considered for inclusion in a type set as Mint State coins are readily available. Circulated pieces are often dull and/or blotchy whereas there are beautiful gems available.

Aspects of Striking and Appearance: The silver content was sufficient to give the finished pieces a bright, deeply lustrous finish not much different from that found on contemporary dimes, quarters, and half dollars. The metal was softer than the normal nickel-content alloy, resulting in many pieces being struck with very sharp design details including the steps on the Monticello building. Mint State coins are usually well struck and often of exceptional beauty.

Proof Coins: Proof strikings were made only in 1942. Until recent decades, it was not unusual for dealers to obtain quantity groups of the 1942-P. However, by now most have been dispersed. Attractive Proofs are readily available singly.

Market Value: Circulation Strikes

VF-20	EF-40	AU-50	MS-60	MS-63	MS-64FS
$2	$3.50	$4	$6	$12	$20
MS-65	**MS-65FS**	**MS-66**	**MS-66FS**	**MS-67**	**MS-67FS**
$20	$37	$30	$50	$50	$125

Market Value: Proof Strikes

PF-63	PF-64	PF-65	PF-66	PF-67
$90	$95	$110	$160	$275

Retail Price Trends

Year	EF-40	MS-60	PF-65
1960	$0.60	$0.75	$7.50
1970	$1	$1	$60
1980	$2	$2.75	$150
1990	$1	$7	$400

Year	EF-40	MS-60	PF-65
2000	$2	$6	$100
2010	$1.75	$6	$100
2019	$3.50	$6	$110

Jefferson, Monticello Reverse, With Designer's Initials (1966–2003)

Circulation-Strike Mintage: 37,810,302,313

Proof Mintage: 16,724,214

Field Population: Circulated, billions; Mint State, hundreds of millions, if not billions; Proof, millions

Designer: Felix Schlag. **Weight:** 5 grams. **Composition:** .750 copper, .250 nickel. **Diameter:** 21.2 mm. **Edge:** Plain. **Mints:** Philadelphia, Denver, San Francisco.

Key to Collecting: Mint State coins are very common, including gems.

Aspects of Striking and Appearance: Vary, but superb pieces are readily available.

Proof Coins: Gems are common.

Notes: In 1971, 1972, 1977, and 1982, slight modifications were made to the dies to sharpen the details. In 1968 the mintmark position, formerly to the right of the building on the reverse, was moved to the lower right of the obverse.

Market Value: Circulation Strikes

MS-63	MS-64FS	MS-65	MS-65FS	MS-66
$0.25	$8	$1	$10	$12

Market Value: Proof Strikes

PF-65	PF-66	PF-67Cam
$2	$7	$12

Retail Price Trends

Year	MS-63	MS-65	PF-65
1970	$0.05	$0.10	$1.50
1980	$0.05	$0.10	$0.75
1990	$0.05	$0.10	$0.75
2000	$0.05	$0.10	$0.75
2010	$0.25	$1	$2
2019	$0.25	$1	$2

Jefferson, Westward Journey (2004–2005)

2004, Obverse
Designer: Felix Schlag.

Field Population:
Nearly all of original mintage

2005, Obverse
Designer: Joe Fitzgerald.

2004, Peace Medal
Reverse designer: Norman E. Nemeth.

Circulation-Strike Mintage:
733,440,000

Proof Mintage:
2,992,069

2004, Keelboat
Reverse designer: Al Maletsky.

Circulation-Strike Mintage:
711,600,000

Proof Mintage:
2,965,422

2005, American Bison
Reverse designer: Jamie Franki.

Circulation-Strike Mintage:
936,000,000

Proof Mintage:
3,344,679

2005, "Ocean in View"
Reverse designer: Joe Fitzgerald.

Circulation-Strike Mintage:
805,200,000

Proof Mintage:
3,344,679

Designers: See image captions for designers. **Weight:** 5 grams. **Composition:** .750 copper, .250 nickel. **Diameter:** 21.2 mm. **Edge:** Plain. **Mints:** Philadelphia, Denver, San Francisco.

Key to Collecting: In 2004 special designs commemorating the Westward Journey (Lewis and Clark expedition) were introduced. They utilized the previous obverse design paired with two different reverse designs, one representing the Peace Medals given out by Lewis and Clark, the other showing the keelboat that provided much of their transportation. Two new reverse designs were introduced for 2005, showing the American bison and a representation of Clark's journal entry upon spotting what he thought was the Pacific Ocean (in actuality, they were still approximately 20 miles from the coast). They were paired with a new obverse, a tightly cropped profile of Jefferson facing right. Mint State coins are very common, including gems. All basic dates and mintmarks were saved in roll quantities.

Aspects of Striking and Appearance: Generally well struck and attractive. Some have a matte-like finish. On the obverse, check for weakness on the portrait.

Proof Coins: Gems are common. All have mirror fields. Most have frosted or cameo contrast on the higher features.

WESTWARD JOURNEY, all types

Market Value: Circulation Strikes

MS-63	MS-65	MS-66
$0.25	$0.75	$5

Market Value: Proof Strikes

PF-65	PF-67	PF-69DC
$8	$12	$25

Jefferson, Monticello Reverse, Modified Portrait (2006 to Date)

Circulation-Strike Mintage:
Tens of billions, still being minted

Proof Mintage:
Tens of millions, still being minted

Field Population:
Circulated, tens of billions; Mint State, hundreds of millions; Proof, tens of millions

Designers: ***Obverse:*** Jamie Franki; ***Reverse:*** Felix Schlag. **Weight:** 5 grams. **Composition:** .750 copper, .250 nickel. **Diameter:** 21.2 mm. **Edge:** Plain. **Mints:** Philadelphia, Denver, San Francisco.

Key to Collecting: 2006 saw the return of Felix Schlag's reverse design showing a front view of Jefferson's home, Monticello. It also featured the debut of another new Jefferson portrait on the obverse, this time in three-quarters profile. Mint State coins are very common, including gems.

Aspects of Striking and Appearance: Generally well struck and attractive.

Proof Coins: Gems are common. All have mirror fields. Most have frosted or cameo contrast on the higher features.

Market Value: Circulation Strikes

MS-63	MS-65	MS-66
$0.25	$0.75	$3

Market Value: Proof Strikes

PF-65	PF-67	PF-69DC
$4	$12	$30

13
Half Dimes
1792-1873

Overview of the Denomination

Half dimes or five-cent silver coins were provided for in the Mint Act of April 2, 1792. The spelling was stated as "half *disme*," with *disme* probably being pronounced as we say *dime* today. The same word was used for the silver 10-cent piece or *disme*, today's dime. The *disme* term was used intermittently in government correspondence for years afterward, but on coins it later appeared only as *dime*.

Although in later years, some numismatists were fond of calling the 1792 half disme a *pattern*, no facts corroborate that contention. The pieces were made in quantity, believed to be 1,500, and, per the president of the United States, were made for *circulation*. Moreover, nearly all examples in existence today show signs of wear, often extensive.

As to whether you wish to include a 1792 half disme in your type set, you can have an escape clause, so to speak, if you elect not to: as the Philadelphia Mint was not yet a reality in the summer of 1792 when these were struck, they were made off-premises in the shop owned by John Harper, a Philadelphia sawmaker who had connections to the Mint and its personnel. In the strictest sense, it is a *federal coin* authorized under the 1792 legislation but is not a product made within the walls of the first Mint building. On the other hand, Thomas Jefferson referred to the temporary facility at the Harper shop as "the Mint," in a memorandum of July 11, 1792, in which he wrote of taking "75 D to the Mint" to be coined into half dismes.[10]

Next in line comes the Flowing Hair half dime design of 1794 and 1795, thought to have been devised by Mint engraver Robert Scot. The obverse and reverse motifs were also used on the half dollars and dollars of the same dates. Miss Liberty, facing to the right, has hair "flowing" downward. On the reverse is an eagle perched on a rock, wings outspread, with the tips intersecting the surrounding wreath.

In 1796 and 1797, the Draped Bust obverse, Small Eagle reverse design was employed on the half dime, also by engraver Scot. The obverse depicts Miss Liberty facing to the right, her bosom draped in cloth, her hair tied behind her head, said to have been from a sketch of Mrs. William Bingham (the former Ann Willing), furnished by artist Gilbert Stuart. On the reverse is what collectors call the "Small Eagle" motif, with the eagle indeed smaller than on the preceding, and now perched or somehow situated on a cloud. The same design was used on other silver denominations, including the dime and half dollar in 1796 and 1797, the quarter dollar in 1796, and the silver dollar from 1795 to 1798.

There were no half dimes minted with the dates 1798 or 1799. The 1800 to 1805 half dimes continued the Draped Bust obverse as preceding, but now with the Heraldic Eagle reverse adapted from the Great Seal of the United States. Then followed a long hiatus in which silver half dimes were absent from the coinage scene.

In 1829 production resumed with the Capped Bust design created by John Reich and first used years earlier on the 1807 half dollar. Miss Liberty wears a cloth cap, a *mob cap* in early parlance, a popular item for indoor wear by women. The reverse displays a perched eagle holding an olive branch and arrows. This style was continued through part of 1837.

At the Philadelphia Mint in 1837 and at the New Orleans Mint in 1838, the Liberty Seated design, without obverse stars, was used in combination with a wreath design on the reverse. The engraver was Christian Gobrecht; the obverse was a miniature version of his famous "Gobrecht dollar" of 1836. The same design was used at the same time for dimes.

In 1838 stars were added to the obverse of the half dime. This constitutes a new type, with stars and without drapery at Miss Liberty's elbow, that would be used until 1840, at which time drapery was added. This new type was made through and including 1859. A different type within the series was created 1853 to 1855 when arrowheads were added alongside the date to indicate a weight reduction.

The final type in the half dime series was introduced in 1860 from dies modified by James B. Longacre. The inscription UNITED STATES OF AMERICA replaced the obverse stars, and on the reverse, a "cereal wreath" was employed, the latter apparently being the suggestion of numismatist Harold P. Newlin. This motif was used through early 1873, at which time the half dime was abolished under the Coinage Act of that year.

Collecting a Type Set of Half Dimes

Collecting a set of the different half dime types is a challenging sport. The 1792 half disme may be optional for you (see above), but if it is not, you will quickly find that many on the market have problems—such as nicks, cuts, and marks. However, when you finally acquire an example you like, the coin will be very satisfying to own and contemplate.

The 1794 and 1795 Flowing Hair half dimes are fairly scarce at all levels and are quite rare in choice Mint State. Then come the Draped Bust obverse, Small Eagle reverse half dimes of 1796 and 1797. In the late 1960s, when Jim Ruddy was gathering pictures for his *Photograde* grading guide (released in 1970), he found that of the various silver types (including the more famous 1796 and 1797 half dollars), half dimes of this type were the hardest to complete a photographic set of, from the lowest grades to the highest.

Draped Bust obverse, Heraldic Eagle reverse half dimes of the 1800 to 1805 years are scarce in all grades, more so than generally realized. In Mint State they are very rare, although on occasion some dated 1800 turn up (not often for the others). Finding a *sharply struck* example is next to impossible, and you may have to give up on this aspect of your search and settle for one that has some weakness in areas.

Capped Bust half dimes and the several variations of Liberty Seated half dimes will pose no problem at all, and with some small amount of patience, you will be able to find a sharply struck example in just about any grade desired.

BEYOND A TYPE SET

Collecting half dimes by early die varieties 1794 to 1837, and/or by dates and mintmarks (beginning with the 1838-O), has captured the fancy of many numismatists over the years.

Among early half dimes, the rarest and most expensive is the 1802. Most are well worn, and I am not aware of even a single Mint State example. Other early half dimes range from rare to very rare.

Capped Bust half dimes of the years 1829 to 1837 are all easily available as dates, but some of the die varieties are very rare. Today, most half dimes on the market are not attributed by varieties, making the search for such things rewarding when a rarity is found for the price of a regular coin. Liberty Seated issues are collectible, although some are rare. The 1870-S is unique. Proofs are available for dates from 1858 to 1873, and earlier Proofs are occasionally offered.

Half Disme (1792)

Circulation-Strike Mintage: 1,500 per Thomas Jefferson's records, which must be viewed as correct

Field Population: Circulated, 200 to 300; Mint State, 14 to 22

Designer: Unknown (possibly Robert Birch). **Weight:** 1.35 grams. **Composition:** .8924 silver, .1076 copper. **Diameter:** 16.5 mm. **Edge:** Reeded. **Mint:** John Harper's shop, Philadelphia.

Key to Collecting: The 1792 half disme is one of the more fascinating early federal issues, mainly because facts concerning it are scarce and legends and rumors abound. It has been said that Martha Washington posed for the obverse, but if this is true, her image on the coin is not even remotely similar to illustrations of her made from life in the same era. Some have said that President Washington took his own silverware to the Mint, where it was melted down and converted to half dismes, which were then given to him. And so it goes, with widely ranging accounts of this denomination's history.

The point of mentioning all of this here is that the 1792 half dime is shrouded in a good deal of mystery—and such things contribute to the fascination of numismatics and, indeed, here and there among other designs, to the formation and enjoyment of a type set.

Probably 200 to 300 circulated coins exist, mostly in grades such from G to F, often with dents and marks. Mint State coins are exceedingly rare, with probably fewer than two dozen in existence. Several of these are memorable and qualify as choice or gem grades.

Aspects of Striking and Appearance: Usually fairly well struck except for some lightness on the eagle's breast. Some have adjustment marks from filing the planchet prior to striking. For this coin, I suggest that you disregard seeking a sharp one and concentrate instead on finding one with overall good eye appeal and without problems.

Market Value: Circulation Strikes

VF-20	EF-40	MS-60	MS-62	MS-63
$80,000	$100,000	$165,000	$185,000	$275,000

Retail Price Trends

Year	G-4	F-12	MS-63
1946	$50	$100	$250
1950	$50	$100	$2,500
1960	$115	$225	$5,000
1970	$575	$950	$10,000
1980	$1,200	$2,500	$35,000

Year	G-4	F-12	MS-63
1990	$1,400	$4,000	$40,000
2000	$4,500	$7,000	$100,000
2010	$20,000	$43,000	$325,000
2019	$20,000	$40,000	$275,000

Flowing Hair (1794–1795)

Circulation-Strike Mintage: 86,416

Field Population: Circulated, 2,200 to 3,500; Mint State, 250 to 400

Designer: Unknown. **Engraver:** Robert Scot.
Weight: 1.35 grams. **Composition:** .8924 silver, .1076 copper.
Diameter: Approximately 16.5 mm. **Edge:** Reeded. **Mint:** Philadelphia.

Key to Collecting: Most circulated coins are dated 1795. Typical grades are G to F or so. EF and AU grades are elusive. Probably somewhere between 250 and 400 Mint State coins exist, the vast preponderance being of the 1795 date. Although most hover around low Mint State levels, and others might be better called AU, there are a few choice and gem pieces around. However, in relation to the great demand for these pieces they are quite difficult to obtain, and the appearance of a choice one is an important numismatic event.

Aspects of Striking and Appearance: Many have problems of one sort or another, including adjustment marks from filing the planchet, and/or light striking in some areas, most particularly the breast of the eagle. It may not be possible to find a *needle-sharp* example, but with some extensive searching, a fairly decent strike can be obtained. In summary, a sharply struck coin is a goal, not necessarily a reality.

Notes: There is no indication of the denomination of this coin on the obverse, reverse, or edge.

Market Value: Circulation Strikes

AG-3	G-4	VG-8	F-12	VF-20	EF-40	AU-50	MS-60	MS-62	MS-63	MS-64	MS-65
$550	$1,350	$1,600	$2,000	$3,250	$6,000	$8,000	$11,500	$13,500	$18,000	$22,500	$37,500

Retail Price Trends

Year	G-4	F-12	MS-63
1946	$6	$10	$50
1950	$7.50	$15	$65
1960	$30	$50	$200
1970	$155	$325	$1,000
1980	$275	$525	$5,000

Year	G-4	F-12	MS-63
1990	$575	$1,000	$10,000
2000	$550	$925	$7,500
2010	$1,200	$2,400	$19,500
2019	$1,350	$2,000	$18,000

Draped Bust, Small Eagle Reverse (1796–1797)

Circulation-Strike Mintage: 54,757

Field Population: Circulated, 1,200 to 1,500; Mint State, 60 to 90

Designer: Probably Gilbert Stuart. **Engraver:** Robert Scot. **Weight:** 1.35 grams. **Composition:** .8924 silver, .1076 copper. **Diameter:** Approximately 16.5 mm. **Edge:** Reeded. **Mint:** Philadelphia.

Key to Collecting: This very scarce type in the half dime series has received a lot of attention over the years. Interestingly, most pieces on the market seem to be in grades from VG to VF, not often lower or higher, most with medium wear. Nicks and scratches can be a problem. Select an example with pleasing light or medium gray surfaces. Several different star arrangements exist for the 1797, but these are not considered to be different types. Probably no more than a few dozen truly choice Mint State coins exist. As with other early silver types, beware deeply toned or vividly iridescent toned pieces for which the true surface character cannot be determined with accuracy, but which are offered as Mint State. I recommend acquiring examples only with rich luster on the surfaces, either lightly toned or brilliant. However, *any* fully brilliant piece is so by virtue of having been dipped—not necessarily negative, although repeated dipping tends to make coins dull and lifeless.

Aspects of Striking and Appearance: Most coins are weak in one area or another, although there are some marvelous exceptions. As not many people take notice of striking sharpness, such coins can often be acquired for only a modest premium. Points to check for sharpness include the hair of Miss Liberty, the centers of the stars, and, on the reverse, the eagle. Also check for adjustment marks, but these are infrequent. Denticles around the border are usually decent on this type, but may vary in strength from one part of the border to another. Many have Mint-caused planchet-adjustment marks. In summary, a sharply struck coin is a goal, not necessarily a reality.

Market Value: Circulation Strikes

AG-3	G-4	VG-8	F-12	VF-20	EF-40	AU-50	MS-60	MS-62	MS-63	MS-64	MS-65
$700	$1,500	$1,800	$3,450	$4,750	$8,750	$12,500	$16,000	$19,000	$25,000	$40,000	$80,000

Retail Price Trends

Year	G-4	F-12	MS-63
1946	$10	$17.50	$100
1950	$10	$25	$120
1960	$27.50	$60	$225
1970	$160	$325	$2,000
1980	$325	$600	$5,000
1990	$700	$1,100	$8,000
2000	$650	$1,100	$9,000
2010	$1,200	$2,250	$25,000
2019	$1,500	$3,450	$25,000

Draped Bust, Heraldic Eagle Reverse (1800-1805)

Circulation-Strike Mintage: 124,270

Field Population: Circulated, 1,500 to 1,800; Mint State, 125 to 175

Designer: Robert Scot. **Weight:** 1.35 grams. **Composition:** .8924 silver, .1076 copper. **Diameter:** Approximately 16.5 mm. **Edge:** Reeded. **Mint:** Philadelphia.

Key to Collecting: Examples are scarce in all grades and rare in Mint State. Most examples on the market are in worn grades, often showing extensive circulation, marks, and porosity. Finding a "nice" example can be done but may involve looking over several candidates in order to select a winner. Coins in grades of EF and AU are mostly of the 1800 date. Again, 1800 comes to the fore when Mint State coins are offered as most are of this date. Examples of other dates are virtually non-existent in choice or gem Mint State and are first-class rarities even in MS-60.

Aspects of Striking and Appearance: Most coins of this type are lightly struck in one area or another. The obverse stars usually show some weakness. On many coins, the central details of Miss Liberty are not sharp. On the reverse, the upper right of the shield and the adjacent part of the eagle's wing are often soft, and several or even most stars may be lightly defined (sharp stars show sharply peaked centers). Denticles are likely to be weak or missing in areas. Expect to compromise on the striking issue. Even more, many have Mint-caused planchet-adjustment marks. Finding a "nice" coin will be a challenge.

Notes: There is no indication of the denomination on the obverse, reverse, or edge.

Market Value: Circulation Strikes

AG-3	G-4	VG-8	F-12	VF-20	EF-40	AU-50	MS-60	MS-62	MS-63	MS-64	MS-65
$450	$1,100	$1,500	$2,000	$3,000	$6,000	$8,500	$12,500	$15,000	$20,000	$25,000	$47,500

Retail Price Trends

Year	G-4	F-12	MS-63
1946	$7	$12.50	$50
1950	$8	$15	$65
1960	$25	$65	$225
1970	$130	$250	$1,000
1980	$225	$450	$3,000
1990	$575	$900	$5,000
2000	$475	$750	$8,000
2010	$725	$1,750	$20,000
2019	$1,100	$2,000	$20,000

Capped Bust (1829-1837)

Circulation-Strike Mintage: 13,058,700

Proof Mintage: Several hundred

Field Population: Circulated, 80,000 to 120,000; Mint State, 10,000 to 20,000; Proof, 75 to 125

Engraver: William Kneass, after a design by John Reich. **Weight:** 1.35 grams (changed to 1.34 grams in 1837). **Composition:** .8924 silver, .1076 copper (changed to .900 silver, .100 copper in 1837). **Diameter:** Approximately 15.5 mm. **Edge:** Reeded. **Mint:** Philadelphia.

Key to Collecting: Half dimes of this design were first struck in the wee small hours of the morning of July 4, 1829, to have a supply on hand for insertion in the cornerstone of the new (second) Philadelphia Mint building and, presumably, to have some inexpensive coins on hand for distribution as souvenirs. There are no rare dates in this range, but some die varieties are elusive. Finding a nice example for your type set will be no problem. Examples abound in all grades. As these are not expensive, you will want to consider a higher level, say at least VF. There are many Mint State coins on the market.

Aspects of Striking and Appearance: Most half dimes of this type are fairly well struck. Points to check include the hair details and star centers on the obverse and the eagle on the reverse. Denticles range from well defined to somewhat indistinct, and, in general, are sharper on the obverse than on the reverse.

Proof Coins: Proof coins were struck in limited numbers for presentation purposes and for distribution to numismatists. Insist on a coin with deep and full (not partial) mirror surfaces. Seek one that is well struck and has good contrast. Avoid deeply toned pieces (deep toning often masks the true nature of a coin).

Market Value: Circulation Strikes

G-4	VG-8	F-12	VF-20	EF-40	AU-50	MS-60	MS-62	MS-63	MS-64	MS-65	MS-66
$50	$65	$80	$115	$175	$275	$400	$525	$850	$1,250	$2,500	$4,000

Market Value: Proof Strikes

PF-60	PF-63	PF-64	PF-65
$4,500	$10,000	$18,000	$27,500

Retail Price Trends

Year	F-12	EF-40	MS-64
1946	$0.60	$1	$3.25
1950	$0.75	$1.50	$3.75
1960	$3	$5	$12
1970	$11	$30	$700
1980	$25	$70	$1,500

Year	F-12	EF-40	MS-64
1990	$23	$100	$2,500
2000	$28	$110	$1,700
2010	$75	$165	$1,100
2019	$80	$175	$1,250

Liberty Seated, No Stars on Obverse (1837–1838)

Circulation-Strike Mintage: 1,475,000

Proof Mintage: Fewer than 60

Field Population: Circulated, 12,000 to 16,000; Mint State, 2,000 to 3,500; Proof, 30 to 40

Designer: Christian Gobrecht. **Weight:** 1.34 grams. **Composition:** .900 silver, .100 copper. **Diameter:** 15.5 mm. **Edge:** Reeded. **Mints:** Philadelphia, New Orleans.

Key to Collecting: The Liberty Seated design without obverse stars was used in the half dime and dime series only at the Philadelphia Mint in 1837 and the New Orleans Mint in 1838 (1838-O). Miss Liberty has no drapery at her elbow. These coins are very attractive, and the starless obverse gives them a cameo-like appearance. Circulated coins are plentiful in the context of the era. All grades are available, with EF and AU examples being scarcer than lower grades. Enough Mint State pieces are available, so that finding one will be no problem. Two thousand or more exist, most of which are lustrous and quite attractive, a field of opportunity wider than for the related dimes. Nearly all are dated 1837.

Aspects of Striking and Appearance: Usually seen well struck, except for the denticles, which are often mushy. Points to check include the denticles on obverse and reverse and the highest parts of the Liberty Seated figure and the leaves.

Proof Coins: It is likely that at least several dozen Proofs were made of the 1837 half dime, although perhaps more were made of the related dime. Today, attractive examples exist and are rare. Nearly all I have seen called Proofs are, indeed, Proofs. If you aspire to acquire one, select an example with deep mirror surfaces.

Market Value: Circulation Strikes

G-4	VG-8	F-12	VF-20	EF-40	AU-50	MS-60	MS-62	MS-63	MS-64	MS-65	MS-66
$40	$55	$80	$145	$250	$450	$600	$750	$850	$1,200	$2,500	$3,650

Market Value: Proof Strikes

PF-60	PF-63	PF-64	PF-65
$7,000	$12,500	$20,000	$32,500

Retail Price Trends

Year	F-12	EF-40	MS-64
1946	$2	$3	$6
1950	$2.50	$5	$12
1960	$21	$35	$75
1970	$80	$90	$700
1980	$70	$200	$1,500
1990	$45	$200	$3,000
2000	$45	$190	$2,000
2010	$80	$235	$1,800
2019	$80	$250	$1,200

Liberty Seated, Stars on Obverse, No Drapery (1838–1840)

Circulation-Strike Mintage: 6,057,189

Proof Mintage: *About 20*

Field Population:
Circulated, 30,000 to 40,000;
Mint State, 2,500 to 4,000;
Proof, 10 to 15

Designer: Christian Gobrecht. **Weight:** 1.34 grams. **Composition:** .900 silver, .100 copper. **Diameter:** 15.5 mm. **Edge:** Reeded. **Mints:** Philadelphia, New Orleans.

Key to Collecting: Half dimes of the first type with stars, but still without drapery, were minted to the extent of six million or so coins and they are plentiful in all grades. Mint State coins are also plentiful, though scarcer than the next type. Finding an attractive example that is just right should present no problem.

Aspects of Striking and Appearance: Most are well struck and are very pleasing in appearance, usually with satiny luster rather than a deep flashy frost.

Proof Coins: A few Proofs were made of each of the years of this type.

Market Value: Circulation Strikes

G-4	VG-8	F-12	VF-20	EF-40	AU-50	MS-60	MS-62	MS-63	MS-64	MS-65	MS-66
$18	$21	$28	$45	$125	$200	$280	$350	$475	$800	$1,350	$3,000

Market Value: Proof Strikes

PF-60	PF-63	PF-64	PF-65
8,500	$10,500	$25,000	$35,000

Retail Price Trends

Year	F-12	EF-40	MS-64	PF-64
1946	$0.50	$1	$2	$50
1950	$0.75	$1.50	$3.75	$150
1960	$3	$7	$14	$500
1970	$5.50	$20	$500	$4,000
1980	$12	$50	$700	$12,000

Year	F-12	EF-40	MS-64	PF-64
1990	$12.50	$55	$1,800	$20,000
2000	$20	$60	$1,100	$24,000
2010	$27	$75	$800	$25,000
2019	$28	$125	$800	$25,000

Liberty Seated, Stars on Obverse, Drapery (1840–1853; 1856–1859)

Circulation-Strike Mintage: 36,618,585

Proof Mintage: Fewer than 2,000 pieces

Field Population: Circulated, 150,000 to 225,000; Mint State, 10,000 to 14,000; Proof, 1,100 to 1,400

Designer: Christian Gobrecht. **Weight:** ***1840–1853:*** 1.34 grams; ***1856–1859:*** 1.24 grams. **Composition:** .900 silver, .100 copper. **Diameter:** 15.5 mm. **Edge:** Reeded. **Mints:** Philadelphia, New Orleans.

Key to Collecting: Half dimes of this type were minted in large quantities, so finding a nice example for a type set will be easy enough to do. Mint State coins are plentiful as a type, although certain dates and varieties are rare. Most on the market are dated in the 1850s.

Aspects of Striking and Appearance: Vary widely. Generally, the earlier dates are better struck and sharper than later issues, but there are exceptions. Points to check include the star centers, the head and other details of the Liberty Seated figure, the leaves on the reverse, and the denticles on both sides. Luster varies.

Proof Coins: Proofs were first widely sold to collectors in 1858 in which year an estimated 210 silver sets were distributed. It is believed that 800 Proofs were struck of 1859, of which slightly more than 400 found buyers. Proofs were made of earlier dates, but in much smaller numbers. The quality of Proofs on the market varies widely, and patience and care are needed to find a choice example.

Market Value: Circulation Strikes

G-4	VG-8	F-12	VF-20	EF-40	AU-50	MS-60	MS-62	MS-63	MS-64	MS-65	MS-66
$18	$22	$25	$35	$60	$115	$175	$225	$285	$400	$700	$950

Market Value: Proof Strikes

PF-60	PF-63	PF-64	PF-65
$550	$1,100	$1,500	$2,500

Retail Price Trends

Year	F-12	EF-40	MS-64	PF-64
1946	$0.35	$0.75	$2	$15
1950	$0.50	$0.75	$2	$16.50
1960	$1.25	$3	$7.50	$37.50
1970	$5	$10	$200	$1,000
1980	$10	$32.50	$500	$2,000

Year	F-12	EF-40	MS-64	PF-64
1990	$9	$40	$750	$3,000
2000	$12	$50	$825	$2,500
2010	$25	$75	$700	$2,200
2019	$25	$60	$400	$1,500

Liberty Seated, Stars on Obverse, Arrows at Date (1853–1855)

Circulation-Strike Mintage: 25,060,020

Proof Mintage: Fewer than 200, mostly dated 1854

Field Population: Circulated, 80,000 to 120,000; Mint State, 4,000 to 6,000; Proof, 90 to 125

Designer: Christian Gobrecht. **Weight:** 1.24 grams. **Composition:** .900 silver, .100 copper. **Diameter:** 15.5 mm. **Edge:** Reeded. **Mints:** Philadelphia, New Orleans.

Key to Collecting: Half dimes of the 1853 to 1855 With Arrows type are plentiful today in circulated grades, less so in Mint State. These are still easy enough to find, mostly in grades MS-60 to MS-63. Gems are not rare, but are in the minority. Most Mint State coins are of the 1853 Philadelphia issue, which recorded by far the largest mintage.

Aspects of Striking and Appearance: Vary widely. Often with one or more problems such as weak stars, weak head of Miss Liberty, light definition on the higher leaf details, and mushy denticles. Many are not sharp and some are struck from "tired" dies. Cherrypicking is strongly advised, although there will be many candidates from which to choose.

Proof Coins: Exceedingly rare. Most bear the 1854 date. Proofs are well struck, and choice examples have a pleasing appearance.

Market Value: Circulation Strikes

G-4	VG-8	F-12	VF-20	EF-40	AU-50	MS-60	MS-62	MS-63	MS-64	MS-65	MS-66
$20	$25	$30	$35	$70	$140	$190	$240	$310	$450	$850	$1,250

Market Value: Proof Strikes

PF-60	PF-63	PF-64	PF-65
$4,000	$7,500	$8,500	$10,000

Retail Price Trends

Year	F-12	EF-40	MS-64	PF-64
1946	$0.35	$0.75	$1.50	$35
1950	$0.45	$1	$2.25	$37.50
1960	$1.65	$5	$12	$140
1970	$4	$15	$300	$1,500
1980	$9.50	$37.50	$700	$4,000

Year	F-12	EF-40	MS-64	PF-64
1990	$8	$40	$1,500	$8,000
2000	$11	$40	$900	$10,500
2010	$25	$65	$725	$12,000
2019	$30	$70	$450	$8,500

Liberty Seated, Legend on Obverse (1860–1873)

Circulation-Strike Mintage: 15,552,600

Proof Mintage: 10,040

Field Population: Circulated, 100,000 to 175,000; Mint State, 12,000 to 16,000; Proof, 7,000 to 8,500

Designer: Christian Gobrecht. **Weight:** 1.24 grams.
Composition: .900 silver, .100 copper. **Diameter:** 15.5 mm.
Edge: Reeded. **Mints:** Philadelphia, New Orleans, San Francisco.

Key to Collecting: Half dimes of this type were made for slightly more than a decade, beginning in 1860. After spring 1862, no silver coins of any kind circulated in the East and Midwest, although they remained in commerce on the West Coast. Half dimes were first struck at the San Francisco Mint in 1863. The Coinage Act of 1873 ended the denomination. Finding a nice example for your type set will be no problem. Mint State coins are readily available, usually dated 1860 to 1862 or in the early 1870s.

Aspects of Striking and Appearance: Usually fairly well struck. Points to check include the head of Miss Liberty on the obverse, the wreath details on the reverse (particularly in the lower areas), and the denticles. Generally, Mint State coins have excellent luster.

Proof Coins: Proofs are available in proportion to their mintages. Choice and gem examples can be found much more readily than in the larger Liberty Seated denominations.

Market Value: Circulation Strikes

G-4	VG-8	F-12	VF-20	EF-40	AU-50	MS-60	MS-62	MS-63	MS-64	MS-65	MS-66
$16	$20	$25	$30	$50	$85	$175	$225	$300	$400	$600	$900

Market Value: Proof Strikes

PF-60	PF-63	PF-64	PF-65	PF-65CAM
$350	$550	$750	$1,100	$1,400

Retail Price Trends

Year	F-12	EF-40	MS-64	PF-64
1946	$0.75	$1	$2	$6
1950	$0.75	$1	$2	$7.50
1960	$2.50	$4	$7.50	$25
1970	$5.25	$15	$400	$200
1980	$12	$30	$1,100	$900

Year	F-12	EF-40	MS-64	PF-64
1990	$12	$30	$1,000	$3,000
2000	$14	$30	$1,000	$2,000
2010	$25	$43	$800	$1,600
2019	$25	$50	$400	$750

14
Dimes
1796 to Date

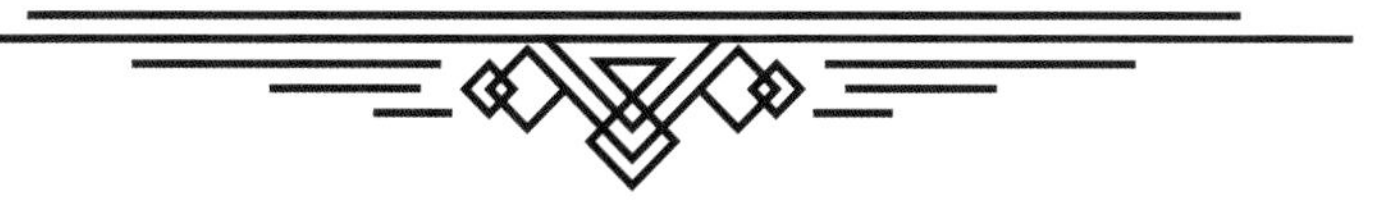

Overview of the Denomination

Dimes or ten-cent pieces were first struck in 1796, too late to include the Flowing Hair design used on the 1794 and 1795 coinages of other silver denominations. The first dimes of 1796 and 1797 display the Draped Bust obverse, Small Eagle reverse type as used on other silver issues of the same years. The obverse of the 1796 dime has 15 stars, while those of 1797 have either 13 or 16 stars. However, the 1796 and 1797 are nearly always combined as a single type.

In 1798 a new type appeared, combining the Draped Bust obverse with the Heraldic Eagle reverse, the latter modeled after the Great Seal of the United States and first used in federal coinage with the 1796 quarter eagle. This motif was produced through 1807, excepting 1799. No dimes were made in 1808. In 1809 the Capped Bust type was introduced, following the motif introduced by John Reich on the silver half dollar coinage of 1807. On the reverse, a perched eagle was employed, grasping arrows and an olive branch in its talons. Dimes of this style were made intermittently through 1828, in which year the border details were slightly modified. The revised type was continued through 1837.

The Liberty Seated motif, without obverse stars, was used in 1837 at the Philadelphia Mint and in 1838 at the New Orleans Mint (1838-O), the obverse following Christian Gobrecht's design first used on the silver dollar of 1836. Why this motif was used for just a short time is not known today, for there seem to have been no major problems in production, and today the style seems to be quite attractive. To this point, and continuing through the 1860s, the motifs on the dimes closely followed those used on the half dimes, although the dates of the different types varied. The reverse of this type, used on later types to 1860, employed an open wreath enclosing ONE / DIME in two lines, with UNITED STATES OF AMERICA around the border.

In 1838 stars were added to the obverse, but there was no drapery at the elbow, this being Gobrecht's original design. Drapery was added later by an outside artist, and some dimes of 1840 have this feature as do all later dimes (except for a Proof 1841 variety), creating a type that was continued to 1860, except for certain issues of 1853 and all of 1854 and 1855 which had arrowheads added to the date, in response to the Coinage Act of February 21, 1853. From 1850 until spring 1853, no silver coins were seen in circulation as their melt-down or bullion value was more than their face value. Dimes and other silver coins made under the 1853 legislation had slightly lower weights, making them unattractive to hoarders. Although this lower weight was continued in later years, the arrows were discontinued after 1855.

In 1860 the Liberty Seated motif was revised again, this time by Chief Engraver James B. Longacre. Around the obverse border UNITED STATES / OF AMERICA appeared, replacing the stars. On the reverse, a "cereal wreath" composed of several grains was used, following a suggestion made to Mint Director James Ross Snowden by numismatist Harold P. Newlin. This general type was continued through 1891. However, in 1873 the authorized weight was increased slightly, and some 1873 dimes and all of 1874 have arrowheads at the date to reflect this. No arrowheads were used for the rest of the span, 1875 to 1891, although the higher weight remained the standard.

In 1891 the Treasury Department issued a nationwide call for new coin designs. Many were received and reviewed, but none were found to be satisfactory. It fell to Chief Engraver Charles E. Barber to devise a design, which he did, loosely following the Liberty Head motif used on certain French coins. This was widely criticized in its time and pleased hardly anyone, but it launched a coinage that extended to 1916. Barber dimes were not popular with numismatists in that era and few coins were saved at the time of issue, except for Proofs in sets. Today, many Barber dimes are rare in high grades.

In 1916 in response to concerns raised by the numismatic community and others, the Treasury Department revised the current silver designs, consisting of the dime, quarter, and half dollar. Sculptor Adolph A. Weinman was tapped to create artistic motifs for the dime and the half dollar. For the dime, he used a female portrait modeled after Elsie (Mrs. Wallace) Stevens, now fitted with a winged cap symbolizing freedom or liberty of thought. The reverse displayed a fasces of ancient Roman tradition. Well-received, the "Mercury" dime, as it came to be called, although the messenger-god Mercury of fame was a *male*, was used through 1945.

In the latter year, President Franklin D. Roosevelt died. In 1946 it was decided to memorialize him with a portrait on the 10-cent piece, in view of his work with the March of Dimes campaign to combat polio, with which the president was afflicted. John R. Sinnock created the Roosevelt dime, which endures to this day. After 1964 silver was discontinued in view of the rising worldwide price of that metal. Later issues are of a clad composition, save for certain Proofs struck in silver for collectors.

COLLECTING A TYPE SET OF DIMES

From 1796 to date, a type set of dimes includes many interesting issues. None are in the super-rare category, but earlier motifs can be a challenge.

The 1796 and 1797 dime with Draped Bust obverse, Small Eagle reverse is the rarest of the dime types by far, with fewer than 50,000 pieces minted in an era in which there was no numismatic interest in saving such coins. Finding a choice example in whatever grade you select will require time and effort, which, of course, is a desirable concept in any area of numismatics—the thrill of the chase!

Then comes the Draped Bust obverse, Heraldic Eagle reverse type, made from 1798 through 1807 (except for 1799). Today, these are available easily enough in circulated grades but are elusive in Mint State. Nearly all are lightly struck—another challenge. Capped Bust dimes of the 1809 to 1828 years also require connoisseurship to locate a sharply struck specimen. For all of these early types, some compromise is required, but try to find the nicest examples you can.

Later Capped Bust dimes of 1828 to 1837 can be found well struck as can the later variations within the Liberty Seated type. Barber, Mercury, and Roosevelt dimes will be easy to find in just about any grade desired.

Proofs are available from the Liberty Seated era to present and are sometimes included in type sets, usually answering the call for sharply struck pieces, as most (but not all) were made with care.

Beyond a Type Set

Dimes have been a very popular denomination to collect on a systematic basis. Generally, interest is separated into different eras. Those of the early years, the Draped Bust and Capped Bust issues 1796 to 1837, are enthusiastically sought not only for dates but also for major varieties. Among early varieties, the 1796, 1797 16 stars, and 1797 13 stars are each rare in all grades. Dimes with the Heraldic Eagle reverse of 1798 to 1807 are generally scarce but not prohibitively rare, although Mint State coins are elusive. Among the reverse dies, some were shared with contemporary quarter eagles of like design and diameter—feasible as there is no indication of denomination on them. Indeed, there was no mark of value on any dime until 1809.

Among Classic Head dimes of 1809 to 1828, the 1822 is the key date and is especially rare in high grades. Among the modified Classic Head dimes of 1829 to 1837, varieties are available without difficulty.

Liberty Seated dimes of the various types have been a popular specialty over a long period of time. There are no impossible rarities save for the unique 1873-CC Without Arrows; some varieties are very hard to find, including early 1870s Carson City issues.

Barber dimes can be collected by date and mint from 1892 to 1916, except for the 1894-S, of which only 24 are believed to have been struck, with only about 10 accounted for today. The other varieties range from common to scarce. Mercury dimes of 1916 to 1945 have an enthusiastic following. The key issues are 1916-D (in particular); 1921; 1921-D; 1942, 2 Over 1; and 1942-D, 2 Over 1. A commemorative gold version struck in 2016 is not typically collected as a separate type. Roosevelt dimes from 1946 to date can be easily collected by date and mint and are very popular.

Draped Bust, Small Eagle Reverse (1796–1797)

Circulation-Strike Mintage: 47,396

Field Population: Circulated, 1,200 to 1,500; Mint State, 120 to 150

Designer: Probably Gilbert Stuart. **Engraver:** Robert Scot. **Weight:** 2.7 grams. **Composition:** .8924 silver, .1076 copper. **Diameter:** Approx. 19 mm. **Edge:** Reeded. **Mint:** Philadelphia.

Key to Collecting: Dimes were first minted in 1796, with no known fanfare or publicity at the time. Some are from prooflike dies, suggesting that they may have been "presentation pieces," but no documentation exists. Likely, most were simply produced for routine commercial purposes. This type is the rarest and most expensive in the dime series. Within any desired grade, examples should be selected with great care, as many have problems of one sort or another. Most in the marketplace are in lower grades, from G to VG or F, and often with problems such as dull and porous surfaces. Choice VF, EF, and AU examples are rare. Mint State coins are rare, but when seen are usually dated 1796 and sometimes have prooflike surfaces. Some very choice examples exist and attract a lot of attention when offered. Specimens dated 1797 are exceedingly rare.

Aspects of Striking and Appearance: Striking is better on dimes of 1796 than those of 1797. Most dimes of this type have weakness or problems in one area or another. It will pay you to select carefully. Once again, not many of your competitors in the search will care much about sharpness, and certification services make no note of it at all, so you may be able to make a really good buy. Points to check for sharpness include the hair of Miss Liberty, the centers of the stars, and, on the reverse, the eagle. Also check for adjustment marks. In summary, a sharply struck coin is a goal, not necessarily a reality.

Notes: There is no indication of the denomination of this coin on the obverse, reverse, or edge.

Market Value: Circulation Strikes

AG-3	G-4	VG-8	F-12	VF-20	EF-40	AU-50	MS-60	MS-62	MS-63	MS-64
$1,100	$2,750	$3,500	$5,000	$6,500	$10,000	$15,000	$23,000	$27,500	$35,000	$45,000

Retail Price Trends

Year	G-4	F-12	MS-63
1946	$17.50	$35	$100
1950	$20	$40	$175
1960	$60	$130	$500
1970	$245	$575	$2,000
1980	$475	$900	$5,000

Year	G-4	F-12	MS-63
1990	$850	$1,400	$8,000
2000	$900	$1,750	$13,000
2010	$2,000	$4,000	$32,000
2019	$2,750	$5,000	$35,000

Draped Bust, Heraldic Eagle Reverse (1798–1807)

Circulation-Strike Mintage: 422,010

Field Population: Circulated, 6,000 to 10,000; Mint State, about 500

Designer: Robert Scot. **Weight:** 2.7 grams. **Composition:** .8924 silver, .1076 copper. **Diameter:** Approximately 19 mm. **Edge:** Reeded. **Mint:** Philadelphia.

Key to Collecting: Nearly all dimes of this type were struck casually, with the result that most have some areas of lightness—a rusticity or naiveté that, of course, contributes to the charm of such pieces. Many examples beckon for inclusion in a type set, but you will be challenged if you want to acquire one with a combination of attractive surfaces and a decent strike—not needle sharp, but above average. Circulated coins of this type are scarce, but enough exist that finding one will not be a problem. The years 1805 and 1807 are the least expensive. Many are nicked, marked, porous, or have other problems. Mint State coins are fairly scarce and when seen are often dated 1805 or 1807. Examples of other dates are virtually non-existent in choice or gem Mint State and are first-class rarities even in MS-60, this being especially true of the 1801 to 1804 years. The combination of choice or gem Mint State with *sharp strike* is so rare as to be hardly if ever seen!

Aspects of Striking and Appearance: Just about every coin in existence has one area of light striking or another. The obverse stars usually show some weakness. On many coins, the details of Miss Liberty's hair are not sharp. On the reverse, the upper right of the shield and the adjacent part of the eagle's wing are often soft, and several or even most stars may be lightly defined (sharp stars show sharply peaked centers). Denticles are likely to be weak or missing in areas. Expect to compromise on the striking issue. In summary, a sharply struck coin is a goal, not necessarily a reality.

Market Value: Circulation Strikes

AG-3	G-4	VG-8	F-12	VF-20	EF-40	AU-50	MS-60	MS-62	MS-63	MS-64
$250	$550	$850	$1,300	$1,750	$2,750	$3,250	$5,500	$7,000	$9,500	$14,000

Retail Price Trends

Year	G-4	F-12	MS-63
1946	$4	$12	$30
1950	$5	$12.50	$40
1960	$15	$32.50	$90
1970	$90	$135	$500
1980	$175	$300	$1,000
1990	$475	$850	$3,000
2000	$375	$600	$5,000
2010	$500	$1,000	$10,000
2019	$550	$1,300	$9,500

Capped Bust, Wide Border (1809–1828)

Circulation-Strike Mintage: 5,566,844, including 1828, Modified Design

Proof Mintage: *Fewer than 150*

Field Population: Circulated, 50,000 to 80,000; Mint State, 3,000 to 5,000; Proof, 50 to 70

Designer: John Reich. **Weight:** 2.7 grams. **Composition:** .8924 silver, .1076 copper. **Diameter:** Approximately 19 mm. **Edge:** Reeded. **Mint:** Philadelphia.

Key to Collecting: Circulated coins are widely available for the higher mintage dates in grades from G to F. Mint State coins are fairly scarce, even in the range of MS-60 to MS-63. Choice and gem pieces are rare, and sharply struck examples are especially so. Most pieces are attractive, especially in higher grades. Striking varies (details are given below), but with some searching, a nice example can be located, an enjoyable pursuit. The dies were made by hand, as were earlier dies in the series. Accordingly, careful viewing under low power magnification will reward you with interesting details.

Aspects of Striking and Appearance: Places to check for light striking on the obverse include the center of the portrait and around the brooch, the star centers, and the denticles. On the reverse check the eagle, especially the area in and around the upper right of the shield. Denticles are sometimes weak, but are usually better refined on the reverse than on the obverse.

Proof Coins: Proof coins were struck in limited numbers for presentation purposes and for distribution to numismatists. Insist on a coin with deep and full (not partial) mirror surfaces. Search for one that is well struck, and has good contrast. Avoid deeply toned pieces (deep toning often masks the true nature of a coin). More than just a few pieces attributed as "Proofs" are not Proofs, in my opinion. *Be careful.*

Market Value: Circulation Strikes

G-4	VG-8	F-12	VF-20	EF-40	AU-50	MS-60	MS-62	MS-63	MS-64	MS-65
$65	$125	$135	$250	$650	$1,000	$2,000	$3,000	$4,000	$6,500	$12,500

Market Value: Proof Strikes

PF-60	PF-63	PF-64	PF-65
$7,500	$15,000	$20,000	$35,000

Retail Price Trends

Year	G-4	F-12	MS-63
1946	$1.50	$5	$11
1950	$1.75	$6	$12.50
1960	$5	$15	$27.50
1970	$19	$100	$600
1980	$35	$145	$1,000

Year	G-4	F-12	MS-63
1990	$25	$275	$2,000
2000	$35	$275	$4,000
2010	$35	$60	$2,200
2019	$65	$135	$4,000

Capped Bust, Modified Design (1828–1837)

Circulation-Strike Mintage: 6,778,350, including 1828, Wide Border

Proof Mintage: *Fewer than 200*

Field Population: Circulated, 80,000 to 110,000; Mint State, 10,000 to 14,000; Proof, 100 to 130

Designer: John Reich, as modified by William Kneass.
Weight: ***1828–1836:*** 2.7 grams; ***1837:*** 2.69 grams.
Composition: ***1828–1836:*** .8924 silver, .1076 copper; ***1837:*** .900 silver, .100 copper. **Diameter:** 18.5 mm.
Edge: Reeded. **Mint:** Philadelphia.

Key to Collecting: Examples are readily available in just about any grade desired, through and including choice and gem Mint State, with higher grade coins being rarer. There are quite a few on the market, mostly in lower grade ranges. Choice and gem examples are offered with some frequency, but finding an example with good eye appeal can be a challenge.

Aspects of Striking and Appearance: Generally quite well struck, but sometimes light on the portrait. Check the hair, brooch, and other details.

Proof Coins: Similar to other Capped Bust denominations, there are some nice Proof dimes in existence for the years here studied, but there are more than just a few deeply toned (deep gray, black, vividly iridescent, etc.) circulation strikes masquerading as Proofs. The entire field of early Proofs has many traps. Be careful.

Market Value: Circulation Strikes

G-4	VG-8	F-12	VF-20	EF-40	AU-50	MS-60	MS-62	MS-63	MS-64	MS-65
$30	$45	$50	$100	$275	$450	$1,000	$1,400	$2,000	$3,250	$7,500

Market Value: Proof Strikes

PF-60	PF-63	PF-64	PF-65
$7,500	$15,000	$20,000	$30,000

Retail Price Trends

Year	G-4	F-12	MS-63
1946	$1	$1.75	$4
1950	$0.75	$2	$5
1960	$1.75	$4	$14
1970	$9.50	$50	$300
1980	$25	$85	$700
1990	$20	$175	$1,000
2000	$20	$175	$600
2010	$30	$45	$1,600
2019	$30	$50	$2,000

Liberty Seated, No Stars on Obverse (1837–1838)

Circulation-Strike Mintage: 1,088,534

Proof Mintage: *Fewer than 75*

Field Population: Circulated, 7,000 to 11,000; Mint State, 700 to 1,100; Proof, 30 to 40

Designer: Christian Gobrecht. **Weight:** 2.67 grams. **Composition:** .900 silver, .100 copper. **Diameter:** 17.9 mm. **Edge:** Reeded. **Mints:** Philadelphia, New Orleans.

Key to Collecting: The Liberty Seated design without obverse stars was used in the half dime and dime series only at the Philadelphia Mint in 1837 and the New Orleans Mint in 1838 (1838-O). The 1837-dated coins are very attractive, and the starless obverse gives them a cameo-like appearance. The 1838-O dimes are often grainy and dull; few truly attractive specimens exist. Circulated coins are plentiful in the context of the era. All grades are available, with EF and AU examples being scarcer than lower grades. Probably nearly a thousand Mint State coins exist, although coins with eye appeal can be hard to find. Nearly all are dated 1837. Gems are rare, and gems with excellent surfaces are rarer still. Mint State 1838-O dimes are rarities and are often of unsatisfactory luster.

Aspects of Striking and Appearance: Usually seen well struck, although the denticles can sometimes be weak (but are generally sharper than on the related half dimes). Points to check include the denticles on obverse and reverse and the highest parts of the Liberty Seated figure and the leaves.

Proof Coins: Proofs of 1837 (but not 1838-O) were struck in an unknown small quantity, but seemingly more than the related 1837 half dime. Most have deep mirror surfaces and are quite attractive. Avoid deeply toned pieces.

Market Value: Circulation Strikes

G-4	VG-8	F-12	VF-20	EF-40	AU-50	MS-60	MS-62	MS-63	MS-64	MS-65	MS-66
$45	$55	$100	$275	$500	$750	$1,100	$1,400	$1,800	$4,000	$7,750	$10,000

Market Value: Proof Strikes

PF-60	PF-63	PF-64	PF-65
$6,000	$12,000	$15,000	$35,000

Retail Price Trends

Year	G-4	F-12	MS-63
1946	$3	$6	$15
1950	$3.50	$8	$25
1960	$30	$50	$120
1970	$95	$300	$750
1980	$75	$275	$700
1990	$50	$300	$1,500
2000	$65	$475	$1,800
2010	$45	$100	$1,800
2019	$45	$100	$1,800

Liberty Seated, Stars on Obverse, No Drapery, (1838–1840)

Circulation-Strike Mintage: 6,525,115

Proof Mintage: *About 20*

Field Population: Circulated, 20,000 to 30,000; Mint State, 1,500 to 2,500; Proof, 10 to 12

Designer: Christian Gobrecht. **Weight:** 2.67 grams. **Composition:** .900 silver, .100 copper. **Diameter:** 17.9 mm. **Edge:** Reeded. **Mints:** Philadelphia, New Orleans.

Key to Collecting: Liberty Seated dimes of the type with obverse stars, but without drapery at Miss Liberty's left elbow, were minted to the extent of over six million pieces. Enough were produced that examples today are readily available in all grades, although gems are scarce. Most are quite pleasing in appearance.

Aspects of Striking and Appearance: Most are well struck, but there are exceptions. Points to check include the star centers, head and other details of the Liberty Seated figure, the leaves on the reverse, and the denticles on both sides. Luster is usually satiny rather than deeply frosty.

Market Value: Circulation Strikes

G-4	VG-8	F-12	VF-20	EF-40	AU-50	MS-60	MS-62	MS-63	MS-64	MS-65
$20	$25	$30	$48	$145	$300	$475	$600	$850	$1,100	$3,000

Market Value: Proof Strikes

PF-60	PF-63	PF-64	PF-65
$5,000	$10,000	$12,500	$17,500

Retail Price Trends

Year	F-12	EF-40	MS-64	PF-64
1946	$1.25	$2.50	$5	$50
1950	$1.25	$2.50	$6	$75
1960	$3.50	$7	$18	$700
1970	$7	$20	$400	$6,000
1980	$10	$40	$600	$11,000
1990	$10	$40	$1,000	$16,000
2000	$12	$50	$800	$14,000
2010	$30	$110	$950	$11,000
2019	$30	$145	$1,100	$12,500

Liberty Seated, Stars on Obverse, Drapery, (1840–1853; 1856–1860)

Circulation-Strike Mintage: 36,437,000

Proof Mintage: *Fewer than 2,000 pieces*

Field Population: Circulated, 150,000 to 210,000; Mint State, 5,000 to 7,000; Proof, 1,100 to 1,400

Designer: Christian Gobrecht, as modified by Robert Ball Hughes.
Weight: ***1840–1853:*** 2.67 grams; ***1856–1860:*** 2.49 grams.
Composition: .900 silver, .100 copper. **Diameter:** 17.9 mm.
Edge: Reeded. **Mints:** Philadelphia, New Orleans, San Francisco.

Key to Collecting: Liberty Seated dimes saw a makeover by Robert Ball Hughes, an artist in the private sector, who modified Christian Gobrecht's design. The shield, formerly leaning sharply to the left, now leans slightly to the right, and extra drapery has been added to Miss Liberty's elbow. Half dimes were similarly changed. Higher denomination coins were modified as well but not as dramatically. Dimes of this type were minted in large numbers and were popular in the American monetary system. Circulated examples are plentiful today. Most are very attractive. Mint State coins are also plentiful, although certain dates and varieties are rare. Most on the market are dated in the 1850s and are often in choice and gem grades.

Aspects of Striking and Appearance: Vary widely. Generally, dates before 1853 are sharper than later issues, but there are exceptions. Points to check include the star centers, head and other details of the Liberty Seated figure, the leaves on the reverse, and the denticles on both sides. Luster varies.

Proof Coins: Proofs are available and are usually dated 1859, less often 1858, and rarely of earlier years. Quality is usually low from repeated dipping over the years. Finding an example up to PF-63 will be easy enough to do, but locating a higher-grade Proof with high-quality surfaces will be a challenge.

Market Value: Circulation Strikes

G-4	VG-8	F-12	VF-20	EF-40	AU-50	MS-60	MS-62	MS-63	MS-64	MS-65
$16	$18	$20	$30	$50	$130	$300	$450	$550	$850	$1,850

Market Value: Proof Strikes

PF-60	PF-63	PF-64	PF-65
$900	$1,250	$1,500	$2,250

Retail Price Trends

Year	F-12	EF-40	MS-64	PF-64
1946	$0.65	$1.25	$3	$12
1950	$0.50	$1	$3.50	$30
1960	$0.65	$2	$8	$70
1970	$4.50	$10	$300	$1,000
1980	$7.50	$30	$600	$2,500

Year	F-12	EF-40	MS-64	PF-64
1990	$9	$40	$700	$4,000
2000	$10	$35	$1,000	$1,950
2010	$20	$50	$825	$2,000
2019	$20	$50	$850	$1,500

Liberty Seated, Stars on Obverse, Arrows at Date (1853–1855)

Circulation-Strike Mintage: 21,493,010

Proof Mintage: *Fewer than 200*

Field Population: Circulated, 100,000 to 150,000; Mint State, 3,000 to 5,000; Proof, 80 to 115

Designer: Christian Gobrecht. **Weight:** 2.49 grams. **Composition:** .900 silver, .100 copper. **Diameter:** 17.9 mm. **Edge:** Reeded. **Mints:** Philadelphia, New Orleans.

Key to Collecting: Dimes of the years 1853 to 1855 With Arrows type are plentiful today in circulated grades, less so in Mint State. These are still easy enough to find, though mostly in grades MS-60 to MS-64. Gems are not rare, but are in the minority. Most Mint State coins are of the 1853 Philadelphia issue.

Aspects of Striking and Appearance: The quality of this type varies widely. Examples are often seen with one or more problems such as weak stars, weak head of Miss Liberty, light definition on the higher leaf details, and mushy denticles. Many of the 1853 date were struck from over-used dies and have somewhat "shiny" grainy surfaces rather than deep frosty luster. In contrast, most later issues are better struck. Finding a sharp example will be a pleasant challenge.

Proof Coins: Such pieces are seldom encountered except when great collections come on the market. Most are of the 1854 date. Proofs were well struck, and choice examples have a pleasing appearance with deep mirror surfaces. Some prooflike 1853 coins have been called "Proofs"; beware of such.

Market Value: Circulation Strikes

G-4	VG-8	F-12	VF-20	EF-40	AU-50	MS-60	MS-62	MS-63	MS-64	MS-65
$20	$23	$25	$30	$50	$175	$325	$450	$675	$950	$1,700

Market Value: Proof Strikes

PF-60	PF-63	PF-64	PF-65
$6,000	$10,000	$15,000	$25,000

Retail Price Trends

Year	F-12	EF-40	MS-64	PF-64
1946	$0.50	$1	$2.50	$400
1950	$0.50	$1.50	$3.75	$800
1960	$1.85	$4	$12	$1,750
1970	$4.75	$20	$200	$2,000
1980	$10	$45	$500	$5,000

Year	F-12	EF-40	MS-64	PF-64
1990	$7.50	$40	$700	$10,000
2000	$10	$40	$800	$19,000
2010	$20	$50	$925	$14,500
2019	$25	$50	$950	$15,000

Liberty Seated, Legend on Obverse (1860–1873; 1875–1891)

Circulation-Strike Mintage: 175,575,277

Proof Mintage: 25,403

Field Population: Circulated, more than 2,000,000; Mint State, 35,000 to 50,000; Proof, 16,000 to 21,000

Designer: Christian Gobrecht. **Weight:** ***1860–1873:*** 2.49 grams; ***1875–1891:*** 2.5 grams. **Composition:** .900 silver, .100 copper. **Diameter:** 17.9 mm. **Edge:** Reeded. **Mints:** Philadelphia, New Orleans, San Francisco, Carson City.

Key to Collecting: Dimes of this type are very plentiful today, this being especially true of dates after 1874. Finding a choice example in any desired grade will be no problem. Mint State examples exist in large numbers in the marketplace, especially dates after 1874, and even more especially for certain high-mintage issues of the 1880s.

Aspects of Striking and Appearance: Usually fairly well struck for the earlier years, somewhat erratic in the 1870s, and better from the 1880s to 1891. Many Civil War issues have parallel die striae, this being true of virtually all silver and gold issues of that period. Points to check include the head of Miss Liberty on the obverse, the wreath details on the reverse, and the denticles. Generally, Mint State coins have excellent luster.

Proof Coins: Proofs exist in relation to their mintages. Certain examples of the 1870s can be lightly struck in areas, a curious situation. Quality varies. Seek an example with deep mirror Proof surfaces and frosty devices. Avoid deeply toned coins.

Market Value: Circulation Strikes

G-4	VG-8	F-12	VF-20	EF-40	AU-50	MS-60	MS-62	MS-63	MS-64	MS-65
$15	$18	$20	$25	$35	$80	$150	$200	$250	$425	$650

Market Value: Proof Strikes

PF-60	PF-63	PF-64	PF-65	PF-65Cam
$300	$600	$750	$1,000	$1,150

Retail Price Trends

Year	VF-20	EF-40	MS-65	PF-65
1946	$0.75	$1	$2.25	$4.25
1950	$0.80	$1	$1.75	$4.50
1960	$2	$3	$60	$20
1970	$4.50	$8	$450	$200
1980	$12	$27.50	$500	$600
1990	$12	$20	$900	$1,000
2000	$17.50	$30	$700	$1,250
2010	$20	$30	$600	$850
2019	$25	$35	$650	$1,000

Liberty Seated, Legend on Obverse, Arrows at Date (1873–1874)

Circulation-Strike Mintage: 6,041,608

Proof Mintage: 1,500

Field Population: Circulated, 25,000 to 40,000; Mint State, 2,200 to 3,300; Proof, 1,000 to 1,250

Designer: Christian Gobrecht, as modified by James B. Longacre, with the arrows added during the chief engravership of William Barber. **Weight:** 2.5 grams. **Composition:** .900 silver, .100 copper. **Diameter:** 17.9 mm. **Edge:** Reeded. **Mints:** Philadelphia, San Francisco, Carson City.

Key to Collecting: In 1873 the authorized weights of the silver dime, quarter, and half dollar were increased slightly to make them come out in more or less even figures in terms of the metric system. To signify this change, arrows were placed at the date of later 1873 dimes and all dated 1874. Circulated coins are easily available in any grade desired from the two high-mintage Philadelphia issues. Mint State coins are fairly scarce, as the mintage, although extensive, was much smaller than preceding and later without-arrows coins. At the gem category, such coins are rare. Choice Mint State coins are rarer than equivalent Proofs.

Aspects of Striking and Appearance: Most are well struck, but there are exceptions. The details on Miss Liberty's head are sometimes weak.

Proof Coins: Probably 75% or more of the mintage of 1,500 pieces survive.

Market Value: Circulation Strikes

G-4	VG-8	F-12	VF-20	EF-40	AU-50	MS-60	MS-62	MS-63	MS-64	MS-65
$18	$22	$25	$55	$150	$300	$550	$600	$900	$1,650	$4,000

Market Value: Proof Strikes

PF-60	PF-63	PF-64	PF-65	PF-65Cam
$700	$1,000	$1,500	$3,750	$4,750

Retail Price Trends

Year	VF-20	EF-40	MS-65	PF-65
1946	$1.25	$1.75	$3	$6
1950	$2	$3	$5	$7.50
1960	$15	$25	$47.50	$80
1970	$37.50	$50	$700	$2,000
1980	$45	$90	$1,200	$6,100

Year	VF-20	EF-40	MS-65	PF-65
1990	$45	$100	$1,750	$3,000
2000	$45	$125	$2,500	$4,620
2010	$50	$140	$3,700	$3,250
2019	$55	$150	$4,000	$3,750

Barber or Liberty Head (1892–1916)

Circulation-Strike Mintage: 504,515,075

Proof Mintage: 17,353

Field Population: Circulated, several million; Mint State, 60,000 to 110,000; Proof, 12,000 to 14,000

Designer: ***Obverse:*** Charles E. Barber. ***Reverse:*** James B. Longacre, created in 1860 for the Liberty Seated dime. **Weight:** 2.5 grams. **Composition:** .900 silver, .100 copper (net weight: .07234 oz. pure silver). **Diameter:** 17.9 mm. **Edge:** Reeded. **Mints:** Philadelphia, Denver, New Orleans, San Francisco.

Key to Collecting: Barber dimes are much more available today than are quarters and half dollars. Today, among circulation-strike Barber dimes probably 90% or more in existence are G-4 or below, a curious situation repeated in the quarter and half dollar series. A wide range of possibilities awaits you, as there are relatively inexpensive varieties available from the first year, 1892, to the last, 1916. Contemplate the dates and mints and pick an interesting one—perhaps the 1906-D, representing the first year of the Denver Mint, or another favorite. Mint State coins are somewhat scarce, this being especially true of the mintmarked issues.

Aspects of Striking and Appearance: The obverse of the typical Barber dime is well struck, although the higher details of the hair should be checked. The reverse is usually sharp. If weakness is seen, it is usually in the wreath details. The denticles are usually sharp on the obverse and reverse.

Proof Coins: Proof coins survive in proportion to their mintages. Choice and gem specimens are found more easily among dimes than quarters and half dollars of this type. All were originally sold in silver-coin sets. The Proofs of 1892 to 1901 usually have cameo contrast between the designs and the mirror fields. Later Proofs vary in contrast.

Market Value: Circulation Strikes

G-4	VG-8	F-12	VF-20	EF-40	AU-50	MS-60	MS-62	MS-63	MS-64	MS-65
$4	$5	$6	$10	$24	$75	$125	$160	$225	$275	$425

Market Value: Proof Strikes

PF-60	PF-63	PF-64	PF-65	PF-65Cam
$285	$500	$725	$1,000	$1,150

Retail Price Trends

Year	VF-20	EF-40	MS-65	PF-65
1946	$0.75	$1	$3	$6
1950	$0.75	$1	$2.25	$6
1960	$1	$1.75	$9	$35
1970	$2	$3.50	$300	$400
1980	$6.50	$17.50	$400	$800

Year	VF-20	EF-40	MS-65	PF-65
1990	$6	$18	$600	$1,000
2000	$7	$20	$500	$1,500
2010	$9	$22	$400	$900
2019	$10	$24	$425	$1,000

Winged Liberty Head or "Mercury" (1916–1945)

Circulation-Strike Mintage: 2,677,153,970

Proof Mintage: 78,558

Field Population: Circulated, many millions; Mint State, millions; Proof, 55,000 to 65,000

Designer: Adolph A. Weinman. **Weight:** 2.5 grams.
Composition: .900 silver, .100 copper. **Diameter:** Approximately 17.9 mm.
Edge: Reeded. **Mints:** Philadelphia, Denver, San Francisco.

Key to Collecting: Circulated coins are very common and are not of importance due to the plentitude of Mint State coins. For inclusion in a type set, there are many later dates available in gem grades for relatively low cost, although many individual dates and mints are rare. Among coins of the early 1940s, there are many opportunities to acquire gem pieces with sharply struck features.

Aspects of Striking and Appearance: Many if not most Mercury dimes exhibit areas of light striking, most notably in the center horizontal band across the fasces, less so in the lower horizontal band. The bands are composed of two parallel lines with a separation or "split" between. The term FB, or Full Bands, denotes coins with both parallel lines in the center band distinctly separated. *In addition*, some Mercury dimes may display weak striking in other areas (often not noticed by certification services or others), including at areas of the obverse rim and the date. For a really deluxe specimen, find one with FB *plus* sharp striking in other areas as well. A gold version, struck in 2016 for the design's centennial, is considered an interesting standalone within the series, not necessary for a type set.

Proof Coins: Readily available within the context of the mintage. Struck only from 1936 to 1942, with the later issues having higher production. The Proofs are from completely polished dies, including the portrait.

Market Value: Circulation Strikes

F-12	VF-20	EF-40	AU-50	MS-60	MS-63	MS-64FB
$2.75	$3.00	$3.25	$4.50	$6	$15	$25

MS-65	MS-65FB	MS-66	MS-66FB	MS-67	MS-67FB
$30	$50	$45	$55	$65	$150

Market Value: Proof Strikes

PF-63	PF-64	PF-65	PF-66	PF-67
$140	$160	$175	$200	$300

Retail Price Trends

Year	VF-20	EF-40	MS-65	PF-65
1946	$0.10	$0.10	$0.35	$1.75
1950	$0.10	$0.10	$0.30	$1.50
1960	$0.10	$0.15	$0.50	$7.50
1970	$0.20	$0.35	$5	$150
1980	$0.85	$1	$30	$425
1990	$1.25	$3	$65	$750
2000	$0.80	$1.25	$15	$250
2010	$2.50	$2.75	$25	$200
2019	$3	$3.25	$30	$175

Roosevelt, Silver (1946–1964; 1992 to Date, Proofs Only)

Circulation-Strike Mintage: 6,595,617,673

Proof Mintage: *1946–1964:* **19,837,717** *1992 to Date:* **Tens of millions, still being minted**

Field Population: Circulated, more than a billion; Mint State, many millions; Proof, 1946 to 1964, about 18,000,000; Proof, 1992 to date, most of total mintage

Designer: John R. Sinnock. **Weight:** 2.5 grams. **Composition:** .900 silver, .100 copper (net weight: .07234 oz. pure silver). **Diameter:** 17.9 mm. **Edge:** Reeded. **Mints:** Philadelphia, Denver, San Francisco, West Point.

Key to Collecting: Roosevelt dimes were first issued in 1946 from dies by Chief Engraver John R. Sinnock. Although the motif was not highly acclaimed when it was released, perhaps as the classic "Mercury" dime was a favorite, the new Roosevelt dimes became widely collected. From this point until the alloy was changed after 1965, production took place at the Philadelphia, Denver, and San Francisco mints.

In 1955, when it was announced that the San Francisco Mint would cease coinage, perhaps forever, the Lincoln cents and Roosevelt dimes of 1955-S became wildly popular in numismatic circles, and many were saved.

Circulated coins are very common but not relevant for type set purposes as Mint State and Proof coins are plentiful and inexpensive. Today, a run of date and mintmark varieties contains no rarities, although the 1949, 1949-S, and 1950-S are considered somewhat scarce in the context of the series. Proofs in silver have been struck at the San Francisco Mint from 1992 to date and can be considered as belonging to this type, type, as can the 2015 silver Proof struck at West Point.

Aspects of Striking and Appearance: Fortunately (some might say), not much attention has been paid to which little features may or may not be sharply struck. Points to check include the high parts of the hair (not well defined in the design to begin with) and the high parts of the torch and the leaves.

Proof Coins: Very plentiful and usually quite attractive.

Market Value: Circulation Strikes

EF-40	MS-63	MS-65	MS-66	MS-67	MS-67FT
$2	$3	$5	$12	$30	$115

Market Value: Proof Strikes

PF-65	PF-66	PF-66Cam	PF-67
$5	$8	$25	$10

Retail Price Trends

Year	VF-20	MS-65	PF-65
1980	$0.90	$1	$1
1990	$1.20	$2	$2
2000	$0.75	$1	$1.25
2010	$2	$5	$4.50
2019	$1.50	$5	$5

Roosevelt, Copper-Nickel (1965 to Date, Including Proofs)

Circulation-Strike Mintage: Tens of billions, still being minted

Proof Mintage: Tens of millions, still being minted

Field Population: Circulated, tens of billions; Mint State, billions; Proof, tens of millions

Designer: John R. Sinnock. **Weight:** 2.27 grams. **Composition:** Outer layers of copper-nickel (.750 copper, .250 nickel) bonded to inner core of pure copper. **Diameter:** 17.9 mm. **Edge:** Reeded. **Mints:** Philadelphia, Denver, San Francisco, West Point.

Key to Collecting: Beginning in 1965 and continuing to this day, Roosevelt dimes have been made in copper-nickel-clad composition. Such coins are both familiar and inexpensive, and finding a choice example can be done at the outset of building a type set. From 1965 to today, well over 150 copper-nickel-clad Roosevelt dime date-and-mintmark issues have been produced. For type-set purposes, you can take your time and for face value, you can find a superb gem—or for a modest premium, a dealer can sell you one. Although coins made in our own time are sometimes viewed as ordinary or passé, in actuality, a full set of modern dimes can be quite impressive.

While the majority of dimes of this era are inexpensive, there are several challenges, notably Proofs of 1968, 1970, and 1975, which should have had S mintmarks but don't because of errors at the Mint. The zinger coin is the 1975, which is worth more than $46,000. This reflects that not all expensive rarities are from many generations ago. More affordable, at about $200, is the 1982 circulation strike that lacks the normal P or D mintmark. While these scarcities and rarities are interesting to contemplate, the majority of collectors will simply opt for one of each basic regular issue—easy enough to acquire and, as noted, impressive when viewed all at once.

Aspects of Striking and Appearance: Usually fairly well struck. The clad composition is more resistant to nicks and bagmarks than was the earlier silver alloy.

Proof Coins: Common. Usually well struck and very attractive.

Market Value: Circulation Strikes

MS-65	MS-66	MS-67	MS-67FT
$2	$3	$4	$10

Market Value: Proof Strikes

PF-65	PF-66	PF-66Cam	PF-67
$2	$4	$5	$6

15
Twenty-Cent Pieces
1875–1878

Overview of the Denomination

In 1874 a new denomination, the silver twenty-cent piece, seemed like a good idea—especially to Senator John P. Jones of Nevada, the district known as "the Silver State." At the time, the price of silver metal was spiraling downward on world markets. The economy of Virginia City, the epicenter of the silver mining and refining activity, was suffering. In February of that year, Jones introduced a bill calling for the twenty-cent piece for use in the West. At that time in the East and Midwest, no silver coins of any kind were seen in general circulation, and Fractional Currency bills largely took their place. However, silver was plentiful in the West, and it was thought that the twenty-cent piece would be a useful denomination, although in retrospect it did nothing that could not be accomplished by tendering two dimes. For whatever reasons, Mint Director Henry R. Linderman supported the twenty-cent piece in his *Annual Report of the Director of the Mint*, and legislators went along as well. The coin became a reality on March 3, 1875.

Chief Engraver William Barber prepared the design, copying Christian Gobrecht's Liberty Seated figure for the obverse and his own eagle from the 1873 trade dollar for the reverse. The edge of the new denomination was plain, rather than reeded, a departure from other Liberty Seated coins of the time.

In the first year, 1,155,000 pieces were struck at the San Francisco Mint, 133,290 at Carson City, but only 36,910 (plus 2,790 Proofs) in Philadelphia, the coins not being needed for circulation in the East. Almost immediately, the public confused the new coin with the Liberty Seated quarter dollar of similar size. In July 1876, a proposal to withdraw the twenty-cent piece was introduced in Congress but was laid over. Finally, the Act of May 2, 1878, abolished the denomination.

In the meantime, circulation coinage for the second year of the coin's existence, 1876, fell to just 10,000 at Carson City (most of which were later melted) and 14,640 at Philadelphia (most probably melted as well). None were made in San Francisco. Proofs were produced for collectors in 1875 and 1876 and also for two later years, 1877 and 1878, when no circulation strikes were made.

The twenty-cent piece might have been successful had there been no quarters in circulation, for it was a logical fractional division of the popular $20 bill and gold double eagle. However, quarters were firmly ensconced in commerce, and soon the twenty-cent coins were forgotten.

SELECTING A COIN FOR YOUR TYPE SET

Only one example is needed for inclusion in your type set. By far the most available in Mint State is the 1875-S, followed by the 1875-CC. These are often somewhat lightly struck on the reverse, particularly near the top of the eagle's wings. The 1875 and 1876 Philadelphia coins are occasionally encountered in Mint State and are usually well struck.

Proofs are readily available for all years 1875 to 1878.

BEYOND A TYPE SET

A full date and mintmark set of twenty-cent pieces consists of the 1875, 1875-CC, 1875-S, 1876, 1876-CC, 1877, and 1878, the last two years being available only in Proof format. The great challenge in forming a set is the 1876-CC, of which 10,000 were minted, but, seemingly, all but about two dozen were melted. Those that do survive are typically encountered in Mint State and are widely heralded when they are offered at auction.

Liberty Seated (1875–1878)

Circulation-Strike Mintage: 1,349,840

Proof Mintage: 5,000

Field Population: Circulated, 25,000 to 40,000; Mint State, 6,000 to 9,000; Proof, 3,500 to 4,200

Designer: William Barber. **Weight:** 5 grams. **Composition:** .900 silver, .100 copper. **Diameter:** 22 mm. **Edge:** Plain. **Mints:** Philadelphia, Carson City, San Francisco.

Key to Collecting: Mint State and Proof examples are readily available for inclusion in a type set, the 1875-S circulation strike being the most plentiful, as might be expected from its overwhelmingly large mintage, and the 1875-CC a distant second, although the 1875 and 1876 Philadelphia pieces are offered now and then. Grades usually range from VF to AU. This denomination did not circulate long enough to generate many well-worn pieces, such as AG-3 or G-4. Mint State coins are available for 1875, 1875-CC, 1875-S, and 1876 (the 1876-CC being a rarity). Generally, the 1875-CC and 1875-S (in particular) are the most often seen, in grades from MS-60 upward.

Aspects of Striking and Appearance: These characteristics vary from coin to coin. Points to check include the eagle's wing feathers, especially at the top of the wings, and the letters around the border. Generally, the 1875 and 1876 Philadelphia coins are the best struck and have the deepest luster.

Proof Coins: The easiest to find are the 1875 and 1876. The 1877 and 1878 are of lower mintages and are also in greater demand due to their Proof-only status (no related circulation strikes were made). Avoid dark and deeply toned pieces. Quality can be a problem.

Market Value: Circulation Strikes

G-4	VG-8	F-12	VF-20	EF-40	AU-50	MS-60	MS-62	MS-63	MS-64	MS-65	MS-66
$85	$100	$130	$150	$250	$400	$650	$875	$1,100	$1,350	$2,350	$6,000

Market Value: Proof Strikes

PF-60	PF-63	PF-65
$1,300	$2,500	$7,500

Retail Price Trends

Year	VF-20	EF-40	MS-65	PF-65
1946	$3	$3.50	$6	$22
1950	$4	$5	$9	$25
1960	$12.50	$16.50	$45	$75
1970	$50	$67.50	$150	$3,000
1980	$95	$165	$1,000	$7,000

Year	VF-20	EF-40	MS-65	PF-65
1990	$90	$190	$2,500	$7,500
2000	$100	$160	$3,000	$8,300
2010	$175	$250	$5,000	$12,000
2019	$150	$250	$2,350	$7,500

16

Quarter Dollars
1796 to Date

Overview of the Denomination

Although authorized by the Mint Act of April 2, 1792, silver quarter dollars were not struck until 1796. At the time, the Mint did not coin silver or gold for its own account; it produced pieces only at the specific request of depositors. Those with bulk silver, usually in the form of foreign coins, typically selected the largest denomination—the dollar.

The first quarter dollar of 1796 featured the Draped Bust obverse in combination with the Small Eagle reverse. Nearly all were made with prooflike surfaces, this being the nature of the dies, making high-grade pieces especially attractive to numismatists today. However, as only 6,146 were struck, examples are elusive.

No further quarter dollars were made until 1804, at which time a new reverse was used: the Heraldic Eagle style. The Draped Bust obverse design as used in 1796 was continued. This type was made only through 1807. Similar to half dimes, dimes, and half dollars of the same design, quarters of this era were not well struck. Examples in numismatic hands today are nearly always weak in one area or another.

The next production of quarter dollars was in 1815, using John Reich's Capped Bust motif first employed on half dollars of 1807. From then through 1828, coinage was intermittent. Then followed a gap until 1831, when a new design or modification appeared, with a smaller diameter and now lacking the motto E PLURIBUS UNUM above the eagle on the reverse. This style was produced each year through 1838.

The Liberty Seated motif, Christian Gobrecht's *magnum opus*, was inaugurated part way through 1838 and remained a standard for decades afterward. Later modifications included the addition of drapery to the elbow in 1840, arrowheads at the date and rays on the reverse in 1853, to indicate the new reduced weight standard, then arrows only in 1854 and 1855. In 1866 the motto IN GOD WE TRUST was added to the reverse, this being the same year it was first employed in other larger-denomination silver and gold coins. Arrows were added alongside the date of some 1873 and all 1874 quarters to indicate a slight increase in the authorized weight.

Quarter dollars were not seen in circulation in the East and Midwest from early 1862 until April 20, 1876, when the Treasury began to release long-stored coins in quantity. During much of the Civil War and for over a decade afterward, Fractional Currency bills filled the need to make change.

In 1892 Charles E. Barber's Liberty Head design, used on what we today call the "Barber quarter," replaced the time-honored Liberty Seated motif. The Barber coins were made continuously through 1916. In that year, a sweeping revision of silver designs took place at the instigation of the numismatic community and others, most of whom had little appreciation for Barber's work. The Standing Liberty motif by artist Hermon A. MacNeil became the new standard.

On the obverse of the 1916 quarter, Miss Liberty was placed standing, apparently stepping forward, through an opening in a parapet or wall. Her right breast was exposed, a classical touch not much different from the partial nudity seen on certain paper money, in paintings, and in sculpture. Although a later generation of writers would declare that the public was offended by such a display, no contemporary account of such prudery has been found. Partway through 1917, the coin was restyled; Miss Liberty was given a jacket of armor (for "military preparedness" in view of the World War raging in Europe), and the stars on the reverse were rearranged. While the early or Type I quarters of 1916 and early 1917 generally struck up well and exhibit superb design details, the new version presented difficulties. Today, most Standing Liberty quarters of the modified design are weakly defined in one area or another, typically in the details of Miss Liberty's head and the rivets on the shield she holds. A commemorative gold version was struck in 2016.

In 1932 a quarter dollar was issued to observe the 200th anniversary of George Washington's birth. John Flanagan's design was selected. The obverse depicted Washington from the classic bust done by Jean Antoine Houdon in 1785 during a visit to Mount Vernon when he made a life mask of the general. The reverse illustrated a somewhat modern eagle.

The normal alloy of 90% silver and 10% copper continued in use through 1964, after which the composition was changed from silver to a composition of pure copper clad with layers of copper-nickel. In 1976 the Bicentennial design was used for a year, the reverse showing a military drummer from colonial times—thought by many to be the best of the three new motifs of this year, the others being on the half dollar and dollar.

In 1999 the Mint changed Houdon's portrait of Washington and added myriad hair lines and squiggles, completely altering the appearance. Staff engraver William Cousins performed the hairdressing. This change was said to have been done to enhance the sharpness of the design. No doubt sculptor Houdon, creator of the enduring original classic bust, turned over in his grave!

Beginning in the same year, 1999, the 50 State Quarters® program saw the production of five different reverses each year, each observing a different state and the order in which it entered the Union. Each state was to select the motifs employed. Amid many suggestions, controversies, and discussions, the new pieces were made, no two alike, and each reflecting some aspect of a state's history. The entire program was and is a wonderful addition to the spectrum of American coinage. Similar programs followed celebrating the District of Columbia, the U.S. territories, and various national parks and other historic sites.

COLLECTING A QUARTER DOLLAR TYPE SET

There are no super-rarities among the different types of quarter dollars, but the first one, the 1796 with Draped Bust obverse and Small Eagle reverse, is hard to find and expensive in all grades. The values are, of course, justified by the great demand for this single-year type.

Finding a decent strike will be your greatest challenge in the short-lived 1804 to 1807 type with Heraldic Eagle reverse. Enough were made that examples from these years are not rarities, but nearly all are weakly struck. Quarters of the 1815 to 1828 Capped Bust type, large planchet, are available easily enough in worn grades but are scarce to rare in Mint State. Some cherrypicking will be needed to find a sharp strike.

Respite from the difficulty of finding sharp strikes is at last found with the 1831 to 1838 type, Capped Bust, small diameter, and without E PLURIBUS UNUM. Most are quite nice. For the first time, Mint State coins are generally available with frequency in the marketplace, although ones with good eye appeal are in the distinct minority.

The Liberty Seated quarters of the several types made from 1838 to 1891 are generally available in proportion to their mintages, with an allowance for the earlier dates being scarcer than the later ones—as they had a longer time to become worn or lost. Many quarters of earlier dates were melted circa 1850 to 1853 when the price of silver rose on international markets, and such coins were worth slightly more in melt-down value than face value.

Barber quarters of 1892 to 1916 will present no difficulty, except to find an example with sharp striking overall, including in the telltale area on the reverse at and near the eagle's leg to the right. Gem Mint State Barber quarters are scarcer than generally known. Proofs were sold to collectors and saved, and thus they are available in proportion to their mintages, with probably 70% to 80% surviving.

The Type I Standing Liberty quarter is a rarity if dated 1916, for only 52,000 were struck, and not many were saved. The feasible alternative is the 1917 Type I, which is often seen in Mint State, sharply struck, and exceedingly beautiful. Standing Liberty quarters of the Type II design, minted from part way through 1917 to 1930, are often weakly struck on the head of Miss Liberty and on the shield rivets, and sometimes other places as well. Searching is needed to locate a nice example.

Washington quarters, on the other hand, will be easy enough to locate. The recent State, D.C., territorial, and America the Beautiful reverses are appealing in their diversity and make a fascinating study in themselves.

BEYOND A TYPE SET

Generally, even angels would fear to tread in the formation of a specialized collection of quarter dollars from 1796 to date, by dates, mints, and major varieties. As a class, quarters are considerably more difficult to acquire than are either dimes or half dollars.

The 1796 is rare and popular both as a date and a type. The 1804, although elusive in worn grades, is of commanding importance if AU or Mint State. The 1823, 3 Over 2, is a classic rarity and is nearly always encountered well-worn. In the same decade, the 1827 is famous. A few years ago, Karl Moulton demonstrated that the obverse die was an overdating of the 1823, 3 Over 2, making it 1827, 7 Over 3 Over 2, a most curious circumstance. Although Mint records indicate that 4,000 circulation strikes were produced in calendar year 1827, they were probably struck from 1825-dated or earlier dies, as no unequivocal example has ever been located. There are, however, a dozen or so Proofs. Originals are distinguished by having the 2 in the 25 C. denomination with a curved base, while restrikes, also very rare, have a square-base 2.

One unsolved mystery in numismatics involves quarter dollars dated 1815 (the die variety known as Browning-1) and 1825, 5 Over 3 (Browning-2), which are often seen counterstamped, above the cap, with either an E or an L. Hundreds exist. As other quarter dollar die varieties were made during this period, but only these two bear counterstamps, it may be that this was done either at the Mint or otherwise before they were generally distributed.

The panorama of Liberty Seated quarters from 1838 to 1891 is highlighted by several rarities, notably the 1842 Small Date (known only in Proof format) and the 1873-CC Without Arrows (of which only four or five are known, at least three being Mint State). The others are generally available, but some can be almost impossible to find in Mint State, the 1849-O, certain early San Francisco issues, and Carson City coins of the early 1870s being well known in this regard. From the mid-1870s onward Mint State coins are generally available, including choice and gem pieces. Proofs from 1858 onward can be found in proportion to their mintages, with later dates often being seen with higher numerical designations than are earlier ones.

Barber quarters are collectible by date and mint, although the "big three" rarities, the 1896-S, 1901-S, and 1913-S, are expensive and hard to find.

Standing Liberty quarters 1916 to 1930 represent a short-lived series. Most are easy enough to collect in grades up to MS-63, except for the rare 1918-S, 8 Over 7, overdate. Finding higher-grade coins that are sharply struck is another matter entirely, and over the years, few sets of this nature have been assembled. A commemorative gold version struck in 2016 is generally not collected as a separate type.

Washington quarters are all collectible, with no great rarities. However, in relation to the demand for them, certain early issues are elusive, the 1932-D being best known in this regard. Modern issues, including the Bicentennial and State coins, are at once plentiful, inexpensive, and interesting to own.

For a more detailed study of each Washington quarter, including recent programs, see the *Guide Book of Washington Quarters.*

Draped Bust, Small Eagle Reverse (1796)

Circulation-Strike Mintage: 6,146

Field Population: Circulated, 250 to 325; Mint State, 250 to 300

Designer: Probably Gilbert Stuart. **Engraver:** Robert Scot.
Weight: 6.74 grams. **Composition:** .8924 silver, .1076 copper.
Diameter: Approximately 27.5 mm. **Edge:** Reeded. **Mint:** Philadelphia.

Key to Collecting: Among the pieces needed for a type set of United States coins the 1796 quarter is one of the most elusive. It is also among the most famous. The combination of the Draped Bust obverse and Small Eagle reverse is unique to this year. In one coin, we have the first year of issue of the denomination, the only year of the design type, and a variety with an enticingly low mintage figure of just 6,146. How exciting! Hundreds of circulated examples exist, but as the demand is so extensive, any specimen meets with enthusiasm when it is offered. Hundreds of high-grade examples also exist, *nearly all* of which are prooflike. Most are quite attractive. In his 1988 *Encyclopedia*, Walter Breen noted: "Many of these were saved as the first of their kind. When Col. E.H.R. Green inherited his mother's millions, he became a collector of (among other things) railroad cars, pornographic films, and among his immense numismatic holdings was a hoard of over 200 Uncirculated 1796 quarter dollars, of which at least 100 were more or less prooflike—their fields more mirrorlike than on the others. A. Kosoff and Andre DeCoppet dispersed many of these to date and type collectors in the 1940s."[11] Even in the 1950s, such coins were seen with some frequency. However, by now they are widely dispersed, and the appearance of even a single choice or gem specimen is an event of importance.

Aspects of Striking and Appearance: Most are quite well struck except for the head of the eagle on the reverse, which can be shallow or flat, especially on the Browning-2 variety (there are two known die varieties for this year, Browning-1 being the rarer). However, *all* aspects should be checked prior to making a purchase. A few pieces have planchet striations or carbon streaks; these should be avoided, or bought at a discount. As noted, Mint State coins are prooflike, sometimes *very mirrorlike*, and not lustrous or frosty. Lower-grade coins can be porous or granular. Some have Mint-caused planchet-adjustment marks.

Market Value: Circulation Strikes

AG-3	G-4	VG-8	F-12	VF-20	EF-40	AU-50
$7,500	$11,000	$17,000	$25,000	$32,500	$48,500	$62,500
AU-55	**AU-58**	**MS-60**	**MS-62**	**MS-63**	**MS-64**	**MS-65**
$70,000	$72,500	$80,000	$100,000	$125,000	$200,000	$375,000

Retail Price Trends

Year	VF-20	MS-65
1946	$27.50	$120
1950	$35	$225
1960	$265	$1,500
1970	$725	$10,000
1980	$1,500	$40,000

Year	VF-20	MS-65
1990	$3,500	$65,000
2000	$3,750	$60,000
2010	$30,000	$300,000
2019	$32,500	$375,000

Draped Bust, Heraldic Eagle Reverse (1804–1807)

Circulation-Strike Mintage: 554,900

Field Population: Circulated, 2,500 to 4,000; Mint State, 300 to 450

Designer: Robert Scot. **Weight:** 6.74 grams. **Composition:** .8924 silver, .1076 copper. **Diameter:** Approximately 27.5 mm. **Edge:** Reeded. **Mint:** Philadelphia.

Key to Collecting: Quarter dollars of the several dates combining the Draped Bust obverse with Heraldic Eagle reverse were made in sufficient quantities that none is a rarity today, although the 1804 is considered to be scarcer than the others. Examples of the dates 1805 to 1807 abound in the marketplace, generally in circulated grades, and nearly always with weak striking, this being particularly true of the last year, 1807. Get ready, get set, go! A challenge awaits you!

Aspects of Striking and Appearance: The majority of coins of this type have problems. Check the striking details on the portrait and on the eagle, the border stars and letters, and the denticles. Finding a sharply struck coin will test your patience, but when the game is caught and in your hand you'll be very proud. Meanwhile, most of your competitors in the marketplace will be concentrating on grading numbers, not *quality*, giving you a great advantage. For my money, I would rather own a sharply struck AU than a flatly struck MS-63! Mint State coins are virtually impossible to find for 1804, but are occasionally seen for the years 1805 to 1807. Luster is often good, but striking is apt to be miserable, and therefore cherrypicking is required. This will be a special challenge. A sharply struck coin is a goal, not necessarily a reality. As if these challenges are not sufficient, many have Mint-caused planchet-adjustment marks.

Market Value: Circulation Strikes

AG-3	G-4	VG-8	F-12	VF-20	EF-40	AU-50
$225	$500	$650	$950	$1,800	$3,750	$5,500

AU-55	MS-60	MS-62	MS-63	MS-64	MS-65
$6,500	$11,000	$15,000	$20,000	$32,500	$85,000

Retail Price Trends

Year	G-4	F-12	MS-63
1946	$2.50	$5	$35
1950	$3.50	$7.50	$55
1960	$14	$30	$175
1970	$55	$125	$650
1980	$100	$225	$2,750

Year	G-4	F-12	MS-63
1990	$250	$500	$6,000
2000	$200	$400	$7,000
2010	$450	$825	$14,500
2019	$500	$950	$20,000

Capped Bust, Large Diameter (1815–1828)

Circulation-Strike Mintage: 1,834,584

Proof Mintage: Fewer than 100

Field Population: Circulated, 10,000 to 15,000; Mint State, 2,000 to 3,000

Designer: John Reich. **Weight:** 6.74 grams. **Composition:** .8924 silver, .1076 copper. **Diameter:** Approximately 27 mm. **Edge:** Reeded. **Mint:** Philadelphia.

Key to Collecting: As a class, all are fairly scarce. However, these have never been in the limelight, thus creating an opportunity to acquire a scarce to rare coin for less than might otherwise be the case. As a class Mint State coins are very scarce. Most are in lower levels such as MS-60 to MS-62. Really nice MS-63 and higher specimens are rare, and gems even more so.

Aspects of Striking and Appearance: Striking is apt to vary. Check the hair details of Miss Liberty, the star centers, and the denticles. On the reverse, the details of the eagle should be examined (but are often superbly defined), the integrity of the scroll or ribbon above the eagle's head should be checked for weak or light areas, and the lettering should be inspected as well, not to overlook the denticles.

Proof Coins: Proof coins were struck in limited numbers for presentation purposes and for distribution to numismatists. Insist on a coin with deep and full (not partial) mirror surfaces, well struck, and with good contrast. Avoid deeply toned pieces (deep toning often masks the true nature of a coin). This particular range of Capped Bust quarters has many pretenders to the Proof throne, including some that have been certified or have "papers" signed by Walter Breen. Go slowly.

Market Value: Circulation Strikes

AG-3	G-4	VG-8	F-12	VF-20	EF-40	AU-50
$70	$125	$200	$300	$600	$1,600	$2,250

AU-55	MS-60	MS-62	MS-63	MS-64	MS-65
$2,300	$4,000	$4,750	$7,250	$12,000	$25,000

Market Value: Proof Strikes

PF-60	PF-63	PF-64	PF-65
$15,000	$40,000	$60,000	$100,000

Retail Price Trends

Year	F-12	EF-40	MS-64
1946	$3.50	$8	$18
1950	$4	$10	$25
1960	$11	$30	$70
1970	$35	$100	$1,700
1980	$70	$325	$3,000

Year	F-12	EF-40	MS-64
1990	$80	$550	$3,000
2000	$100	$625	$3,500
2010	$160	$1,350	$10,000
2019	$300	$1,600	$12,000

Capped Bust, Reduced Diameter, Motto Removed (1831–1838)

Circulation-Strike Mintage: 4,202,400

Proof Mintage: Fewer than 150

Field Population: Circulated, 30,000 to 45,000; Mint State, 4,000 to 6,500; Proof, 60 to 80

Designer: William Kneass. **Weight:** 6.74 grams (changed to 6.68 grams, .900 fine, in 1837). **Composition:** .8924 silver, .1076 copper. **Diameter:** 24.3 mm. **Edge:** Reeded. **Mint:** Philadelphia.

Key to Collecting: Typical grades range from VF to AU in the circulated category, and in lower ranges of Mint State. Choice and gem pieces do exist, including quite a few of the first year of issue, 1831.

Aspects of Striking and Appearance: Quarter dollars of this type in higher grades are generally well struck, much more so than the preceding. However, it is desirable to check the portrait details and stars on the obverse, the eagle on the reverse, and the denticles on both sides.

Proof Coins: Proof coins were struck in limited numbers for presentation purposes and for distribution to numismatists. Insist on a coin with deeply and fully (not partially) mirror surfaces, well struck, and with good contrast. Avoid deeply toned pieces (deep toning often masks the true nature of a coin). Some pieces attributed as "Proofs" are not Proofs, in my opinion. True Proofs are often very attractive.

Market Value: Circulation Strikes

G-4	VG-8	F-12	VF-20	EF-40	AU-50	AU-55
$70	$100	$125	$150	$400	$750	$950

MS-60	MS-62	MS-63	MS-64	MS-65	MS-66
$2,000	$2,500	$4,250	$8,500	$22,500	$40,000

Market Value: Proof Strikes

PF-60	PF-63	PF-64	PF-65
$15,000	$25,000	$60,000	$90,000

Retail Price Trends

Year	F-12	EF-40	MS-64
1946	$2	$3	$7.50
1950	$2	$3	$7.50
1960	$4.75	$12	$25
1970	$24	$80	$400
1980	$50	$160	$1,000

Year	F-12	EF-40	MS-64
1990	$50	$225	$2,500
2000	$225	$5,000	$3,500
2010	$125	$400	$8,500
2019	$125	$400	$8,500

Liberty Seated, No Motto Above Eagle, No Drapery (1838–1840)

Circulation-Strike Mintage: 1,339,346

Proof Mintage: *Fewer than 8*

Field Population: Circulated, 6,000 to 9,000; Mint State, 700 to 1,000; Proof, 4 to 6

Designer: Christian Gobrecht. **Weight:** 6.68 grams. **Composition:** .900 silver, .100 copper. **Diameter:** 24.3 mm. **Edge:** Reeded. **Mints:** Philadelphia, New Orleans.

Key to Collecting: Liberty Seated quarters of 1838 and 1839, and some of 1840, lack drapery at Miss Liberty's elbow, thus constituting a separate type. These are fairly scarce today, but enough exist that finding one in just about any grade except gem Mint State will present no difficulty, especially an attractive VF, EF, or AU example for type set purposes. Individual varieties of Mint State coins range from scarce to rare, but securing a solitary example for a type set will be no problem.

Aspects of Striking and Appearance: The quality of striking varies but is generally good. Check the features of Miss Liberty on the obverse, including her hair details, and examine the stars around the borders. On the reverse check the eagle, particularly the area to the lower left of the shield. The denticles are usually sharp.

Proof Coins: Exceedingly rare and not a realistic acquisition expectation.

Market Value: Circulation Strikes

G-4	VG-8	F-12	VF-20	EF-40	AU-50	AU-55	MS-60	MS-62	MS-63	MS-64	MS-65
$35	$50	$75	$175	$450	$950	$1,200	$1,700	$2,500	$4,000	$9,000	$35,000

Market Value: Proof Strikes

PF-60	PF-63	PF-64	PF-65
	$250,000		

Retail Price Trends

Year	F-12	EF-40	MS-64
1946	$2	$3.50	$9
1950	$2	$4	$10
1960	$5.50	$18	$23
1970	$14	$80	$700
1980	$25	$135	$1,500
1990	$25	$135	$3,000
2000	$27	$275	$4,000
2010	$65	$400	$9,000
2019	$75	$450	$9,000

Liberty Seated, No Motto Above Eagle, Drapery (1840–1853; 1856–1865)

Circulation-Strike Mintage: 45,341,187

Proof Mintage: Fewer than 5,500

Field Population: Circulated, 200,000 to 300,000; Mint State, 10,000 to 15,000; Proof, 3,500 to 4,300

Designer: Christian Gobrecht. **Weight:** ***1840–1853:*** 6.68 grams; ***1856–1865:*** 6.22 grams. **Composition:** .900 silver, .100 copper. **Diameter:** 24.3 mm. **Edge:** Reeded. **Mints:** Philadelphia, New Orleans, San Francisco.

Key to Collecting: Liberty Seated quarters from this early span of years are much scarcer than are related half dimes, dimes, and half dollars, although this is not generally realized. However, enough are around that finding one will be no problem. Circulated coins in VF, EF, or AU are sufficiently available for type set purposes. Individual Mint State pieces range from scarce to rare, but the span of years is such that you will have no trouble finding one.

Aspects of Striking and Appearance: The quality of striking varies widely due to the range of years involved. In general, check the features of Miss Liberty on the obverse, including her hair details, and examine the stars around the borders. On the reverse, check the eagle, particularly the area to the lower left of the shield. The denticles are usually sharp, especially for earlier and later years but should be checked as well.

Proof Coins: Proofs were first produced in significant numbers beginning in 1858 and are thus available from that year through 1865 in proportion to their mintages. Truly choice and gem pieces without distracting hairlines are the minority and will require some searching.

Market Value: Circulation Strikes

G-4	VG-8	F-12	VF-20	EF-40	AU-50	AU-55	MS-60	MS-62	MS-63	MS-64	MS-65
$25	$30	$35	$45	$75	$185	$225	$350	$450	$600	$1,000	$2,750

Market Value: Proof Strikes

PF-60	PF-63	PF-64	PF-65
$700	$1,200	$2,000	$4,000

Retail Price Trends

Year	VF-20	EF-40	MS-65	PF-65
1946	$0.85	$1	$3.25	$12.50
1950	$3	$4	$7.50	$10
1960	$4	$5	$10	$400
1970	$15	$20	$300	$2,750
1980	$25	$55	$900	$5,500

Year	VF-20	EF-40	MS-65	PF-65
1990	$20	$50	$1,500	$4,000
2000	$25	$50	$3,000	$4,500
2010	$48	$85	$3,750	$4,800
2019	$45	$75	$2,750	$4,000

Liberty Seated, Arrows at Date, Rays Around Eagle (1853)

Circulation-Strike Mintage: 16,542,000

Proof Mintage: Fewer than 10

Field Population: Circulated, 70,000 to 100,000; Mint State, 3,000 to 4,000; Proof, 4 to 6

Designer: Christian Gobrecht, as slightly modified by James B. Longacre or someone else on the Mint staff. **Weight:** 6.22 grams. **Composition:** .900 silver, .100 copper. **Diameter:** 24.3 mm. **Edge:** Reeded. **Mints:** Philadelphia, New Orleans.

Key to Collecting: Quarter dollars of this one-year type with arrows on the obverse and rays on the reverse were produced in large quantities, primarily at the Philadelphia Mint, plus some of 1853-O. Although examples are quite numerous on the market today, most were struck in haste, and quality suffered. Accordingly, at any given grade range, it is important to select a sharp example, such coins being in the minority. Even most Mint State pieces have lightness of strike or grainy or otherwise lifeless luster. Cherrypicking is advised.

Aspects of Striking and Appearance: Quality of striking played second fiddle to high-speed production for this issue, and from the viewpoint of a connoisseur, most examples today have problems of one sort or another. Check the details of Miss Liberty, including her head, and the stars. Many of these were struck from "tired" dies, giving a grainy aspect to them, quite lifeless, even on choice and gem pieces. On the reverse, the striking is usually better than the obverse, but check the details of the eagle, especially at the lower left.

Proof Coins: Proofs are exceedingly rare. Sometimes prooflike circulation strikes have been offered as Proofs. Be careful.

Market Value: Circulation Strikes

G-4	VG-8	F-12	VF-20	EF-40	AU-50	AU-55	MS-60	MS-62	MS-63	MS-64	MS-65
$25	$30	$35	$50	$175	$350	$450	$1,000	$1,250	$2,000	$4,000	$10,000

Market Value: Proof Strikes

PF-65
$100,000

Retail Price Trends

Year	VF-20	EF-40	MS-64	PF-65
1946	$1.75	$2.50	$3	$12
1950	$3	$4	$4	$25
1960	$14	$18	$15	$200
1970	$27.50	$40	$600	$6,000
1980	$35	$100	$1,000	$25,000

Year	VF-20	EF-40	MS-64	PF-65
1990	$40	$150	$1,400	$40,000
2000	$40	$175	$3,000	$85,000
2010	$50	$175	$4,250	$125,000
2019	$50	$175	$4,000	$100,000

Liberty Seated, Arrows at Date, No Rays (1854–1855)

Circulation-Strike Mintage: 17,293,400

Proof Mintage: Fewer than 140

Field Population: Circulated, 80,000 to 120,000; Mint State, 2,000 to 3,000; Proof, 65 to 90

Designer: Christian Gobrecht, with the arrows added by someone on Mint staff. **Weight:** 6.22 grams. **Composition:** .900 silver, .100 copper. **Diameter:** 24.3 mm. **Edge:** Reeded. **Mints:** Philadelphia, New Orleans, San Francisco.

Key to Collecting: Today, examples are available in just about every grade desired, except that Mint State pieces are somewhat scarce. Many are quite attractive—significantly more so than the typical example of the preceding type. Select one with deep frosty luster and sharp striking. Mint State coins in all numerical categories are scarcer than those of 1853, but when found, they tend to be of better eye appeal.

Aspects of Striking and Appearance: The usual areas should be checked, including the details of Miss Liberty, the stars, and the eagle, but in general, the striking is better than on the preceding.

Proof Coins: Proof coins were made in small quantities and sometimes come on the market today. These are extremely rare and highly desirable. Most have very nice eye appeal.

Market Value: Circulation Strikes

G-4	VG-8	F-12	VF-20	EF-40	AU-50	AU-55	MS-60	MS-62	MS-63	MS-64	MS-65
$25	$30	$35	$45	$85	$250	$350	$625	$900	$1,200	$2,100	$6,500

Market Value: Proof Strikes

PF-60	PF-63	PF-64	PF-65
$8,500	$15,000	$25,000	$30,000

Retail Price Trends

Year	VF-20	EF-40	MS-64	PF-64
1946	$1	$1.50	$3	$45
1950	$1.50	$2	$4	$45
1960	$7	$9	$15	$45
1970	$12.50	$50	$600	$2,000
1980	$30	$70	$1,000	$3,000

Year	VF-20	EF-40	MS-64	PF-64
1990	$35	$115	$1,400	$5,000
2000	$30	$80	$2,000	$4,750
2010	$45	$85	$2,500	$20,000
2019	$45	$85	$2,100	$25,000

Liberty Seated, Motto Above Eagle (1866–1873; 1875–1891)

Circulation-Strike Mintage: 72,680,181

Proof Mintage: 20,923

Field Population: Circulated, more than 1,000,000; Mint State, 14,000 to 22,000; Proof, 16,000 to 19,000

Designer: Christian Gobrecht, as modified by James B. Longacre.
Weight: ***1866–1873:*** 6.22 grams; ***1875–1891:*** 6.25 grams.
Composition: .900 silver, .100 copper. **Diameter:** 24.3 mm.
Edge: Reeded. **Mints:** Philadelphia, San Francisco, Carson City.

Key to Collecting: Although quarter dollars of this era are significantly scarcer than dimes and half dollars, enough exist that there will be no problem finding a choice example for a type set. Quite similar to the situation in the half dollar denomination, most of the higher-grade pieces are dated 1879 and later, which also coincides with a period of lower mintages. Circulated coins are scarce as a class and typically found of the higher-mintage dates (completely opposite the situation for Mint State coins!). Many Mint State examples exist but, interestingly, are from the lower-mintage issues from 1879 through 1891. Earlier dates, including some of very generous mintages, are much less often seen, particularly at the gem level. Many Mint State coins, particularly 1879 and later, are highly prooflike.

Aspects of Striking and Appearance: Generally good, but the details of Miss Liberty, the stars, and the eagle should be checked.

Proof Coins: Proofs were made on a regular basis for collectors from 1866 onward. Today, they exist in proportion to the mintages. Some Proofs were rather carelessly struck, and although these are in the minority, it does pay to check for quality.

Market Value: Circulation Strikes

G-4	VG-8	F-12	VF-20	EF-40	AU-50	AU-55	MS-60	MS-62	MS-63	MS-64	MS-65
$25	$30	$35	$45	$65	$160	$215	$275	$400	$550	$900	$1,300

Market Value: Proof Strikes

PF-60	PF-63	PF-64	PF-65
$475	$750	$950	$1,400

Retail Price Trends

Year	VF-20	EF-40	MS-64	PF-65
1946	$1	$1.25	$2.50	$10
1950	$1.50	$2	$3.50	$7.50
1960	$2.25	$3	$8.25	$33
1970	$6.50	$20	$200	$700
1980	$20	$40	$400	$1,700
1990	$20	$40	$700	$1,900
2000	$25	$45	$1,200	$2,000
2010	$45	$65	$875	$1,350
2019	$45	$65	$900	$1,400

Liberty Seated, Arrows at Date (1873–1874)

Circulation-Strike Mintage: 2,302,822

Proof Mintage: 1,240

Field Population: Circulated, 10,000 to 15,000; Mint State, 2,000 to 3,000; Proof, 900 to 1,100

Designer: Christian Gobrecht, as modified by James B. Longacre, with the arrows added during the chief engravership of William Barber. **Weight:** 6.25 grams. **Composition:** .900 silver, .100 copper. **Diameter:** 24.3 mm. **Edge:** Reeded. **Mints:** Philadelphia, San Francisco, Carson City.

Key to Collecting: In 1873 the authorized weights of the silver dime, quarter, and half dollar were increased slightly to make them come out in more or less even figures in terms of the metric system. To signify this change, arrows were placed at the date of later 1873 quarters and all quarters dated 1874. Although the slightly higher weight remained the standard, the arrows were discontinued after 1874. Mint State coins are rare, as the mintage was much smaller than preceding and later (especially) without-arrows coins. Today, choice Mint State coins are not often seen, and gems are very rare, the quarters of this type being much more difficult to locate than are dimes and half dollars of the same design. Circulated coins are available, often dated 1873 (the highest mintage).

Aspects of Striking and Appearance: Most are well struck, but there are exceptions. The details on Miss Liberty's head are sometimes weak. Also check the star centers and the lower parts of the eagle.

Proof Coins: Probably 75% or more of the mintage of 1,240 pieces survives.

Market Value: Circulation Strikes

G-4	VG-8	F-12	VF-20	EF-40	AU-50	AU-55	MS-60	MS-62	MS-63	MS-64	MS-65
$25	$30	$40	$65	$200	$450	$600	$850	$1,000	$1,350	$1,850	$3,500

Market Value: Proof Strikes

PF-60	PF-63	PF-64	PF-65
$900	$1,350	$2,500	$5,500

Retail Price Trends

Year	VF-20	EF-40	MS-65	PF-65
1946	$1.50	$2	$4.50	$10
1950	$2.50	$3.50	$7	$12
1960	$30	$40	$75	$110
1970	$45	$75	$600	$2,000
1980	$65	$150	$1,000	$8,500

Year	VF-20	EF-40	MS-65	PF-65
1990	$55	$150	$1,500	$6,000
2000	$60	$180	$3,000	$5,800
2010	$65	$200	$4,000	$7,750
2019	$65	$200	$3,500	$5,500

Barber (1892–1916)

Circulation-Strike Mintage: 264,670,792

Proof Mintage: 17,299

Field Population: Circulated, several million; Mint State, 50,000 to 100,000; Proof, 11,000 to 13,000

Designer: Charles E. Barber. **Weight:** 6.25 grams. **Composition:** .900 silver, .100 copper (net weight .18084 oz. pure silver). **Diameter:** 24.3 mm. **Edge:** Reeded. **Mints:** Philadelphia, Denver, New Orleans, San Francisco.

Key to Collecting: Today, among circulation-strike Barber quarters, probably 90% or more in existence are G-4 or below, a curious situation repeated in the dime and half dollar series. Although contemporary listings hardly ever mention this, assembling a set of dates and mintmarks in VF, EF, or AU grade might well take a year or more to do! Mint State coins are quite scarce, this being especially true of the mintmarked issues. Among type coins dated in the twentieth century, a gem Mint State Barber quarter is one of the scarcest. Choice and gem coins are usually of Philadelphia Mint varieties or, if of branch mints, dated after 1905. For some reason, those of the final several years are often quite "baggy," with numerous marks, this being especially true of the 1916.

Aspects of Striking and Appearance: The obverse of the typical Barber quarter is usually fairly well struck, although the higher hair details and star centers should be checked. The reverses of most Barber quarters are fairly well struck except for the lower right area of the eagle, including the leg and talons. The upper right area of the shield and nearby wing can also be weak. The denticles are usually sharp on the obverse and reverse.

Proof Coins: Proofs exist in proportion to their mintages. More choice examples tend to be of later dates. Most are sharply struck. The Proofs of 1892 to 1901 usually have cameo contrast between the designs and the mirror fields. Later Proofs vary in contrast.

Market Value: Circulation Strikes

G-4	VG-8	F-12	VF-20	EF-40	AU-50	MS-60	MS-62	MS-63	MS-64	MS-65
$9	$14	$26	$40	$70	$120	$240	$275	$350	$525	$800

Market Value: Proof Strikes

PF-60	PF-63	PF-64	PF-65	PF-65CAM
$350	$650	$850	$1,250	$1,450

Retail Price Trends

Year	VF-20	EF-40	MS-65	PF-65
1946	$1	$1.50	$3.50	$9
1950	$1.50	$2	$4	$10
1960	$2	$2.50	$12	$45
1970	$4	$11	$300	$400
1980	$20	$50	$700	$800

Year	VF-20	EF-40	MS-65	PF-65
1990	$16	$50	$1,000	$1,200
2000	$25	$60	$1,300	$1,700
2010	$40	$60	$900	$2,100
2019	$40	$70	$800	$1,250

Standing Liberty, No Stars Below Eagle (1916–1917)

Circulation-Strike Mintage: 12,253,200

Field Population: Circulated, several hundred thousand; Mint State, 35,000 to 70,000

Designer: Hermon A. MacNeil. **Weight:** 6.25 grams. **Composition:** .900 silver, .100 copper (net weight .18084 oz. pure silver). **Diameter:** 24.3 mm. **Edge:** Reeded. **Mints:** Philadelphia, Denver, San Francisco.

Key to Collecting: This is the coin that everybody loves—an absolutely gorgeous design that usually comes well struck and, if in Mint State, deeply lustrous.

Although quarters of this design were produced in limited quantity in 1916, just to the extent of 52,000 pieces, most of this type are dated 1917, although a close examination of the 1917 issues will reveal *slight* differences. Enough were saved that examples are fairly plentiful in all grades, through and including gem Mint State. However, the demand for them is so great that at any given time a dealer is not apt to have more than one, two, or a few in stock. Among the issues needed for a type set of twentieth-century copper, nickel, and silver coins, this is one of the top several scarcest, perhaps exceeded only by the Mint State Barber quarter and half dollar in terms of elusive nature. Most Mint State pieces are beautiful to behold. However, there are some exceptions.

Aspects of Striking and Appearance: This design is generally well struck, although the rare 1916 is not as sharp as the issues of 1917. Places to check for sharpness include the head of Miss Liberty, the rivets in the shield, and the central part of her gown. On the reverse, the details of the eagle can be checked. The luster is typically satiny and beautiful.

Market Value: Circulation Strikes

G-4	VG-8	F-12	VF-20	EF-40	AU-50	MS-60
$18	$30	$50	$70	$90	$140	$225

MS-63	MS-63FH	MS-64	MS-64FH	MS-65	MS-65FH
$325	$400	$400	$525	$700	$900

Retail Price Trends

Year	EF-40	MS-65
1946	$2.25	$4
1950	$2.25	$4
1960	$4.25	$12
1970	$14.50	$300
1980	$75	$750

Year	EF-40	MS-65
1990	$60	$700
2000	$60	$700
2010	$120	$750
2019	$90	$700

Standing Liberty, Stars Below Eagle (1917–1930)

Circulation-Strike Mintage: **214,516,400**

Field Population: **Circulated, millions; Mint State, 150,000 to 250,000**

Designer: Hermon A. MacNeil. **Weight:** 6.25 grams.
Composition: .900 silver, .100 copper (net weight .18084 oz. pure silver).
Diameter: 24.3 mm. **Edge:** Reeded. **Mints:** Philadelphia, Denver, San Francisco.

Key to Collecting: In 1917 the motif was significantly modified. Miss Liberty appears sheathed in a jacket of armor, further suggesting military preparedness in view of the World War then raging in Europe, to which America was busily supplying munitions to the Allies (England, France and others). On the reverse, the position of the eagle was modified and the stars rearranged. In 1925 a further modification was made, and the date was placed in a slightly recessed position, to help with the effects of wear. By this time, the dates were becoming difficult to discern on the earlier dates. The Standing Liberty quarter was discontinued after 1930, not having endured for the 25 years that, per law, a basic design was supposed to be in effect. Circulated examples abound. For type-set purposes, you may wish to opt for a high grade EF or AU, carefully selected. Mint State coins are also plentiful, the 1926-D (one of the lower mintage issues) being the most common of all due to old-time holdings.

Aspects of Striking and Appearance: Luster is usually fairly good. However, striking can range from poor to miserable. Careful selection is strongly recommended! While the collecting fraternity loves shortcuts and nicknames, and the term "Full Head" is used by certification services and others to indicate pieces on which the hair and face details of Miss Liberty are quite sharp (not always *full*), in reality, this is just part of the equation. Also check the rivets on the left side of the shield, which can be weak or even missing even if the head details are sharp! Moreover, check the date area. Sometimes this can be weak, particularly toward the left side. The reverse details should be checked as well. While coins of the years 1917 to 1924 were sometimes weakly struck at the date, after 1925 the dates were generally sharp.

Market Value: Circulation Strikes

G-4	VG-8	F-12	VF-20	EF-40	EF-40	AU-50
$7	$8	$9	$17	$35	$35	$65
MS-60	**MS-63**	**MS-63FH**	**MS-64**	**MS-64FH**	**MS-65**	**MS-65FH**
$120	$175	$275	$225	$375	$425	$675

Retail Price Trends

Year	EF-40	MS-65
1946	$1	$2.25
1950	$1.50	$3
1960	$3	$9
1970	$6.75	$150
1980	$20	$250

Year	EF-40	MS-65
1990	$25	$400
2000	$25	$500
2010	$36	$475
2019	$35	$425

Washington, Eagle Reverse, Silver (1932–1964; 1992–1998, Proofs Only)

Circulation-Strike Mintage: 8,259,676,501

Proof Mintage:
1932–1964: 19,911,592
1992–1998: 5,939,737

Field Population: Circulated, hundreds of millions; Mint State, many millions; Proof, well over 20,000,000

Designer: John Flanagan. **Weight:** 6.25 grams.
Composition: .900 silver, .100 copper (net weight .18084 oz. pure silver).
Diameter: 24.3 mm. **Edge:** Reeded. **Mints:** Philadelphia, Denver, San Francisco.

Key to Collecting: The Washington quarter dollar, first minted in 1932 to honor the 200th anniversary of the birth of the Father of Our Country, enjoyed a long design life and was produced, with a metal change in 1965, through the year 1998. The design was by John Flanagan, a sculptor whose statuary was widely acclaimed. The Standing Liberty motif, not minted since 1930, was promptly forgotten! From that point onward, Washington quarters were made in large quantities, with the silver version being produced continuously through 1964, with the solitary exception of the 1933 year. Examples abound in every grade imaginable, but circulated coins are not relevant for type-set purposes as Mint State pieces and Proofs are so inexpensive that these form a worthwhile option. Coins such as this enable you to fill in some of your type set quickly. Proofs in silver have been struck at the San Francisco Mint from 1992 to 1998 and can be considered as belonging to this type.

Aspects of Striking and Appearance: The details of this design were not sharp to begin with. However, most examples are fairly well struck within this context. Little numismatic attention has been paid to the aspect of striking.

Proof Coins: Very plentiful and usually very attractive. Dates available are 1936 to 1942, 1950 to 1964, and 1992 to 1998 (San Francisco Mint).

Market Value: Circulation Strikes

EF-40	AU-50	MS-60	MS-63	MS-64	MS-65	MS-66	MS-67
$7	$8	$9	$10	$12	$15	$33	$85

Market Value: Proof Strikes

PF-64	PF-65	PF-66	PF-67
$10	$11	$20	$30

Retail Price Trends

Year	MS-65	PF-65
1970	$1	$2
1980	$2	$3
1990	$2.50	$5
2000	$3.25	$3.50
2010	$12	$8
2019	$15	$11

Washington, Eagle Reverse, Copper-Nickel (1965–1998, Including Proofs)

Circulation-Strike Mintage: 37,420,766,593

Proof Mintage: 93,516,827

Field Population: Circulated, billions; Mint State, billions; Proof, tens of millions

Designer: John Flanagan. **Weight:** 5.67 grams. **Composition:** Outer layers of copper nickel (.750 copper, .250 nickel) bonded to inner core of pure copper. **Diameter:** 24.3 mm. **Edge:** Reeded. **Mints:** Philadelphia, Denver, San Francisco.

Key to Collecting: Due to the rising price of silver, use of this metal was discontinued beginning in 1965, and circulating quarter dollars from that time onward have been made of a clad composition consisting of outer layers of 75% copper and 25% nickel bonded to a center section of pure copper, in effect creating a sandwich. The new alloy proved to be very durable, and coins in circulation held up to wear better than did their earlier silver counterparts. This design and metal composition were used through and including 1998, after which year the portrait was severely altered. Circulated coins are extremely common, but not of relevance for type-set purposes due to the availability of Mint State pieces. Readily available in just about any grade desired.

Aspects of Striking and Appearance: Usually well struck and with attractive surfaces. Finding a choice piece will be easy.

Proof Coins: Easily available in proportion to the mintage of Proof sets. Those of the 1965 to 1972 era have slight relief and detail differences from the general circulation strikes. Examples with deeply frosted portraits and eagle are especially desired.

Market Value: Circulation Strikes

MS-63	MS-65	MS-66	MS-67
$1	$7	$18	$30

Market Value: Proof Strikes

PF-65	PF-67Cam	PF-68CAM	PF-68DC
$4	$8	$14	$16

Retail Price Trends

Year	MS-65	PF-65
2000	$0.50	$1
2010	$4	$3
2019	$7	$4

Washington, Bicentennial, Copper-Nickel (1776–1976)

Circulation-Strike Mintage: 1,669,902,855

Proof Mintage: 7,059,099

Field Population: Circulated, hundreds of millions; Mint State, hundreds of millions; Proof, 6,000,000 to 6,750,000

Designers: ***Obverse:*** John Flanagan. ***Reverse:*** Jack L. Ahr. **Weight:** 5.67 grams. **Composition:** Outer layers of .750 copper, .250 nickel bonded to inner core of pure copper. **Diameter:** 24.3 mm. **Edge:** Reeded. **Mints:** Philadelphia, Denver, San Francisco.

Key to Collecting: Much attention was paid in the early 1970s to the forthcoming 200th anniversary of American independence. For the occasion special reverse designs were made for the quarter dollar, half dollar, and dollar, and on the obverse of each the curious double date, 1776-1976, was placed. In view of anticipated demand, many coins were *prestruck* in calendar year 1975. Many numismatists consider the reverse motif of the quarter dollar to be the most attractive used on the three denominations made for this event. Circulated coins abound but are not relevant for type-set purposes as Mint State pieces are common and are available in all grades.

Aspects of Striking and Appearance: Usually well struck and of good appearance.

Proof Coins: Proofs were made in large quantities and were plentiful on the market for years afterward, with retail shops at the different mints having examples on display and for sale for several years after the bicentennial ended. One reason for this is that the coin market was in the doldrums in 1976, a down point in the market cycle, and large quantities that might otherwise have been absorbed weren't. This translates into good news for you today, as gem coins can be had for a pittance.

Market Value: Circulation Strikes

MS-63	MS-65	MS-66	MS-67
$1	$6	$15	$50

Market Value: Proof Strikes

PF-65	PF-67Cam	PF-68CAM	PF-68DC
$5	$10	$16	$20

Retail Price Trends

Year	MS-63	MS-65	PF-65
1980	$0.50	$0.50	$1.75
1990	$1	$0.50	$1.75
2000	$1.50	$0.50	$1.25

Year	MS-63	MS-65	PF-65
2010	$1	$6	$3
2019	$1	$6	$5

Washington, Bicentennial, Silver (1776–1976)

Circulation-Strike Mintage: 11,000,000

Proof Mintage: 4,000,000

Field Population: Circulated, several hundred thousand; Mint State, nearly 10,000,000; Proof, 3,400,000 to 3,700,000

Designers: ***Obverse:*** John Flanagan. ***Reverse:*** Jack L. Ahr. **Weight:** 5.75 grams. **Composition:** Outer layers of .800 silver, .200 copper bonded to inner core of .209 silver, .791 copper (net weight .0739 oz. pure silver). **Diameter:** 24.3 mm. **Edge:** Reeded. **Mint:** San Francisco.

Key to Collecting: This is simply a special-metal version of the preceding design, struck in a silver-clad composition for sale to numismatists and those desiring souvenirs. All were struck at the San Francisco Mint and bear an S mintmark. Circulated coins are exceedingly rare—unavailable, unless someone spent a coin collection! On the other hand, Mint State coins are very common.

Aspects of Striking and Appearance: Usually excellent.

Proof Coins: Common.

Market Value: Circulation Strikes

MS-63	MS-64	MS-65
$4	$5	$7

Market Value: Proof Strikes

PF-65
$8

Retail Price Trends

Year	MS-65	PF-65
1980	$2	$5
1990	$2	$5
2000	$2.25	$3
2010	$7	$8
2019	$7	$8

Washington, State, D.C., and Territorial (1999–2009)

Circulation-Strike Mintage: Millions for each type.

Proof Mintage: Hundreds of thousands for each type.

Field Population: Circulated, tens of billions; Mint State, hundreds of millions; Proof, tens of millions

Designers: ***Obverse:*** John Flanagan, as altered by William Cousins, who added extensive hair details. The initials WC were added to those of Flanagan, now appearing run together as JFWC. The W is of unusual appearance and is not easily recognizable as such. ***Reverse:*** See image captions for reverse designers. **Weight:** ***Clad issue:*** 5.67 grams; ***silver Proofs:*** 6.25 grams. **Composition:** ***Clad issue:*** Outer layers of copper-nickel (.750 copper, .250 nickel) bonded to inner core of pure copper; ***silver Proofs:*** .900 silver, .100 copper (net weight .18084 oz. pure silver). **Diameter:** 24.3 mm. **Edge:** Reeded. **Mints:** ***Clad issue:*** Philadelphia, Denver; ***silver Proofs:*** San Francisco.

The 50 State Quarters® Program

Beginning in 1999, the 50 State Quarters® Program was launched by the United States Mint. Each year five states of the Union were each to suggest designs for the reverse of the quarter dollar, the motifs to depict some aspect of history, tradition, nature, or fame. Prohibitions included busts, state seals, state flags, logotypes, and depictions of living people.

Generally, citizens were invited to submit suggestions to be reviewed by the governor and advisors, after which a design would be selected. This would then be submitted to the Commission of Fine Arts (an advisory group), the Citizens Commemorative Coin Advisory Committee (through 2002) and the Citizens Coinage Advisory Committee (after 2002), and the United States Mint, after which certain modifications might be made.

Each year each of the five quarters was released in the order the state joined the Union, with the launching with an appropriate ceremony attended by Mint officials and dignitaries. The launch times were spaced throughout the year. Circulation strikes were made at the Philadelphia and Denver mints, while at the San Francisco Mint Proofs were struck for collectors and others, in copper-nickel-clad composition as well as silver.

Mint Director Philip M. Diehl wrote this comment concerning the genesis of the program:

> The idea of a circulating commemorative has been around the hobby for decades, but frankly, good ideas are a dime a dozen. Far more rare is the ability to move an idea to reality, especially in the rough and tumble environment of Washington, D.C.
>
> From my vantage point, the lion's share of the credit for making the 50 States Quarters® program a reality goes to David Ganz, for his persistence as an advocate, and Congressman Michael Castle for championing the proposal through Congress. David gradually persuaded me of the merits of the proposal, and we at the Mint, in turn, convinced Treasury and the Hill it was doable. There are other claimants, to be sure, but the hobby owes a debt of gratitude to Congressman Castle and Mr. Ganz.[12]

Jay Johnson, director of the Mint in 2000 and 2001, shared his reminiscences of the program in its infancy:

> One of my favorite lines I gave in speeches about the state quarters was that they were both collectible coins and circulating coins. I used to refer folks (if the audience was old enough to remember) to that old commercial for a breath mint (get it? Mint director talking about mints!) which said, 'Is it a breath mint or a candy mint? It's both. It's two, it's two, it's two mints in one!'
>
> That's what I used to say of the quarters—as I held a coin in each hand and clicked them together: 'Is it a circulating coin, or a commemorative coin? It's both, it's two, it's two coins in one!'
>
> Anyone who remembered the Certs commercial got the connection, and it was an easy way of explaining 'circulating' and 'commemorative' coins to the non-numismatist.
>
> Non-numismatic audiences also got a smile out of a line I used to use in speeches after talking about the popularity of the 50 state quarters and the numbers of people

collecting them. I would add, 'Why, these days, practically everybody is calling himself a numismatist!' To many people who couldn't think of even pronouncing numismatist, it got a nice smile. Hopefully, it even helped people think about joining the American Numismatic Association.[13]

OBVERSE CHANGES

In 1999 to accommodate the creative designs intended for the reverse of the State quarters, the inscriptions, UNITED STATES OF AMERICA and QUARTER DOLLAR, were relocated to the obverse above and below the portrait, respectively. LIBERTY and IN GOD WE TRUST were moved to new positions. At the same time the Mint decided to "improve" the portrait of Washington by adding little curlicue and squiggle hair details.

At the time I asked why this was done and was told that there had been complaints that the portrait details were not sharp (nor were they sharp on Houdon's original bust used for the design!). Accordingly, the Mint "sharpened" the design in this manner. In 1999, the name of the Mint engraver who created the new die, William Cousins, was memorialized by adding his initials, WC, next to JF (for John Flanagan, the original designer in 1932) on the neck truncation. It is probably correct to call this the "Cousins portrait."

COLLECTING A TYPE SET OF STATE QUARTERS

Regarding the subject of building a type set, this series is wonderful—in that there are so many varieties available in high grades for inexpensive prices. How lucky we all are.

Key to Collecting: As planned, circulation strikes were made at the Philadelphia and Denver mints, while Proofs, both in clad metal and silver, were made at the San Francisco Mint. In all instances, circulation-strike mintages ran into the hundreds of millions and Proofs in the high hundreds of thousands. Accordingly, the four varieties of each issue were readily available in the year they were minted, and after that time the market supply has been generous. Additionally, for the years 2005–2009 (and in 2010, the first year of the America the Beautiful series), Philadelphia and Denver strikes released in uncirculated Mint Sets had a special Satin Finish, distinct from the standard finish. Circulated coins are extremely common, but not of relevance for type-set purposes due to the availability of Mint State pieces, which are available in just about any grade desired.

Aspects of Striking and Appearance: Usually well struck and with attractive surfaces. Finding a choice piece will be easy. For some issues, Denver Mint coins are not sharp in certain areas of the lettering. On some Proofs, over-polishing of dies has eliminated some details, as on part of the WC (for William Cousins) initials on certain 1999 Delaware pieces. Some have interesting die cracks, an example being a 2002-P Tennessee with a large crack from the neck through the Q of QUARTER to border, another die crack from the forehead through the first S of STATES; others could be cited. Quite a few mint errors, such as off-center strikings, are available and are interesting to see.

Proof Coins: Easily available in both copper-nickel-clad composition and silver-content types, in proportion to their mintages.

Market Price Performance (all issues): Not yet any long-term market history to report. General current market values given below.

For More Detailed Information

The *Guide Book of Washington Quarters* (Whitman Publishing) is a good source for history, grading and other information on each State quarter. It includes full-color illustrations, market values, and mintages, along with designer details, behind-the-scenes accounts, and stories about each state.

1999,
Delaware
Reverse designer:
William Cousins.

1999,
Pennsylvania
Reverse designer:
John Mercanti.

1999,
New Jersey
Reverse designer:
Alfred Maletsky.

1999,
Georgia
Reverse designer:
T. James Ferrell.

1999,
Connecticut
Reverse designer:
T. James Ferrell.

2000,
Massachusetts
Reverse designer:
Thomas D. Rogers Sr.

2000,
Maryland
Reverse designer:
Thomas D. Rogers Sr.

2000,
South Carolina
Reverse designer:
Thomas D. Rogers Sr.

2000,
New Hampshire
Reverse designer:
William Cousins.

2000,
Virginia
Reverse designer:
Edgar Z. Steever.

2001,
New York
Reverse designer:
Alfred Maletsky.

2001,
North Carolina
Reverse designer:
John Mercanti.

2001,
Rhode Island
Reverse designer:
Thomas D. Rogers Sr.

2001,
Vermont
Reverse designer:
T. James Ferrell.

2001,
Kentucky
Reverse designer:
T. James Ferrell.

2002,
Tennessee
Reverse designer:
Donna Weaver.

2002,
Ohio
Reverse designer:
Donna Weaver.

2002,
Louisiana
Reverse designer:
John Mercanti.

2002,
Indiana
Reverse designer:
Donna Weaver.

2002,
Mississippi
Reverse designer:
Donna Weaver.

2003,
Illinois
Reverse designer:
Donna Weaver.

2003,
Alabama
Reverse designer:
Norman E. Nemeth.

2003,
Maine
Reverse designer:
Donna Weaver.

2003,
Missouri
Reverse designer:
Alfred Maletsky.

2003,
Arkansas
Reverse designer:
John Mercanti.

2004,
Michigan
Reverse designer:
Donna Weaver.

2004,
Florida
Reverse designer:
T. James Ferrell.

2004,
Texas
Reverse designer:
Norman E. Nemeth.

2004,
Iowa
Reverse designer:
John Mercanti.

2004,
Wisconsin
Reverse designer:
Alfred Maletsky.

2005,
California
Reverse designer:
Don Everhart.

2005,
Minnesota
Reverse designer:
Charles Vickers.

2005,
Oregon
Reverse designer:
Donna Weaver.

2005,
Kansas
Reverse designer:
Norman E. Nemeth.

2005,
West Virginia
Reverse designer:
John Mercanti.

2006,
Nevada
Reverse designer:
Don Everhart.

2006,
Nebraska
Reverse designer:
Charles Vickers.

2006,
Colorado
Reverse designer:
Norman E. Nemeth.

2006,
North Dakota
Reverse designer:
Donna Weaver.

2006,
South Dakota
Reverse designer:
John Mercanti.

2007,
Montana
Reverse designer:
Don Everhart.

2007,
Washington
Reverse designer:
Charles Vickers.

2007,
Idaho
Reverse designer:
Don Everhart.

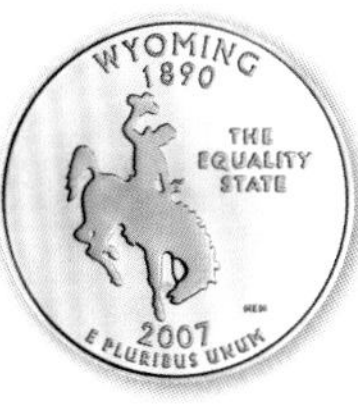

2007,
Wyoming
Reverse designer:
Norman E. Nemeth.

2007,
Utah
Reverse designer:
Joseph Menna.

2008, Oklahoma
Reverse designer:
Phebe Hemphill.

2008, New
Mexico
Reverse designer:
Don Everhart.

2008, Arizona
Reverse designer:
Joseph Menna.

2008, Alaska
Reverse designer:
Charles Vickers.

2008, Hawaii
Reverse designer:
Don Everhart.

2009, District of
Columbia
Reverse designer:
Don Everhart.

2009, Puerto Rico
Reverse designer:
Joseph Menna.

2009, Guam
Reverse designer:
Jim Licaretz.

2009, American Samoa
Reverse designer:
Charles Vickers.

2009, U.S. Virgin
Islands
Reverse designer:
Joseph Menna.

2009, Northern
Mariana Islands
Reverse designer:
Phebe Hemphill.

Market Value:
Circulation Strikes

AU-50	MS-63	MS-65
$0.45	$0.50	$1

Market Value:
Proofs, Copper-Nickel

PF-65	PF-66DC	PF-69DC
$3	$4.50	$18

Market Value:
Proofs, Silver

PF-65	PF-66DC	PF-69DC
$8	$10	$22

Washington, America the Beautiful (2010 to Date)

Circulation-Strike Mintage: Millions for each type.

Proof Mintage: Hundreds of thousands for each type.

Field Population: Circulated, tens of billions; Mint State, hundreds of millions; Proof, tens of millions

Designers: ***Obverse:*** John Flanagan, as altered by William Cousins, who added extensive hair details. The initials WC were added to those of Flanagan, now appearing run together as JFWC. The W is of unusual appearance and is not easily recognizable as such. ***Reverse:*** See image captions for reverse designers. **Weight:** ***Clad issue:*** 5.67 grams; ***silver Proofs:*** 6.25 grams. **Composition:** ***Clad issue:*** Outer layers of copper-nickel (.750 copper, .250 nickel) bonded to inner core of pure copper; ***silver Proofs:*** .900 silver, .100 copper (net weight .18084 oz. pure silver). **Diameter:** 24.3 mm. **Edge:** Reeded. **Mints:** ***Clad issue:*** Philadelphia, Denver, San Francisco; ***silver Proofs:*** San Francisco.

THE AMERICA THE BEAUTIFUL™ PROGRAM

Aware of the wonderful success of the State Quarters Program, even including the somewhat lackluster interest in the D.C. and territorial coins at the end, Representative Michael Castle initiated and promoted a new series. This became H.R. 6184—America's Beautiful National Parks Quarter Dollar Coin Act of 2008. This became PL 110-456 and was signed by President George W. Bush on December 23, 2008.

Oops! After the fact it was realized that some states did not have a national park!

Behind the scenes regrouping took place, and these became known as America the Beautiful quarters. States that did not have national parks were searched for a national something-or-other, such as a national historic site, or river way, or wildlife preserve.

This resulted in the showcasing of may places that many Americans were unfamiliar with—the Chickasaw National Recreation Area (2011), El Yunque National Forest (2011), Kisatchie National Forest (2015), and Bombay Hook National Wildlife Refuge (2015) being several examples. This unique teaming-up of the National Park Service and the U.S. Mint brought educational and promotional opportunities galore.

This was and is a plus situation for anyone who receives a quarter who is interested in learning more. We all know about Yellowstone, Yosemite, Grand Canyon, and some other subjects, but the obscure places invite study.

Some designs do not tell all. For example, the 2013 New Hampshire quarter only says WHITE MOUNTAIN. Depicted is a mountain with a lake in the foreground. There is no peak called White Mountain. Shown is Mount Chocorua, not mentioned either on the coin or the official Mint news releases concerning it. What is intended is the White Mountain National Forest, a range of peaks of which Mount Washington is one of the highest and Mount Chocorua is one of the lowest.

Such things add a lot to the enjoyment of collecting the quarters.

On the negative side, quarters with places few had ever heard of did not engender much public interest. Mintages of the various issues fell far below those of the State quarters issues. Not simplifying matters is the Federal Reserve System's program—which in a way makes sense—of supplying new quarters to member banks that request them. If a bank needs coins it is sent the supply currently on hand, which like it or not has nothing to do with the location of the bank in relation to the showcased subject. When the New Hampshire quarters were released in 2013 I did not learn of a single bank in the state that received a supply—as no new coins were needed.

Beginning with Hot Springs National Park in 2010, the America the Beautiful subjects were issued in the chronological order in which they came under national protection. The Hot Springs were protected under federal authority beginning in 1832, the first such location. However, private businesses exploited the location by setting up private bathhouses (warm-water spas). It was not named as a national park until 1921. The illustration on the coin is of a modern (1936) building. Go figure, as they say! Again, all of this adds interest to the series for anyone who seeks to explore the coins in depth.

Beyond the complications mentioned, the selection of designs was often controversial, as reflected in this article by Debbie Bradley in *Numismatic News*, February 9, 2010:

Design Dilemma

> The very features American parks have in common—mountains, streams, meadows—make them difficult to distinguish on coins. That's what the Commission of Fine Arts is wrestling with as it recommends designs for the 2011 coins in the "America the Beautiful" quarter series. At its January 21 meeting, the CFA reviewed reverse designs for quarters honoring Gettysburg National Military Park in Pennsylvania, Glacier National Park in Montana, Olympic National Park in Washington, Vicksburg National Military Park in Mississippi and Chickasaw National Recreation Area in Oklahoma. It recommended designs for only three of the quarters—Gettysburg, Glacier and Olympic—while giving support to a design for Vicksburg and asking for a redesign of the Chickasaw quarter.
>
> CFA Secretary Tom Luebke said the CFA doesn't support what appears to be a tendency to take photographic images and use them as the basis for the coin design. That results in excessive detail and realism, which isn't appropriate for medallic design, he said. Coin design could instead emphasize key elements and possibly an abstraction or stylization of the iconic elements to convey the essence of the subject, he said… Although the U.S. Mint has adopted a template for the "America the Beautiful" quarters, the CFA is not pleased with the straight bottom in the design area because it is often in conflict with the design composition, Luebke said. And the placement of the state name and E PLURIBUS UNUM presents odd symmetry, he said. "But members acknowledged that is water under the dam," Luebke said.

In summary, for anyone with intellectual curiosity in combination with numismatic enthusiasm, these quarters have a lot to offer!

Collecting a Type Set of America the Beautiful™ Quarter Dollars

Like the State quarters before it, the America the Beautiful series provides collectors with many varieties available in high grades for inexpensive prices.

Key to Collecting: Continuing the production assignments used for State quarters, circulation strikes are made at the Philadelphia and Denver mints; additionally, starting in 2012 and continuing to date, the San Francisco Mint has made relatively small quantities of Uncirculated S-mintmark quarters of each design in the National Park series. These can be purchased by collectors directly from the U.S. Mint, in bags of 100 or rolls of 40 coins, for a premium above face value. Proofs, both in copper-nickel and silver, are made at the San Francisco Mint. In 2010 (as in the years 2005–2009 prior), Philadelphia and Denver strikes released in uncirculated Mint Sets had a special Satin Finish, distinct from the standard finish. Philadelphia and Denver circulation-strike mintages run into the hundreds of millions; San Francisco Proofs are the high hundreds of thousands; Satin Finish mintages are just above half a million per Mint/type, and San Francisco circulation strikes average about a million per type. Accordingly, all varieties of each issue are readily available in the year they were minted, and after that time the market supply has been generous. Circulated coins are extremely common, but not of relevance for type-set purposes due to the availability of Mint State pieces, which are available in just about any grade desired.

Aspects of Striking and Appearance: These quarters can have light striking on the highest area of the obverse. On the reverse there can be weak areas, depending on the design, seemingly more often seen on Denver Mint coins.

Proof Coins: America the Beautiful quarter dollar Proofs are made in San Francisco. For certain later issues, Proofs are available in copper-nickel as well as silver strikings. On some Proofs over-polishing of dies has eliminated some details.

Market Price Performance (all issues): Not yet any long-term market history to report. Individual current market values given below.

For More Detailed Information

The *Guide Book of Washington Quarters* (Whitman Publishing) is a good source for history, grading and other information on each America the Beautiful quarter. It includes full-color illustrations, market values, and mintages, along with designer details, behind-the-scenes accounts, and stories about each state.

2010, Hot Springs National Park (AR)
Reverse designer: Don Everhart.

2010, Yellowstone National Park (WY)
Reverse designer: Don Everhart.

2010, Yosemite National Park (CA)
Reverse designer: Joseph Menna.

2010, Grand Canyon National Park (AZ)
Reverse designer: Phebe Hemphill.

2010, Mt. Hood National Forest (OR)
Reverse designer: Phebe Hemphill.

2011, Gettysburg National Military Park (PA)
Reverse designer: Joel Iskowitz.

2011, Glacier National Park (MT)
Reverse designer: Barbara Fox.

2011, Olympic National Park (WA)
Reverse designer: Susan Gamble.

2011, Vicksburg National Military Park (MS)
Reverse designer: Thomas Cleveland.

2011, Chickasaw National Recreation Area (OK)
Reverse designer: Donna Weaver.

2012, El Yunque National Forest (PR)
Reverse designer: Gary Whitley.

2012, Chaco Culture National Historical Park (NM)
Reverse designer: Donna Weaver.

2012, Acadia National Park (ME)
Reverse designer: Barbara Fox.

2012, Hawai'i Volcanoes National Park (HI)
Reverse designer: Charles L. Vickers.

2012, Denali National Park and Preserve (AK)
Reverse designer: Susan Gamble.

2013, White Mountain National Forest (NH)
Reverse designer: Phebe Hemphill.

2013, Perry's Victory and International Peace Memorial (OH)
Reverse designer: Don Everhart.

2013, Great Basin National Park (NV)
Reverse designer: Ronald D. Sanders.

2013, Fort McHenry National Monument and Historic Shrine (MD)
Reverse designer: Joseph Menna.

2013, Mount Rushmore National Memorial (SD)
Reverse designer: Joseph Menna.

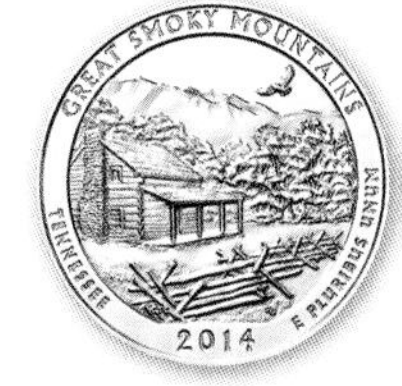

2014, Great Smoky Mountains National Park (TN)
Reverse designer: Chris Costello.

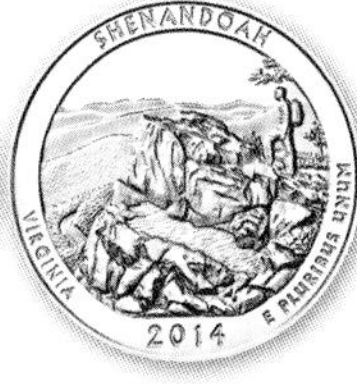

2014, Shenandoah National Park (VA)
Reverse designer: Phebe Hemphill.

2014, Arches National Park (UT)
Reverse designer: Donna Weaver.

2014, Great Sand Dunes National Park (CO)
Reverse designer: Don Everhart.

2014, Everglades National Park (FL)
Reverse designer: Joel Iskowitz.

2015, Homestead National Monument of America (NE)
Reverse designer: Ronald D. Sanders.

2015, Kisatchie National Forest (LA)
Reverse designer: Susan Gamble

2015, Blue Ridge Parkway (NC)
Reverse designer: Frank Morris.

2015, Bombay Hook National Wildlife Refuge (DE)
Reverse designer: Joel Iskowitz.

2015, Saratoga National Historical Park (NY)
Reverse designer: Barbara Fox.

2016, Shawnee National Forest (IL)
Reverse designer: Justin Kunz.

2016, Cumberland Gap National Historic Park (KY)
Reverse designer: Barbara Fox.

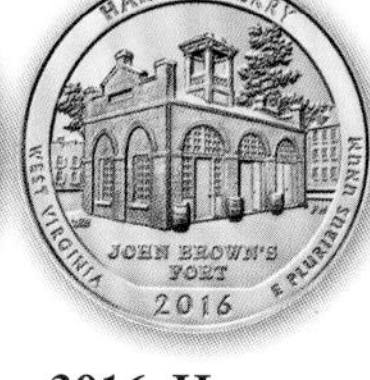

2016, Harpers Ferry National Historical Park (WV)
Reverse designer: Thomas Hipschen.

2016, Theodore Roosevelt National Park (ND)
Reverse designer: Joel Iskowitz.

2016, Fort Moultrie at Fort Sumter National Monument (SC)
Reverse designer: Richard Scott.

2017, Effigy Mounds National Monument (IA)
Reverse designer: Richard Masters.

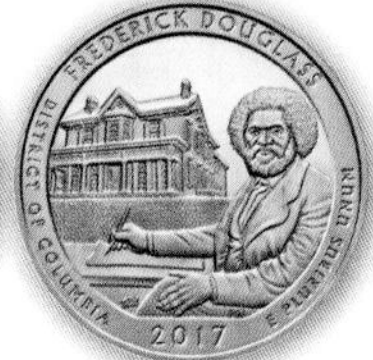

2017, Frederick Douglass National Historic Site (DC)
Reverse designer: Thomas Hipschen.

2017, Ozark National Scenic Riverways (MO)
Reverse designer: Ronald D. Sanders.

2017, Ellis Island (Statue of Liberty National Monument) (NJ)
Reverse designer: Barbara Fox.

2017, George Rogers Clark National Historical Park (IN)
Reverse designer: Frank Morris.

2018, Pictured Rocks National Lakeshore (MI)
Reverse designer: Paul C. Balan.

2018, Apostle Islands National Lakeshore (WI)
Reverse designer: Richard Masters.

2018, Voyageurs National Park (MN)
Reverse designer: Patricia Lucas-Morris.

2018, Cumberland Island National Seashore (GA)
Reverse designer: Donna Weaver.

2018, Block Island National Wildlife Refuge (RI)
Reverse designer: Chris Costello.

2019, Lowell National Historical Park (MA)
Reverse designer: Joel Iskowitz.

2019, American Memorial Park (Northern Mariana Islands)
Reverse designer: Donna Weaver.

2019, War in the Pacific National Historical Park (Guam)
Reverse designer: Joel Iskowitz.

2019, San Antonio Missions National Historical Park (TX)
Reverse designer: Chris Costello.

2019, Frank Church River of No Return Wilderness (ID)
Reverse designer: Emily Damstra.

Market Value: Circulation Strikes

AU-50	MS-63	MS-65
$0.50	$0.75	$1

Market Value: Proofs, Copper-Nickel

PF-65	PF-66DC	PF-69DC
$3	$4.50	$15

Market Value: Proofs, Silver

PF-65	PF-66DC	PF-69DC
$8	$9	$20

17
Half Dollars
1794 to Date

Overview of the Denomination

Half dollars, first struck in 1794, have been produced more or less continuously until the present time. The first United States half dollars were of the Flowing Hair design and were immediately popular. In 1794 an effort was also made to produce silver dollars, but the largest press at the Mint was not of sufficient capability, and the dollars made had severe problems, including light striking. The matter of dollars was given up, and half dollars became more important, at least for a short time.

In the first year, 23,464 Flowing Hair half dollars were made, as compared to only 1,758 silver dollars. In 1795 the production of half dollars of this design rose to 299,680. Then in mid-1795 new equipment was set up, and production of silver dollars commenced strongly (with 160,295 being made). Such silver coins were produced specifically on the request of depositors of this metal. Once silver dollars became a reality, the demand for half dollars dropped precipitously, as the dollars were easier to store and count.

Because of this, in 1796 and 1797 only 3,918 half dollars were produced. These were of a new design, combining the Draped Bust obverse with the Small Eagle reverse. Examples from this limited-production era are of great numismatic rarity and importance today, indeed the most elusive type in the entire silver series save for the 1839 Gobrecht silver dollar.

No half dollars were struck at all in 1798, 1799, or 1800, silver dollars largely taking their place in commerce. In 1801 production of halves resumed, at which time the Heraldic Eagle reverse motif was first used, continuing every year through 1807, except 1804, although there is an overdate, 1805, 5 Over 4. Essentially the same motif was used on the half dime, dime, quarter dollar, and silver dollar. The denominations of this design, from the half dime through the half dollar (but not the silver dollar), did not strike up properly, and virtually all coins are weak in one area or another, one of the greatest challenges in forming a type set. Among these coins those dated 1806 and, in particular, 1807 can be absolutely miserably struck—with much detail missing.

In 1807 a new half dollar design, the Capped Bust obverse, with the Perched Eagle reverse, by John Reich, made its debut, creating a series that became exceedingly popular with numismatists generations later. Interestingly, in 1807 there seems to have been no ceremony, no particular notice, or any other observance of the new style being produced. Pieces quietly slipped into circulation, with the result that today high-grade 1807 half dollars of the new type are quite rare. Most are also lightly struck at the centers.

It is quite curious that the same design type can have so many different characteristics over a period of time. While finding a needle-sharp 1807 Capped Bust half dollar in any grade would be an admirable feat, in contrast, most of 1834 were produced with sharp features and are easy to locate. As you build your type set, study each coin carefully—let it speak to you. Each type is, of course, different—but within a given type there are many interesting distinctions as well.

To this point, and continuing through 1836, half dollars were made with lettered edges, typically saying FIFTY CENTS OR HALF A DOLLAR. Mintages of Capped Bust half dollars continued apace through 1836, with the solitary exception of 1816.

In 1836 steam-powered coining presses were introduced at the Mint, and the new design of the half dollar this year, the Capped Bust motif of smaller diameter, now with a reeded (instead of lettered) edge, was first produced on such a press in November. The modification was made by Christian Gobrecht, an engraver of outstanding talent who had joined the Mint staff in September 1835. The revised style was produced only in late 1836 and in 1837. Then in 1838, continuing through part of 1839, the same obverse was used in combination with a new style of reverse with the denomination expressed HALF DOL. rather than 50 CENTS as on the 1836 and 1837 types.

In 1839 Gobrecht's Liberty Seated motif made its appearance in the half dollar series, copying the same basic depiction of Miss Liberty used on the obverse of the Gobrecht silver dollar of 1836, but with stars around the border. The reverse continued the perched eagle with the denomination spelled as HALF DOL. The earliest coins of 1839 lacked folds of cloth, called drapery in numismatic nomenclature, at Miss Liberty's elbow. In the same year, Robert Ball Hughes was hired to modify Gobrecht's design, and later issues of 1839, continuing to the end of the series, have drapery. With several other modifications, this style was produced through 1891. Variations within that span include 1853 with arrows at date and rays on the reverse, 1854 and 1855 with arrows (but no rays), the addition of the motto IN GOD WE TRUST on the reverse beginning in 1866, and the use of arrows at the date in 1873 and 1874.

Beginning in early 1862, when the outcome of the Civil War was increasingly uncertain, the public hoarded silver and gold coins, and half dollars as well as other pieces disappeared from circulation. Soon a flood of substitutes replaced these coins, including Fractional Currency notes, scrip, Civil War tokens, tickets, and encased postage stamps. Half dollars and other coins and precious metals were available but not at face value in terms of Legal Tender paper money or other bills. Instead, they could be obtained only at a premium through bullion and exchange dealers and banks. Daily quotations were posted as to their value. The exception was the West Coast where paper money was not in use, and throughout this period, half dollars circulated in the region extensively, at par, as did other silver and gold coins.

Although it was hoped that "specie payments" (the term for paying silver and gold coins at par) would be resumed by banks in the East and Midwest after the Civil War, this did not happen. There was so much paper money in circulation, and so much uncertainty as to the solidity of the financial and economic structure, that silver and gold remained at a premium. It was not until April 20, 1876, that silver and paper were again exchangeable at par (and not until December 17, 1878, that gold coins achieved parity). After 1876 silver coins became abundant in the marketplace, and the public, realizing that there was no particular reason to keep hoarding pieces set aside years earlier, turned loose all sorts of early issues, glutting the market. Because of this, mintages of new half dollars dropped sharply in 1879 and remained generally low throughout the rest of the Liberty Seated series.

In 1892 the silver dime, quarter, and half dollar were redesigned by Charles E. Barber. Half dollars of his Liberty Head motif, called "Barber" halves today, were made from that point through 1915. None of his silver coins were particularly popular with either the public or the numismatic community, and many complaints arose. As a result, such pieces were not widely collected in their own time, except for Proofs that were methodically produced each year for numismatic sale. The result is that today many Barber half dollars of relatively high mintages are exceedingly rare in choice and gem Mint State. The entire series is avidly collected now.

In 1913 the New York Numismatic Club, a particularly active organization, became involved in a strong effort to improve the silver coinage, and were soon joined by others in the membership of the American Numismatic Association and elsewhere. Petitions were made to Washington, suggesting that the dime, quarter, and half dollar should be completely redone, to match what had been accomplished on other denominations. By 1913 the Lincoln cent had replaced the Indian Head cent, the Buffalo or Indian Head nickel replaced the Liberty Head nickel, and there were new designs in the gold denominations. These numismatic efforts proved fruitful, and in 1916 new motifs made their debut in the dime, quarter, and half dollar series. For the latter, Adolph A. Weinman, who also created the Winged Liberty Head or "Mercury" dime, created what we now call the Liberty Walking half dollar. Coins of this design were struck from 1916 through and including 1947 but not in all years. The motif proved difficult to strike, with the result that the majority displayed weakness in the higher areas of Miss Liberty on the obverse.

In 1948 Chief Engraver John R. Sinnock created the Franklin half dollar, modeled from a bust by Jean Antoine Houdon, a coin considered by most people to be rather unprepossessing. The new half dollar attracted scant numismatic notice, perhaps because the Liberty Walking design was so admired. Franklin halves were essentially without respect in the hobby for years thereafter, although some investors did acquire bank-wrapped rolls, most particularly the key issues of 1949 and 1949-S. After a relatively short lifetime for an American coin design, the Franklin half was discontinued in 1964 and replaced by the Kennedy motif. Later, Franklin halves would indeed become *very* popular, as they are today. Collectors discovered that many dates were very common in such grades as MS-63, usually extensively bagmarked, but if with relatively few bagmarks and with the lines in the Liberty bell sharp on the reverse, such pieces could be rarities. Also, it was learned that certain Proofs have the head of Franklin polished in the die, while others have cameo appearance. Accordingly, an entire subculture arose devoted to Franklin half dollars, their study, and enjoyment.

The Kennedy half dollar depicts the martyred president on the obverse and a heraldic eagle on the reverse, the latter derived from the Great Seal of the United States and, of course, having many precedents in coinage.

Half dollars of 1964 were of 90% silver content, then in 1965, of a special clad composition with 80% silver exterior (*overall* silver content, including interior, 40%), through 1970, then of a silverless copper-nickel composition since that time, except for silver Proofs made for collectors from 1992 to date. The popularity of President John F. Kennedy was such that upon the issue of these half dollars in 1964 banks had to ration quantities, and the market value quickly jumped to several dollars each. At the time, a Mint State Kennedy half dollar could easily be sold for $5 in Europe, so great was the demand. As years passed, hundreds of millions of Kennedy half dollars were produced, but relatively few ever appeared in day-to-day circulation and commerce, the same being true now.

In 1976 the Bicentennial reverse was employed together with an obverse dated 1776–1976. The reverse displayed Independence Hall, a rather boring (for want of a better word) use of a design familiar in paper money and elsewhere, including on the commemorative gold quarter eagle of 1926. In general, a plan or front-on view of a building, without foliage or much else, makes a poor coin motif—this is my opinion. Few art awards go to such depictions as the Lincoln Memorial on the 1959 cent, Monticello on the 1938 nickel, or Independence Hall on the Bicentennial half dollar.

Collecting a Type Set of Half Dollars

A type set of half dollars is one of the most satisfying in the American series. The panorama is extensive and ranges from the early Flowing Hair issues of 1794 and 1795 down to the present day. The large size of such pieces makes them convenient to view and enjoy. Among the types, the 1794 and 1795 Flowing Hair half is readily available in circulated grades, rare in Mint State, but at any level is hard to find well struck and without adjustment marks. Most on the market are dated 1795. Cherrypicking is advised. Take some time and be choosy.

The next type, the 1796 and 1797 Draped Bust obverse and Small Eagle reverse, is the scarcest in the American silver series excepting the 1839 Gobrecht dollar. However, the latter is available in Proof restrike form, yielding choice and gem examples, so it can be considered in a different category from the circulation-strike 1796 and 1797 half dollar type. It might not be possible to be particular, but if economics permit you to do so, take some time to find a specimen sharply struck on both sides. Needle-sharp striking is more of a theory than a practicality, and as is true with many early types across the American series, some compromise may be necessary.

Half dollars of the 1801 to 1807 type, obverse as above but now with the Heraldic Eagle reverse, are plentiful enough in worn grades but somewhat scarce in Mint State. Striking ranges from average to miserable, seldom needle sharp. Fortunately, there are enough coins in the marketplace that you can take your time on this one. Eventually, you will find a fairly sharp one, and as the majority of buyers know about little other than grading numbers, the premium you need to pay will probably be small. Such are the advantages of being a smart buyer.

Capped Bust half dollars with lettered edge, 1807 to 1836, abound in just about any grade desired. Again, striking is a consideration, and some searching is needed. Generally, those in the late 1820s and the 1830s are better struck than are those of earlier dates, the earlier coins being scarcer and more expensive in any event.

The short-lived type of 1836 and 1837, Capped Bust with reeded edge, denomination spelled as 50 CENTS, is available easily enough through the high-mintage 1837, but most have problems with striking. Again, take your time. Then comes the short-lived 1838 and 1839 type of the same obverse style, reverse modified with a slightly different eagle and with the denomination as HALF DOL. Generally, these are fairly well struck, but again take your time.

Liberty Seated half dollars of the several styles within the series, 1839 to 1891, have no great rarities, save for the 1839 No Drapery in levels of choice Mint State or finer. However, among the earlier types in particular, sharply struck pieces are in the minority. Individual information is given under the respective categories following. Curiously, the most available Mint State Liberty Seated half dollars also are the lowest-mintage issues, the dates 1879 and later!

Barber half dollars of the 1892 to 1915 type were not popular in their time, and while Proofs exist in proportion to their production figures, Mint State coins are quite scarce. In fact, if you opt to build a set of twentieth-century coin designs and demand a Barber half dollar dated 1900 or later, this particular half dollar in Mint State is the scarcest of all silver issues of that century. (As to when a century begins has often been a matter of debate. Strictly speaking, the twentieth century began in the wee hours of the morning on January 1, 1901, but scarcely anyone wanted to wait. Celebrations were held in 1900. In 2000 we all observed the advent of the "new millennium," incorrectly, but happily!) Well-struck choice and gem Barber half dollars are significantly scarcer than generally realized.

Liberty Walking half dollars minted from 1916 to 1947 are plentiful in all grades. Again, some attention should be paid to striking sharpness, at which time the game becomes more intense. Fortunately, there are countless thousands of choice and gem Mint State coins of the 1940s on the market, giving you a wide choice. Then come Franklin half dollars, made only from 1948 to 1963, with a representative coin easy enough to acquire in about any grade desired. Kennedy half dollars then follow, existing in several types, without any problem. Among these and other modern coins, care needs to be taken for value received versus the price paid. If I were building a type set, I would opt to acquire Proof or gem Mint State modern issues in, say, the MS-65 and 66 grades, selected for quality. If I were offered an MS-69 or MS-70 at a high price, based upon a low certified-population figure, I would close my eyes and remember that population figures do not decrease, but increase, and something with "only" 10 pieces certified today might have 100 certified ten years from now. This has happened so often and so many people have been disappointed that it is well worth noting. I have explained many times that "rare" certified coins can become common—true, but a seeming paradox, for few can understand that rare coins can multiply like rabbits. The coins don't change at all in their availability. It is just that more and more move into certified holders, and encapsulated coins become more common, while in precise quantities, fewer non-certified coins are around. Of course, if you love numbers more than anything else, then spend your money on ultra-high grades. The only problem is that unless you have a lot of money, you might not have any left over to buy something such as, for example, a nice Uncirculated Capped Bust or Barber half dollar!

Beyond a Type Set

Collecting half dollars by date and variety has been pursued by many people over the years, and I have quite a few fine memories in this regard. Except for the series of copper cents, half dollars are the most generally available early American coins over a nearly continuous span, making them possible to collect for reasonable cost. Also, enough die varieties exist that these can form another focus of interest and importance.

Among rarities in the early years, the 1796 and 1797 Draped Bust obverse and Small Eagle reverse half dollars are perhaps the most famous, needed for variety collections as well as one example for a type set. Variety enthusiasts aspire to get two of 1796, one with 15 stars on the obverse and the other with 16 stars, plus the 1797. No matter what the grades might be, three varieties in a single collection produce excitement.

Draped Bust half dollars from 1801 through 1807 have a number of rare die varieties (as listed by Overton), but the basic varieties as enumerated in *A Guide Book of United States Coins* are easy enough to find. The 1805, 5 Over 4, overdate is particularly popular, as there was no "perfect date" 1804, and this is the closest one can come to it. Once, dealer B. Max Mehl proclaimed that he had found one. But, alas! It was an 1805, 5 Over 4, with the 5 tooled away.

One of the most vast and interesting playgrounds in early American numismatics is the field of Capped Bust half dollars 1807 to 1836, the style with lettered edge. Several hundred different die combinations exist, and many collectors are active in their pursuit, using the Overton book as a road map. Apart from that, certain of the major varieties—just the tip of the iceberg—can be found listed in the *Red Book.* All are readily collectible except the 1817, 7 Over 4, overdate, of which only about a half dozen exist. The 1815, 5 Over 2, is considered to be the key issue among the specific dates (rather than varieties of dates). The majority of these occur in VF grade, not often lower and not often higher either—a rather curious situation. During the 1820s, vast quantities of these were transferred among banks, with the Second Bank of the United States, headquartered in Philadelphia but with many branches, holding large amounts (presumably, but reports of the bank are not specific). While many if not most of the *Red Book* varieties can be obtained in Mint State, most collectors opt for VF or EF, these grades showing the necessary details but also permitting a budget to be stretched to include more varieties, rather than just a few high-grade pieces. Choice and gem examples can be found here and there, and are most plentiful among the later dates.

Among the Capped Bust half dollars of reduced size, 1836 and 1837, with reeded edge, the 1836 is a key date, and fewer than 5,000 are believed to have been minted. The next type, 1838 and 1839, Capped Bust, reeded edge, with modified eagle on the reverse, includes the famous 1838-O rarity, of which only 20 are said to have been struck. These have a prooflike surface. Interestingly, they were not struck until 1839. In the same year, 1839-O half dollars were also struck, to the extensive quantity of 178,976 pieces, popular to collect today as the mintmark is on the obverse, an unusual placement for the era.

The series of Liberty Seated half dollars from 1839 through 1891 is generally collected by varieties listed in the *Red Book*, although certain dedicated specialists will consult *The Complete Guide to Liberty Seated Half Dollars*, by Randy Wiley and Bill Bugert—a volume that delineates many interesting features, including the number of different reeds on the edges of certain coins.

Among Liberty Seated half dollars, there is just one "impossible" rarity, that being the 1853-O without arrows at the date. Only three exist, and each shows extensive wear. Half dollars were first struck at the San Francisco Mint in 1855 and at the Carson City Mint in 1870. Generally, large quantities of most dates and mintmark varieties of Liberty Seated half dollars were minted, making them readily obtainable today. Except for the later dates, 1879 to 1891, Mint State pieces are generally scarce, gems especially so.

Proof Liberty Seated halves can be collected by date sequence from 1858 onward. Survivors exist in proportion to the mintage quantities. Generally, those before the mid-1870s often come cleaned or hairlined, and more effort is needed in selecting choice specimens than is necessary for the later dates.

Barber half dollars were made continuously from 1892 through 1915, in sufficient quantities that today there are no great rarities. However, a number of issues are quite scarce, even in well-worn grades, and in choice Mint State many are indeed difficult to find. These coins had little honor in the era in which they were issued, and few numismatists saved them.

Proofs were made each year from 1892 to 1915 and can be obtained in proportion to their mintages. However, those of 1914 and 1915 are hard to find choice, for decades ago a Virginia gentleman decided to hoard these two dates, and while doing so polished them to make them "bright." Actually, when chastised for this, he said that his secretary cleaned the coins without his permission.

Liberty Walking half dollars of 1916 through 1947 are popular to collect by date and mint. Scarce varieties include the 1917-S with obverse mintmark, the three issues of 1921, and the low-mintage 1938-D, although the last is not particularly expensive. Uncirculated or Mint State pieces are most available for 1916 and 1917, and then especially so in the 1930s and 1940s. Striking can be a big problem, particularly for issues of the mid-1920s and also the later varieties. Among later coins, the 1940-S and 1941-S are often weakly struck. As certified holders do not take note of such things, opportunities abound for cherrypicking. A commemorative gold version minted in 2016 is not typically included in a type set.

Franklin half dollars minted from 1948 through 1963 have been very popular in recent decades. The complete series of dates and mintmarks is rather short and contains no scarce or rare pieces in grades such as MS-63 and MS-64. Add the element of sharp striking, usually defined as Full Bell Lines (FBL) on the reverse, and certain otherwise common dates become elusive. Proofs can also be collected of the years from 1950 to 1963.

Kennedy half dollars are easily enough collected, and so many have been made by this time that a virtual panorama of dates and mints extends from 1964 to present. My advice on these is to select grades that have a meeting point between a high number such as MS-65 or MS-66 (or equivalent Proofs) and reasonable price. If it were my money, I would not seek ultra grade pieces such as MS-69 or MS-70, as these are apt to cost a lot of money (and, besides, low population numbers will continue to expand over the years as more are certified). Rather, I would use the extra money to collect Franklin half dollars or Liberty Walking issues, or to otherwise expand my horizons. Note that special anniversary versions were struck in 2014; these are not considered necessary additions to a type set.

Flowing Hair (1794–1795)

Circulation-Strike Mintage: 323,144

Field Population: Circulated, 3,500 to 6,000; Mint State, 90 to 110

Designer: Robert Scot. **Weight:** 13.48 grams. **Composition:** .8924 silver, .1076 copper. **Diameter:** Approximately 32.5 mm. **Edge:** FIFTY CENTS OR HALF A DOLLAR with decorations between the words. **Mint:** Philadelphia.

Key to Collecting: Most pieces of this type are dated 1795, although the 1794 is not in the class of great rarities. The design is attractive, and a carefully selected VF or EF piece can be a pleasure to own. Probably 3,500 to 6,000 circulated coins exist. Typical grades are G to F or so. EF and AU grades are elusive in regard to the total population.

Mint State coins are rare. Probably about 100 coins exist at this level, the vast preponderance being of the 1795 date, with just three or four legitimate Mint State 1794's in the picture.[14] Nearly all are in lower Mint State grades. In addition, some AU coins have "graduated" to be called Mint State. However, in relation to the great demand for these pieces, they are quite difficult to obtain, and the appearance of a choice one is an important numismatic event. Finding a really choice example—a decent strike and without adjustment marks or areas of weakness—is a great challenge for this issue. Connoisseurship will pay its rewards, while your competitors will likely be satisfied with ordinary pieces.

Aspects of Striking and Appearance: Many have problems of one sort or another, often severe, including adjustment marks from filing the planchet, and/or light striking in some areas, most particularly the breast of the eagle. Some have mushy, indistinct, or defective rims. Much more so than for the lower-denomination half dime or the higher-denomination silver dollar, a really nice Flowing Hair half dollar is hard to find. It may not be possible to find a needle-sharp example, but with some extensive searching a fairly decent strike can be obtained. In summary, a sharply struck coin is a goal, not necessarily a reality.

Market Value: Circulation Strikes

AG-3	G-4	VG-8	F-12	VF-20	EF-40	AU-50
$650	$1,100	$1,500	$2,750	$3,900	$11,000	$17,500

AU-55	AU-58	MS-60	MS-62	MS-63	MS-64
$21,000	$23,500	$45,000	$62,500	$95,000	$250,000

Retail Price Trends

Year	G-4	F-12	MS-63
1946	$12.50	$20	$150
1950	$7.50	$18.50	$140
1960	$25	$55	$250
1970	$135	$275	$3,000
1980	$285	$525	$10,000
1990	$425	$700	$10,000
2000	$400	$900	$40,000
2010	$1,000	$3,000	$100,000
2019	$1,100	$2,750	$95,000

Draped Bust, Small Eagle Reverse (1796–1797)

Circulation-Strike Mintage: 3,918

Field Population: Circulated, 200 to 300; Mint State, 20 to 25

Designer: Robert Scot. **Weight:** 13.48 grams. **Composition:** .8924 silver, .1076 copper. **Diameter:** Approximately 32.5 mm. **Edge:** FIFTY CENTS OR HALF A DOLLAR with decorations between words. **Mint:** Philadelphia.

Key to Collecting: Among design types of United States silver coins made in circulation-strike format (not Proof finish) this is the Holy Grail, the rarest by far. At the time, most depositors of silver requested dollars, and during this two-year period only 3,918 half dollars were struck. As there was no numismatic interest in them in America, nearly all slipped into circulation and became worn. Most are in grades from well worn to F or VF, some of the latter being generously graded (and equal to simply F of a few decades ago). EF and AU coins are very rare. Some are porous and grainy; avoid these. The total population of this type is only in the hundreds of coins—not many when you consider the demand for them. Relatively few high-grade examples have survived. Mint State coins are exceedingly rare, with fewer than two dozen examples in existence, nearly all of which are dated 1796. Some of 1796 have prooflike surfaces. Due to the great value of such pieces, overgrading and wishful thinking enter into the assigning of numbers. Buy with care, and be sure that a coin is pleasing to your eye.

Aspects of Striking and Appearance: Most specimens are fairly well struck, at least at quick glance. The rarity of this type comes into play, and life is too short to wait for a needle-sharp example. Select one that has decent striking of the features, including star centers, hair of Miss Liberty, and details on the eagle. In summary, a sharply struck coin is a goal, not necessarily a reality. Beyond that, many have Mint-caused planchet-adjustment marks.

Market Value: Circulation Strikes

AG-3	G-4	VG-8	F-12	VF-20	EF-40	AU-50
$23,000	$35,000	$43,500	$52,000	$75,000	$125,000	$165,000

AU-55	AU-58	MS-60	MS-62	MS-63	MS-64
$195,000	$235,000	$290,000	$325,000	$375,000	$500,000

Retail Price Trends

Year	G-4	F-12	MS-63
1946	$125	$200	$800
1950	$135	$225	$900
1960	$235	$485	$1,500
1970	$1,400	$3,500	$30,000
1980	$3,250	$6,500	$50,000
1990	$10,000	$16,500	$90,000
2000	$9,000	$17,000	$150,000
2010	$32,000	$50,000	$400,000
2019	$35,000	$52,000	$375,000

Draped Bust, Heraldic Eagle Reverse (1801–1807)

Circulation-Strike Mintage: 1,600,787

Field Population: Circulated, 10,000 to 14,000; Mint State, 800 to 1,100

Designer: Robert Scot. **Weight:** 13.48 grams. **Composition:** .8924 silver, .1076 copper. **Diameter:** Approximately 32.5 mm. **Edge:** FIFTY CENTS OR HALF A DOLLAR with decorations between words. **Mint:** Philadelphia.

Key to Collecting: Half dollars of this type increase in their general availability from the earlier years, 1801 (rare) and 1802 (very scarce), to 1807, those of 1806 and 1807 being most often seen. Circulated examples abound in various grades, with VF being typical. Although examples are available in just about any grade desired through low Mint State (MS-60 to MS-62), striking details are often weak, and a good amount of enjoyable scouting is needed! Of course, if you don't care, you can buy one in an instant. However, if you are particular, as I hope you will be, this "common" type may take you a long time to acquire. Across much of American numismatics, what used to be AU a generation ago has "graduated" to Mint State, giving great impetus to the resubmission process through the grading services. Choice and gem pieces are rare, and if sharply struck are exceedingly rare.

Aspects of Striking and Appearance: Most show areas of light striking. The most obvious points are the stars on the obverse, the stars above the eagle on the reverse, and also on the reverse the clouds, the details of the shield, and the eagle's wings. However, *all* areas of the coin should be checked, including the denticles. For half dollars of this type, there is no known instance in which pieces were carefully struck either for presentation to dignitaries or for sale to collectors. Such pieces were made on a hand-powered press and struck in a manner to produce as many pieces as quickly as possible. Many have Mint-caused planchet-adjustment marks, a major problem with all early halves through and including this type. In summary, a sharply struck coin is a goal, not necessarily a reality.

Market Value: Circulation Strikes

G-4	VG-8	F-12	VF-20	EF-40	AU-50	AU-55	MS-60	MS-62	MS-63	MS-64
$225	$275	$400	$700	$1,750	$4,500	$5,750	$9,500	$11,000	$20,000	$30,000

Retail Price Trends

Year	G-4	F-12	MS-63
1946	$2	$3	$15
1950	$2.50	$3.50	$22.50
1960	$7.50	$15	$85
1970	$30	$65	$700
1980	$50	$90	$2,000

Year	G-4	F-12	MS-63
1990	$70	$150	$4,000
2000	$125	$200	$10,000
2010	$215	$325	$18,000
2019	$225	$400	$20,000

Capped Bust, Lettered Edge (1807–1836)

Circulation-Strike Mintage: 82,339,124

Proof Mintage: *200–300*

Field Population: Circulated, more than 1,000,000; Mint State, 50,000 to 75,000; Proof, 120 to 160

Designer: John Reich. **Weight:** 13.48 grams. **Composition:** .8924 silver, .1076 copper. **Diameter:** Approximately 32.5 mm. **Edge:** ***1807–1814:*** FIFTY CENTS OR HALF A DOLLAR; ***1814–1831:*** Star added between DOLLAR and FIFTY; ***1832–1836:*** Vertical lines added between words. **Mint:** Philadelphia.

Key to Collecting: Capped Bust half dollars of the 1807 to 1836 years were made in large quantities and today are very easily obtained in nearly any grade, particularly VF through Mint State, the latter very plentiful in the context of early American coinage.

Aspects of Striking and Appearance: Capped Bust half dollars of this era were made quickly. Often, dies were continued in use after they had become worn or "grainy." Quality often suffered. There are quite a few sharply struck coins around, but for every one that is needle-sharp in all points, there are multiples that are not. On the obverse, check the hair details, the star centers, and the denticles. On the reverse, check the eagle, the letters, the motto E PLURIBUS UNUM (the ribbon is often soft in places), and the denticles.

Proof Coins: Proof coins were struck in limited numbers for presentation purposes and for distribution to numismatists. Insist on a coin with deep and full (not partial) mirror surfaces, well struck, and with good contrast. Avoid deeply toned pieces (deep toning often masks the true nature of a coin). *Many* pieces attributed as "Proofs" over the years are not Proofs, in my opinion.

Market Value: Circulation Strikes

G-4	F-12	VF-20	EF-40	AU-50	AU-55	MS-60	MS-62	MS-63	MS-64	MS-65
$60	$80	$110	$180	$375	$500	$1,100	$1,400	$2,000	$3,500	$9,000

Market Value: Proof Strikes

PF-63	PF-64	PF-65
$40,000	$60,000	$75,000

Retail Price Trends

Year	F-12	EF-40	MS-64
1946	$1.50	$2.50	$4.75
1950	$1.50	$3	$5.75
1960	$3.25	$8	$14
1970	$9	$22	$400
1980	$25	$45	$1,000
1990	$37.50	$100	$1,500
2000	$40	$90	$2,000
2010	$80	$175	$3,400
2019	$80	$180	$3,500

Capped Bust, Reeded Edge, 50 CENTS (1836–1837)

Circulation-Strike Mintage: 3,631,020

Proof Mintage: Fewer than 40, mostly dated 1836

Field Population: 20,000 to 30,000; Mint State, 1,500 to 2,500; Proof, 18 to 25

Designer: Christian Gobrecht, modifying John Reich's design. **Weight:** 13.36 grams. **Composition:** .900 silver, .100 copper. **Diameter:** 30 mm. **Edge:** Reeded. **Mint:** Philadelphia.

Key to Collecting: In 1836 relatively few half dollars of this type were made, a number believed to be below 5,000. Then, in 1837, the mintage was an impressive 3,629,820. For type-set purposes, an example of the latter date is the most feasible.

Aspects of Striking and Appearance: The striking of this type is usually quite good, but there are exceptions. Points to check include in particular the stars on the obverse and the details of the eagle on the reverse, after which you can check the hair details of Miss Liberty, the lettering on the reverse, and the denticles. It has been my experience that pieces dated 1836, considered to be rarities, are usually quite well struck, but those dated 1837 can be rather casually made. Extensive cherrypicking will be needed.

Proof Coins: Proofs are occasionally encountered of the year 1836 and are quite rare. Authentic Proofs of 1837 exist but for all practical purposes are unobtainable.

Market Value: Circulation Strikes

G-4	VG-8	F-12	VF-20	EF-40	AU-50	AU-55	MS-60	MS-62	MS-63	MS-64	MS-65
$65	$85	$100	$125	$220	$450	$625	$1,150	$1,500	$2,750	$5,500	$17,500

Market Value: Proof Strikes

PF-60	PF-63	PF-64	PF-65
$30,000	$45,000	$65,000	$90,000

Retail Price Trends

Year	F-12	EF-40	MS-64
1946	$2.50	$3.50	$8
1950	$2.50	$4	$9
1960	$10	$30	$55
1970	$30	$65	$700
1980	$50	$150	$1,000
1990	$45	$150	$3,500
2000	$45	$175	$4,000
2010	$95	$190	$5,500
2019	$100	$220	$5,500

Capped Bust, Reeded Edge, HALF DOL. (1838–1839)

Circulation-Strike Mintage: 5,117,972

Proof Mintage: Fewer than 40, including nearly 20 of the 1838-O

Field Population: Circulated, 22,000 to 32,000; Mint State, 1,000 to 2,000; Proof, 24 to 28

Designer: Christian Gobrecht, modifying John Reich's design. **Weight:** 13.36 grams. **Composition:** .900 silver, .100 copper. **Diameter:** 30 mm. **Edge:** Reeded. **Mint:** Philadelphia.

Key to Collecting: As a class, half dollars of the type with obverse as above, but with restyled reverse, are scarcer in high grades than of the previous type, although the mintages of the new type were higher. Often there is no accounting for what seems to be logic! Specimens are available in just about any grade desired, VF upwards, and in circulated pieces, usually dated 1838, the largest mintage of this short-lived type. Choice and gem pieces are in the distinct minority. The ever-popular 1839-O with obverse mintmark is a possibility for a type set, but is more expensive than, say, a Philadelphia issue of 1838 or 1839. Select with care.

Aspects of Striking and Appearance: Generally the striking of this type is better than on that of the 1836 and 1837 Reeded Edge style, but still care is needed. Check the obverse hair details, stars, and denticles, and on the reverse, the eagle and denticles.

Proof Coins: A few exist, but for all practical purposes they are unobtainable. The 1838-O rarity is generally seen in Proof format.

Market Value: Circulation Strikes

G-4	VG-8	F-12	VF-20	EF-40	AU-50	AU-55	MS-60	MS-62	MS-63	MS-64	MS-65
$65	$85	$100	$125	$220	$450	$675	$1,150	$1,500	$2,750	$4,500	$18,000

Market Value: Proof Strikes

PF-60	PF-63	PF-64	PF-65
$30,000	$45,000	$65,000	$90,000

Retail Price Trends

Year	F-12	EF-40	MS-64
1946	$2.50	$3.50	$7.50
1950	$2.50	$4.50	$9
1960	$10	$30	$50
1970	$30	$65	$700
1980	$50	$150	$1,000

Year	F-12	EF-40	MS-64
1990	$50	$175	$4,000
2000	$50	$185	$4,000
2010	$90	$190	$4,250
2019	$100	$220	$4,500

Liberty Seated, No Motto Above Eagle, No Drapery (1839)

Circulation-Strike Mintage: *600,000*

Proof Mintage: Not recorded

Field Population: Circulated, 2,000 to 3,500; Mint State, 75 to 125; Proof, 1 or 2

Designer: Christian Gobrecht. **Weight:** 13.36 grams. **Composition:** .900 silver, .100 copper. **Diameter:** 30.6 mm. **Edge:** Reeded. **Mint:** Philadelphia.

Key to Collecting: The earliest Liberty Seated half dollars of 1839, comprising an estimated 600,000 pieces (about a third of the total mintage of 1,972,400), lack drapery at Miss Liberty's elbow. In that year, Robert Ball Hughes modified Gobrecht's design by adding this feature, which was continued for the rest of the series. Among other Liberty Seated silver coins, the half dime, dime, and quarter each exist with and without drapery, while the Liberty Seated dollar with perched eagle reverse, introduced in 1840, began with the modified with-drapery style. Today, circulated examples of the 1839 No Drapery half dollar are slightly scarce, but in lower grades, the prices are inexpensive. Mint State pieces are rare. In quite a few years of buying, selling, and auctioning major collections, I have only seen a few choice or finer Mint State pieces.

Aspects of Striking and Appearance: Points to check include the high areas of Miss Liberty, the details of her head, and the stars on the obverse, these usually being fairly sharp. On the reverse, the eagle is often slightly weak at the lower left.

Proof Coins: For all practical purposes Proofs are unobtainable. Perhaps one or two are known today.

Market Value: Circulation Strikes

G-4	VG-8	F-12	VF-20	EF-40	AU-50	AU-55	MS-60	MS-63	MS-64	MS-65
$45	$145	$400	$650	$1,400	$2,000	$4,000	$6,500	$27,500	$55,000	$150,000

Market Value: Proof Strikes

PF-60	PF-63	PF-64	PF-65
$100,000	$135,000	$180,000	$250,000

Retail Price Trends

Year	F-12	EF-40	MS-64
1946	$12	$18	$35
1950	$7.50	$16	$35
1960	$35	$80	$135
1970	$60	$150	$300
1980	$80	$325	$800

Year	F-12	EF-40	MS-64
1990	$80	$600	$15,000
2000	$100	$600	$25,000
2010	$200	$750	$57,000
2019	$400	$1,400	$55,000

Liberty Seated, No Motto Above Eagle, Drapery (1839–1853; 1856–1866)

Circulation-Strike Mintage: 76,238,285 (less an estimated 600,000 for 1839, No Drapery)

Proof Mintage: Fewer than 5,500

Field Population: Circulated, 400,000 to 600,000; Mint State, 10,000 to 20,000; Proof, 3,400 to 4,200

Designer: Christian Gobrecht. **Weight:** ***1839–1853:*** 13.36 grams; ***1856–1866:*** 12.44. **Composition:** .900 silver, .100 copper. **Diameter:** 30.6 mm. **Edge:** Reeded. **Mints:** Philadelphia, New Orleans.

Key to Collecting: Examples can be acquired with no difficulty (note that the 1853 and the 1854 and 1855 are considered to be separate types, and are thus excluded from the present category). Most half dollars of this design are available in proportion to their mintage quantities. The earlier dates are scarcer in higher grades. Many Mint State pieces exist. Those in the 1850s and very early 1860s are most often seen.

Aspects of Striking and Appearance: Striking can be a problem and varies from year to year and die combination to die combination but, as always, this contributes to the appeal of seeking a piece that is just right for your collection. Check the high areas of Miss Liberty, the details of her head, and the stars on the obverse. On the reverse, the eagle is often weak, typically at the lower left. The denticles, usually sharp, should be checked as well. New Orleans coins are typically less well struck than are those from Philadelphia or San Francisco.

Proof Coins: Proofs were made of most of the years in this range, with production beginning in a particularly significant way in 1858. Today, Proofs are readily available from this point through 1865. Quality is often lacking, and care should be given when making a purchase.

Market Value: Circulation Strikes

G-4	VG-8	F-12	VF-20	EF-40	AU-50	AU-55	MS-60	MS-62	MS-63	MS-64	MS-65
$50	$75	$100	$140	$250	$350	$450	$600	$750	$1,100	$2,000	$4,800

Market Value: Proof Strikes

PF-60	PF-63	PF-64	PF-65
$750	$1,600	$2,750	$5,000

Retail Price Trends

Year	VF-20	EF-40	MS-65
1946	$2.50	$3	$5.50
1950	$2	$3	$6
1960	$6	$7.50	$14
1970	$12	$40	$600
1980	$30	$60	$1,500
1990	$35	$65	$3,000
2000	$40	$75	$4,000
2010	$90	$100	$6,000
2019	$90	$100	$4,800

Liberty Seated, Arrows at Date, Rays Around Eagle (1853)

Circulation-Strike Mintage: 4,860,708

Proof Mintage: Fewer than 10

Field Population: Circulated, 25,000 to 35,000; Mint State, 1,800 to 2,400; Proof, 4 to 6

Designer: Christian Gobrecht. **Weight:** 12.44 grams. **Composition:** .900 silver, .100 copper. **Diameter:** 30.6 mm. **Edge:** Reeded. **Mints:** Philadelphia, New Orleans.

Key to Collecting: This is one of relatively few single-year types in the American series. Enough were made that examples can be obtained in just about any grade desired, especially the 1853 Philadelphia circulated coins. Many Mint State pieces survive.

Aspects of Striking and Appearance: The mintage of the 1853 half dollar was accomplished quickly, and little attention was paid to striking them sharply. However, as a class, the half dollars of this year are better defined than are the half dimes, dimes, and quarters. Still, check all of the features of Miss Liberty on the obverse, including the head, check the stars, and on the reverse, check the eagle and other details. The quality of luster and strike varies, so cherrypicking is once again advised.

Proof Coins: A few exist, but most "Proofs" seen are actually prooflike circulation strikes, in my opinion.

Market Value: Circulation Strikes

G-4	VG-8	F-12	VF-20	EF-40	AU-50	AU-55	MS-60	MS-62	MS-63	MS-64	MS-65
$50	$75	$100	$140	$300	$600	$800	$1,500	$2,000	$3,500	$5,000	$22,000

Market Value: Proof Strikes

PF-63	PF-64	PF-65
$50,000	$85,000	$150,000

Retail Price Trends

Year	VF-20	EF-40	MS-65
1946	$2.75	$5	$9
1950	$2.75	$6	$11
1960	$8	$25	$52.50
1970	$20	$75	$300
1980	$35	$250	$1,000

Year	VF-20	EF-40	MS-65
1990	$38	$225	$3,000
2000	$38	$225	$5,000
2010	$130	$275	$25,000
2019	$140	$300	$22,000

Liberty Seated, Arrows at Date, No Rays Around Eagle (1854–1855)

Circulation-Strike Mintage: 12,799,450

Proof Mintage: Fewer than 140

Field Population: Circulated, 55,000 to 80,000; Mint State, 1,500 to 2,200; Proof, 60 to 85

Designer: Christian Gobrecht. **Weight:** 12.44 grams. **Composition:** .900 silver, .100 copper. **Diameter:** 30.6 mm. **Edge:** Reeded. **Mints:** Philadelphia, New Orleans, San Francisco.

Key to Collecting: Enough were made that examples are easily enough found today. However, similar to the above, quality can be another matter entirely. Circulated coins are found in proportion to the mintage. Mint State pieces are plentiful for this issue, and a few decades ago it was not particularly unusual to find them in small groups, particularly the 1854-O (the largest mintage of the type). However, by now nearly all such groups have been dispersed, and coins are found one at a time. Select with care.

Aspects of Striking and Appearance: Check all of the features of Miss Liberty on the obverse, including the head; check the stars; and on the reverse, check the eagle and other details.

Proof Coins: Proofs were made, and today not more than a few dozen exist, mostly of the 1854 date. Such pieces are rarities and when encountered should be carefully studied for quality.

Market Value: Circulation Strikes

G-4	VG-8	F-12	VF-20	EF-40	AU-50	AU-55	MS-60	MS-62	MS-63	MS-64	MS-65
$50	$75	$100	$140	$200	$350	$450	$650	$1,000	$1,500	$2,400	$7,500

Market Value: Proof Strikes

PF-60	PF-63	PF-64	PF-65
$7,500	$12,500	$21,500	$35,000

Retail Price Trends

Year	VF-20	EF-40	MS-65	PF-65
1946	$1	$2	$4	$70
1950	$1.25	$3	$5	$95
1960	$5	$12	$25	$525
1970	$8.50	$50	$400	$3,000
1980	$22	$80	$1,000	$9,000

Year	VF-20	EF-40	MS-65	PF-65
1990	$35	$90	$2,500	$12,000
2000	$35	$90	$3,500	$20,000
2010	$115	$125	$9,000	$37,500
2019	$140	$200	$7,500	$35,000

Liberty Seated, Motto Above Eagle (1866–1873; 1875–1891)

Circulation-Strike Mintage: 56,247,068

Proof Mintage: 20,923

Field Population: Circulated, many hundreds of thousands; Mint State, 15,000 to 25,000; Proof, 15,000 to 18,000

Designer: Christian Gobrecht, with motto added by James B. Longacre or someone else on Mint staff. **Weight:** ***1866–1873:*** 12.44 grams; ***1875–1891:*** 12.5 grams. **Composition:** .900 silver, .100 copper. **Diameter:** 30.6 mm. **Edge:** Reeded. **Mints:** Philadelphia, San Francisco, Carson City.

Key to Collecting: Now, at long last, finding a well-struck Liberty Seated half dollar with good eye appeal will not be much of a problem! The mintage quantities were greatest for the years 1866 through 1878, and today among *worn* specimens these are the most often seen. Later issues, 1879 through 1891, were made in small quantities as there was no call for such pieces in commerce. Mint State coins are quite plentiful, mostly dated during the low-mintage years beginning in 1879, an interesting situation that has a parallel among gold dollars and $3 pieces.

Aspects of Striking and Appearance: Generally, the striking of this type is fairly good. Still, the same usual points should be checked: the details of Miss Liberty (including the head) on the obverse, the stars, and on the reverse, check the eagle.

Proof Coins: Proofs were made of each year and exist in proportion to their mintage figures. Generally, those of the 1880s are choicer than those of earlier years.

Market Value: Circulation Strikes

G-4	VG-8	F-12	VF-20	EF-40	AU-50	AU-55	MS-60	MS-62	MS-63	MS-64	MS-65
$40	$45	$65	$80	$100	$225	$250	$475	$600	$800	$1,250	$3,000

Market Value: Proof Strikes

PF-60	PF-63	PF-64	PF-65
$600	$1,150	$1,600	$2,700

Retail Price Trends

Year	VF-20	EF-40	MS-65	PF-65
1946	$2	$2.75	$5	$12
1950	$2.50	$3	$6	$20
1960	$7	$9	$18	$60
1970	$11	$70	$600	$400
1980	$30	$55	$1,000	$1,200
1990	$30	$60	$1,500	$2,000
2000	$40	$65	$2,500	$2,400
2010	$60	$85	$3,000	$2,900
2019	$80	$100	$3,000	$2,700

Liberty Seated, Motto Above Eagle, Arrows at Date (1873–1874)

Circulation-Strike Mintage: 5,070,310

Proof Mintage: 1,250

Field Population: Circulated, 20,000 to 30,000; Mint State, 1,800 to 2,800; Proof, 900 to 1,100

Designer: Christian Gobrecht, as modified by James B. Longacre or another staff member, with the arrows added during the chief engravership of William Barber. **Weight:** 12.5 grams. **Composition:** .900 silver, .100 copper. **Diameter:** 30.6 mm. **Edge:** Reeded. **Mints:** Philadelphia, San Francisco, Carson City.

Key to Collecting: Circulated coins are available, often dated 1874 (the highest mintage), and in nearly any grade desired through lower Mint State levels. Today, choice Mint State coins are quite scarce, as the mintage, although about five million, was much smaller than preceding and later (especially) without-arrows coins. At the gem category, such coins are very rare but not as rare as quarter dollars of this type.

Aspects of Striking and Appearance: Points to check include the details of Miss Liberty, the obverse stars, and the eagle on the reverse. Many are casually struck, but some are sharp. It will pay to be particular.

Proof Coins: Probably 75% or more of the mintage of 1,250 pieces survive.

Market Value: Circulation Strikes

G-4	VG-8	F-12	VF-20	EF-40	AU-50	AU-55	MS-60	MS-62	MS-63	MS-64	MS-65
$50	$60	$75	$150	$300	$475	$600	$950	$1,250	$1,800	$3,000	$15,000

Market Value: Proof Strikes

PF-60	PF-63	PF-64	PF-65
$1,000	$2,200	$3,500	$9,000

Retail Price Trends

Year	VF-20	EF-40	MS-65	PF-65
1946	$2	$2.75	$5	$12
1950	$2.50	$3	$6	$20
1960	$7	$9	$18	$60
1970	$11	$70	$600	$400
1980	$30	$55	$4,000	$1,200
1990	$30	$60	$2,000	$3,000
2000	$40	$65	$7,500	$4,500
2010	$110	$275	$15,000	$10,500
2019	$150	$300	$15,000	$9,000

Barber or Liberty Head (1892–1915)

Circulation-Strike Mintage: 135,898,889

Proof Mintage: 17,313

Field Population: Circulated, several million; Mint State, 25,000 to 40,000; Proof, 12,000 to 14,000

Designer: Charles E. Barber. **Weight:** 12.5 grams.
Composition: .900 silver, .100 copper. **Diameter:** 30.6 mm.
Edge: Reeded. **Mints:** Philadelphia, Denver, New Orleans, San Francisco.

Key to Collecting: For a twentieth-century type set a choice or gem Mint State Barber half dollar is the rarest issue outside of the gold series. Today, among circulation-strike Barber half dollars probably 90% or more in existence are G-4 or below, a curious situation repeated in the dime and quarter dollar series. Completing a set of Barber half dollars in VF, EF, or AU grade might well take a year or more to do! Mint State half dollars of this type are quite scarce, this being especially true of the mint-marked issues. Choice and gem coins are usually of Philadelphia Mint varieties or, if of branch mints, dated after 1905. In the entire history of American numismatics, no one has ever assembled a full gem set of well-struck Barber half dollars.

Aspects of Striking and Appearance: The obverse does not usually present a problem, although the higher hair details and star centers should be checked. The reverses of most Barber half dollars are fairly well struck except for the lower right area of the eagle, including the leg and talons. The upper right area of the shield and nearby wing can also be weak. The denticles are usually sharp on the obverse and reverse.

Proof Coins: Proofs exist in proportion to their mintages. Choicer examples tend to be of later dates, except for 1914 and 1915, which are often cleaned and hairlined. Most are sharply struck. The Proofs of 1892 to 1901 usually have cameo contrast between the designs and the mirror fields.

Market Value: Circulation Strikes

G-4	VG-8	F-12	VF-20	EF-40	AU-50	AU-55	MS-60	MS-62	MS-63	MS-64	MS-65
$16	$17	$45	$95	$200	$375	$400	$550	$650	$850	$1,150	$2,000

Market Value: Proof Strikes

PF-60	PF-63	PF-64	PF-65
$525	$1,100	$1,400	$2,250

Retail Price Trends

Year	VF-20	EF-40	MS-65	PF-65
1946	$2	$2.75	$5.50	$12
1950	$2	$3	$6	$14
1960	$3.50	$4.75	$22.50	$75
1970	$10	$25	$700	$700
1980	$40	$115	$1,900	$1,500

Year	VF-20	EF-40	MS-65	PF-65
1990	$40	$130	$2,000	$2,500
2000	$65	$120	$2,200	$2,500
2010	$80	$125	$2,500	$3,000
2019	$95	$200	$2,000	$2,250

Liberty Walking (1916–1947)

Circulation-Strike Mintage: 485,320,340

Proof Mintage: 74,400

Field Population: Circulated, more than 100,000,000; Mint State, millions; Proof, 60,000 to 68,000

Designer: Adolph A. Weinman. **Weight:** 12.5 grams.
Composition: .900 silver, .100 copper (net weight .36169 oz. pure silver).
Diameter: 30.6 mm. **Edge:** Reeded. **Mints:** Philadelphia, Denver, San Francisco.

Key to Collecting: Today, examples for a type set are plentiful, particularly those in the late 1930s, and especially, the 1940s. Worn pieces abound, but you should opt for a Mint State coin as they are readily available and inexpensive.

Aspects of Striking and Appearance: Finding a certified gem Mint State coin of a particular date/mintmark might be easy, depending on the year, but finding a *sharply struck* coin can be a virtual impossibility. Check the high parts of Miss Liberty's skirt, the details of her cape, the fingers of her hand, and the details of her head. *Very few* examples will pass muster in this regard. The reverse is usually better struck. Luster varies from issue to issue. Most 1916 and many 1917 halves have wide, flat rims and matte-like luster, quite different from that seen on later dates.

Proof Coins: Proofs were made beginning in 1936 and continuing through 1942 and are usually fairly well struck. Most Proofs of 1941 are from over-polished dies with the AW monogram of the designer no longer present.

Market Value: Circulation Strikes

G-4	VG-8	F-12	VF-20	EF-40	AU-50	AU-55
$9	$10	$11	$16	$18	$25	$30

MS-60	MS-62	MS-63	MS-64	MS-65	MS-66
$45	$60	$75	$90	$210	$325

Market Value: Proof Strikes

PF-64	PF-65	PF-66	PF-67
$450	$500	$600	$800

Retail Price Trends

Year	EF-40	MS-65	PF-65
1946	$0.50	$1.25	$3.50
1950	$0.50	$1.25	$3.75
1960	$0.50	$2.50	$15
1970	$1.50	$25	$200
1980	$4.50	$50	$400

Year	EF-40	MS-65	PF-65
1990	$9	$80	$650
2000	$7	$90	$800
2010	$10	$150	$750
2019	$18	$210	$500

Franklin (1948–1963)

Circulation-Strike Mintage: 465,814,455

Proof Mintage: 15,886,955

Field Population: Circulated, more than 100,000,000; Mint State, tens of millions; Proof, 12,000,000 to 14,000,000

Designer: John R. Sinnock. **Weight:** 12.5 grams. **Composition:** .900 silver, .100 copper (net weight .36169 oz. pure silver). **Diameter:** 30.6 mm. **Edge:** Reeded. **Mints:** Philadelphia, Denver, San Francisco.

Key to Collecting: Franklin half dollars made their debut in 1948 without fanfare. Although notice was routinely given of them in the two leading numismatic journals of the day, reaction by collectors was generally unenthusiastic. Perhaps the artistic beauty could not be compared to the now discontinued Liberty Walking motif.

Although many investors set aside bank-wrapped rolls, and many collectors formed sets by date and mint, there was hardly any notice paid to quality within the Mint State range. When such things became important, it was found that the majority of pieces were nicked and marked and that true gems were scarce. Further, the concept of Full Bell Lines was introduced to the collecting fraternity, giving another aspect to the search.

For type-set purposes, enough Franklin half dollars exist that finding one is easy. Circulated pieces are quite common but not relevant for type-set purposes as Mint State and Proof coins are plentiful and inexpensive. However, most Mint State coins are bagmarked, as this design was susceptible to highlighting even the smallest contact, particularly on the center of the obverse and reverse.

Aspects of Striking and Appearance: This design was not sharply defined in the dies. On the reverse, the horizontal lines at the bottom of the bell are sometimes "full" and sometimes not, the latter resulting when the dies were spaced farther apart. Those with sharp features are popularly designated as having Full Bell Lines (FBL). Some dates and mintmarks are common enough with light striking, but with FBL are very rare (in the context of the series). Nicks and bagmarks are a huge problem with Franklin half dollars, as the relatively plain obverse and the high area of the bell on the reverse were exposed and easily acquired contact marks. Pristine mark-free gems are quite elusive.

Proof Coins: Plentiful, as they were made over a fairly long span of years. Most are well struck. Some have cameo frosted devices and are especially sought for this feature.

Market Value: Circulation Strikes

VF-20	EF-40	MS-60	MS-63	MS-64	MS-64FBL
$9	$10	$14	$25	$28	$38
MS-65	**MS-65FBL**	**MS-66**	**MS-66FBL**	**MS-64**	**MS-65**
$32	$90	$85	$215	$1,150	$2,000

Market Value: Proof Strikes

PF-64	PF-65	PF-65Cam	PF-65DC	PF-66
$18	$25	$45	$100	$30

Retail Price Trends

Year	MS-63	MS-65	PF-65
1970	$2	$3	$5
1980	$4.50	$5	$12
1990	$8	$90	$40
2000	$7	$25	$12
2010	$13	$50	$15
2019	$25	$32	$25

Kennedy, Silver (1964; 1992 to Date, Proofs Only; 2014 50th Anniversary)

Circulation-Strike Mintage: Hundreds of millions, still being minted

Proof Mintage: Tens of millions, still being minted

Field Population: Circulated, more than 100,000,000; Mint State, more than 100,000,000; Proof, 3,000,000 to 3,500,000, plus continuing mintage

Designers: ***Obverse:*** Gilroy Roberts; ***Reverse:*** Frank Gasparro. **Weight:** 12.5 grams. **Composition:** .900 silver, .100 copper (net weight .36169 oz. pure silver). Starting in 2019, silver Proofs are .999 fine. **Diameter:** 30.6 mm. **Edge:** Reeded. **Mints:** Philadelphia, Denver, San Francisco, West Point.

Key to Collecting: Following the assassination of President John F. Kennedy on November 22, 1963, his successor in the office, Lyndon B. Johnson, and others, were enthusiastic about memorializing him on the half dollar. This was done, and the Franklin issue was terminated far short of the standard 25-year minimum then in effect for designs of circulating coins (the same thing happened in 1930 when the relatively short-lived Standing Liberty quarter was ended). Kennedy half dollars were immediately popular not only in the United States but all over the world. Vast quantities were hoarded. Only in the first year, when pieces were made at both Philadelphia and Denver, was the .900 fine silver alloy used for general circulation, thus for a long time 1964 was considered to constitute the short-lived type. However, beginning in 1992 at the San Francisco Mint, silver-content Proofs of this style were made for collectors, a surprising continuation of this type. The U.S. Mint marked the 50th year of the Kennedy half dollar in 2014 with silver coins struck as a Proof, a Reverse Proof, an Enhanced Uncirculated strike, and an Uncirculated strike. Circulated examples of 1964 are very common but not relevant for type-set purposes as Mint State and Proof coins are plentiful and inexpensive.

Aspects of Striking and Appearance: Usually quite well struck.

Proof Coins: Plentiful, well struck, and usually attractive. Those of 1964 were struck at the Philadelphia Mint. Silver Proofs from 1992 to date have been struck at the San Francisco Mint. In 1998, a special Matte Proof silver Kennedy half dollar was struck for inclusion in the Robert F. Kennedy commemorative coin set. The Reverse Proof of the 2014 50th Anniversary set was struck at West Point. In 2019 the Mint changed the silver fineness of its Proof dimes, quarters, and half dollars from .900 to .999.

Market Value: Circulation Strikes

MS-60	MS-63	MS-64	MS-65	MS-66	MS-67
$11	$12	$15	$24	$75	$700

Market Value: Proof Strikes

PF-65	PF-67Cam	PF-68DC	PF-69DC
$20	$60	$400	$2,750

Retail Price Trends

Year	MS-63	MS-65	PF-65
1970	$1.25	$1.50	$2
1980	$2.50	$3.50	$5.75
1990	$4	$7	$16
2000	$5	$4	$8
2010	$13	$50	$15
2019	$25	$32	$25

Kennedy, 40% Silver (1965–1970)

Circulation-Strike Mintage: 848,895,006

Proof Mintage: 8,608,947

Field Population: Circulated, hundreds of millions; Mint State, hundreds of millions; Proof, 7,500,000 to 8,250,000

Designers: ***Obverse:*** Gilroy Roberts; ***Reverse:*** Frank Gasparro. **Weight:** 11.5 grams. **Composition:** Outer layers of .800 silver and .200 copper bonded to inner core of .209 silver, .791 copper (net weight .1479 oz. pure silver). **Diameter:** 30.6 mm. **Edge:** Reeded. **Mints:** Philadelphia, Denver, San Francisco.

Key to Collecting: This type is the same as the preceding, except that a different composition was used, consisting of a planchet with an outer layer of 80% silver and 20% copper, bonded to an inner core of 79.1% copper and 20.9% silver. These figures seem a bit odd until the entire coin is considered—the clad exterior as well as the mostly copper interior; taken as a whole, the half dollars of this type are 40% silver and 60% copper. At the time the price of silver was rising rapidly on the international markets, making it unfeasible to use the old 90% silver alloy throughout. Indeed, other previously silver denominations, the dime and the quarter, went completely silverless in 1965. The 40% silver composition endured through 1970. Circulated coins are very common, but not relevant for type-set purposes as Mint State and Proof coins are plentiful and inexpensive.

Aspects of Striking and Appearance: Usually well struck and attractive.

Proof Coins: Plentiful, but made only from 1968 to 1970 for this type, at the San Francisco Mint.

Market Value: Circulation Strikes

MS-63	MS-65	MS-66
$6	$17	$25

Market Value: Proof Strikes

PF-65	PF-67Cam
$8	$90

Retail Price Trends

Year	MS-63	MS-65	PF-65
1970	$0.65	$0.75	$3
1980	$1	$1.75	$3.25
1990	$1	$2.50	$4
2000	$1.50	$1.75	$3
2010	$4	$6	$8
2019	$6	$17	$8

Kennedy, Copper-Nickel (1971 to Date, Including Proofs)

Circulation-Strike Mintage: Hundreds of millions, still being minted

Proof Mintage: Tens of millions, still being minted

Field Population: Circulated, hundreds of millions; Mint State, hundreds of millions; Proof, tens of millions

Designers: ***Obverse:*** Gilroy Roberts; ***Reverse:*** Frank Gasparro. **Weight:** 11.34 grams. **Composition:** Outer layers of copper-nickel (.750 copper, .250 nickel) bonded to inner core of pure copper. **Diameter:** 30.6 mm. **Edge:** Reeded. **Mints:** Philadelphia, Denver, San Francisco.

Key to Collecting: This type, produced in 1971 and continued to the present time with the exception of the 1776-1976 Bicentennial issue, followed suit with other previously silver denominations. The new composition struck up well, and the pieces made were and are quite pleasing to the eye. Circulated examples are as common as can be, but not in general circulation, where the quarter dollar has virtually replaced the half dollar denomination. For type set purposes, choose a Mint State or Proof coin as both are plentiful and inexpensive. Today, a full specialized set of dates and mints, from the first clad Kennedy half to the present, is very impressive and includes well over 100 different varieties. A few die varieties are listed in the *Red Book* and can be added if desired. A special two-coin set released by the U.S. Mint celebrating the 50th anniversary of the design in 2014 led to High Relief versions being struck at Philadelphia and Denver.

In numismatic periodicals as well as on the Internet, there is always a lot of information about current Kennedy halves—their market values, grades, and, less often, the technical aspects of dies. Stay tuned. The panorama of coinage is constantly changing—great news for type-set collectors. Perhaps sometime soon, if not this year then in the next few years, the 1971-to-date Kennedy half dollar type will be replaced with a new design.

Aspects of Striking and Appearance: Usually well struck and attractive.

Proof Coins: Usually well struck and attractive. Some have frosted surfaces.

Market Value: Circulation Strikes

MS-63	MS-65	MS-66	MS-67
$2	$6	$11	$17

Market Value: Proof Strikes

PF-65	PF-67Cam	PF-68DC	PF-69DC
$3	$12	$18	$20

Kennedy, Bicentennial, Copper-Nickel (1776–1976)

Circulation-Strike Mintage: 521,873,248

Proof Mintage: 7,059,099

Field Population: Circulated, hundreds of millions; Mint State, more than 100,000,000; Proof, 6,000,000 to 6,750,000

Designers: ***Obverse:*** Gilroy Roberts; ***Reverse:*** Seth Huntington. **Weight:** 11.34 grams. **Composition:** Outer layers of copper-nickel (.750 copper, .250 nickel) bonded to inner core of pure copper. **Diameter:** 30.6 mm. **Edge:** Reeded. **Mints:** Philadelphia, Denver, San Francisco.

Key to Collecting: For the Bicentennial, a special Kennedy half dollar was made, incorporating the preceding obverse design, but with the curious double date 1776-1976. On the reverse appeared a depiction of Independence Hall in Philadelphia, a rather boring image no more desirable in its appearance than is the virtually identical design used on the reverse of the 1926 Sesquicentennial quarter eagle. Generally speaking, buildings shown on a front-on or plan view, without foliage, people, or other interesting things, are quite boring when used on coins. Witness also Monticello on the 1938 Jefferson nickel and the Lincoln Memorial on the 1959 cent.

Examples are as common as can be, no problem to get one just right for your collection. Circulating coins are plentiful but of no consequence to you, as Mint State pieces are inexpensive.

Aspects of Striking and Appearance: Usually well struck.

Proof Coins: These are as plentiful as the generous mintage indicates.

Market Value: Circulation Strikes

MS-63	MS-65	MS-66	MS-67
$3	$10	$40	$120

Market Value: Proof Strikes

PF-65	PF-67Cam	PF-68DC	PF-69DC
$4	$13	$18	$20

Retail Price Trends

Year	MS-63	MS-65	PF-65
1980	$0.50	$1	$4
1990	$0.75	$1	$1.50
2000	$1	$0.90	$1.50
2010	$1.50	$2.50	$5
2019	$2	$3	$4

Kennedy, Bicentennial, Silver (1776–1976)

Circulation-Strike Mintage: 11,000,000

Proof Mintage: 4,000,000

Field Population: Circulated, several hundred thousand; Mint State, nearly 10,000,000; Proof, 3,400,000 to 3,700,000

Designers: ***Obverse:*** Gilroy Roberts; ***Reverse:*** Seth Huntington. **Weight:** 11.5 grams. **Composition:** Outer layers of .800 silver, .200 copper bonded to inner core of .209 silver, .791 copper (net weight .14792 oz. pure silver). **Diameter:** 30.6 mm. **Edge:** Reeded. **Mints:** Philadelphia, Denver, San Francisco.

Key to Collecting: This type is similar to the preceding Bicentennial issue, except that it is struck on a 40% silver planchet. Mint State pieces were made at Philadelphia, Proofs at San Francisco. Circulated coins are rare, as these were not placed into circulation and not relevant to building a type set. Mint State coins are very common.

Aspects of Striking and Appearance: Usually well struck.

Proof Coins: Common.

Market Value: Circulation Strikes

MS-63	MS-65
$8	$15

Market Value: Proof Strikes

PF-65	PF-67Cam
$12	$20

Retail Price Trends

Year	MS-63	MS-65	PF-65
1980	$2	$3.50	$6
1990	$3	$3	$5.50
2000	$4	$4	$5

Year	MS-63	MS-65	PF-65
2010	$5	$7	$8
2019	$8	$15	$12

18
Silver Dollars
1794-1935

Overview of the Denomination

Today, silver dollars, particularly of the Morgan type (1878 to 1921) and Peace type (1921 to 1935), are among the all time favorites in American numismatics. And well they should be, for they exist by the millions and are often available in choice and gem Mint State for nominal values. However, the earlier era of silver dollars is sprinkled with pieces that are all scarce, some rare, and some virtually impossible to find. Adding to the interest, in the modern era, silver dollars no longer are of silver (except for some special pieces made for collectors), but are of various other alloys.

The Mint Act of April 2, 1792, provided for the largest silver coin, the dollar, to be of 416 grains weight and 892.4 fineness. By that time, the terms *dollar* and *silver dollar* were in wide use, even though there were no federal examples. Omnipresent in the channels of commerce were the most popular international trade coins ever produced—the Spanish milled dollars. Early Continental Currency paper money, issues of the newly formed federal government, were payable in *Spanish milled dollars.* "Milled" meant raised rim, a bit different from what we think of today as a milled coin (as sometimes the term applies to edge reeding). These coins were produced by the countless millions at mints from Mexico extending down through other Spanish possessions in South America. For the maritime trade, they were the coin of choice, as their value was widely known even in the most remote "pepper ports" of the East Indies.

The first silver dollars, of the Flowing Hair design, were struck in November 1794. Of the production run, 1,758 were kept, and many others were returned to the melting pot. The press was too small for such a large-diameter coin, and none struck up well. These and other early dollars, through 1804, had the edge lettered HUNDRED CENTS ONE DOLLAR OR UNIT.

In the summer of 1795, with a new press on hand, the production of dollars resumed, this time in quantity. The Flowing Hair design remained in use until toward the end of the year when the Draped Bust design took its place. During ensuing years, well over a million silver dollars were minted, through a design change to the use of the Heraldic Eagle reverse beginning in 1798. Today, most surviving early dollars are well worn, with VF-20 to

VF-30 being about the norm. These pieces circulated extensively, but, apparently, mostly outside of the United States. In particular, they were in wide use in the Caribbean islands.

In 1804 the Treasury Department took special notice that the majority of United States silver dollars made up to this point had been used in the export trade, particularly to the West Indies (Caribbean), but also to China, the East Indies, and elsewhere. While coins sent to the West Indies often came back to the United States, most sent to China were melted. During the same era, gold coins were also exported, primarily to Europe. Accordingly, although the Philadelphia Mint had been in business since 1792, relatively little in the way of American coins could be seen in circulation except for copper half cents and cents. By 1804, the further coinage of silver dollars seemed to be an exercise in futility, and the mandate was given to cease making them.

It was hoped that the elimination of the silver dollar would force large depositors of silver to request half dollars instead and that these smaller coins would not be used in maritime commerce—for they would appear puny and would be more cumbersome to count than the Spanish milled dollars. Accordingly, half dollars, unlike silver dollars, might become plentiful in domestic commerce. This did happen, and federal silver dollars from the earlier years were scarcely ever seen.

Taking the place of the silver dollar were, of course, half dollars, plus in even greater quantity, paper bills issued by state-chartered banks and others (often, if entrepreneurs wanted to have a bank authorized, and the state would not do it, they would enter banking anyway—the Owl Creek Bank of Mount Vernon, Ohio, being but one of many examples).

In 1835 the Mint desired to plan for resumption of silver dollar coinage, and Christian Gobrecht, hired as second (not assistant) engraver in September of that year, was set to the task. New motifs were used, incorporating a figure of Miss Liberty in a seated position, sketched by well-known artist Thomas Sully, and the reverse with an eagle in flight, after sketches by artist Titian Peale, said to have been based on "Peter," a mascot eagle in residence at the Philadelphia Mint (who had free access to fly to the outside through openings).

Patterns were produced, some with the signature of the engraver, C. GOBRECHT F. (the F standing for *fecit* or "made it"), prominent in the field above the date. Apparently, there was some commotion about this at the time, and the engraver moved his name to a less conspicuous position, on the base of the seated figure (now with an extraneous period added, as C. GOBRECHT. F.). One of the little mysteries in numismatics today is that not a single *original* example of the name-in-field pattern is known to exist. Happily, restrikes were made at the Mint beginning in spring 1859, and examples are available today, although they are rare.

In December 1836 what collectors call "Gobrecht dollars" were made to the extent of 1,000 pieces, all in mirror Proof format. Numismatic historian R.W. Julian estimates that 400 were saved for presentation and for sale to numismatists (what few there were at the time). Two were given to President Andrew Jackson. The other 600 were deposited in a local bank for face value. In early 1837 a further 600 were made under the new weight standard (see the following), with the dies in a different orientation. Most of these reached circulation as well.

Under the Act of January 18, 1837, the authorized weight of the silver dollar was reduced to 412.5 grains, the alloy composed of 90% silver and 10% copper. This standard was continued for the next century. Although additional patterns were struck in the Gobrecht series, only one more variety was produced for circulation, that dated 1839, and differing slightly in design details. Only 300 were made, again with Proof surfaces. Today, restrikes fill the need for examples for a date or type set.

In 1840 silver dollars were produced in quantity for the first time in many years, with 61,005 being made of this date. The obverse motif featured the Liberty Seated design by Gobrecht, with stars and date. The reverse abandoned the Flying Eagle and substituted a perched eagle similar to that used on the quarter and half dollar. This type was continued through 1865, after which the motto IN GOD WE TRUST was added to the reverse, and production continued until 1873.

Although Liberty Seated silver dollars were common in American commerce in the 1840s, the vast influx of gold to the East beginning in 1849 drove up the price of silver, as that particular metal became "rare" in proportion to its historic value relationship with gold. Beginning in 1850, Liberty Seated silver dollars already struck or about to be, contained more than a dollar worth of silver. This situation remained in effect through the succeeding years in the Liberty Seated series. Accordingly, many earlier pieces were melted. New coins required more than face value to make, and thus were not used in commerce. Instead, nearly all were "trade" coins sent to Canton, China, in exchange for merchandise. After their arrival in China, most were sent to India and melted (part of the despised opium trade, well recorded in the literature). Because of this, the mintages of Liberty Seated silver dollars after 1849 have little relationship to their true availability today. The New Orleans, San Francisco, and Carson City mints produced certain Liberty Seated varieties.

On February 28, 1878, the Bland-Allison Act became law, providing for the government to acquire each year millions of ounces worth of silver and convert the metal into dollars. Such coins were not at all needed for commerce, and the legislation was simply a boondoggle to please Western politicians who were responsible to citizens and mining interests. George T. Morgan, an assistant engraver who came to the Mint from England in 1876 and who in 1877 produced a number of illustrious patterns, created the design for the new coin. Called the "Morgan" dollar today, these pieces were made continuously from 1878 through 1904 and again for a short time in 1921.

In 1918 vast quantities of silver dollars, the total comprising 270,232,722 pieces, went to the melting pot. At the time, silver bullion was valuable, and much of it was shipped to India, a country in which the population loved this metal (but generally disdained gold). Then in 1921 there was a hurry-up call for more silver dollars to be minted. None had been struck since 1904. New dies of the Morgan dollar design were hastily made up. As the old hubs and models were no longer on hand, actual *coins* were copied! The result was a loss of detail. In the meantime, Anthony de Francisci, an artist in the private sector, designed the new motif that made its debut in December, called the Peace dollar. The obverse depicted Miss Liberty facing left, wearing a diadem of spikes. The facial portrait is virtually identical to that used by Augustus Saint-Gaudens on his 1907 $10 (modeled after Hettie Anderson), but de Francisci said that it was actually modeled by his wife, Teresa Cafarelli, and others—a composite depiction. The reverse depicted an eagle perched on a rock, facing to the right. Peace dollars were made intermittently through 1935.

COLLECTING A TYPE SET OF SILVER DOLLARS

Forming a type set of *any* denomination admits of personal options, and perhaps nowhere is this more relevant than whether to decide to include the 1839 Gobrecht silver dollar as a special type—or to ignore it. However, let me pursue the discussion in logical order:

The first silver dollar type, of 1794 and 1795 with Flowing Hair, will be easy enough to obtain in grades from VF through low Mint State. Striking usually ranges from rather poor to barely acceptable, and planchet-adjustment marks are often seen. Accordingly, cherrypicking will be needed to find a good example. As always, as an assimilator of information in this book, you will have an inside track in this regard and will be able to make a better buy for your money.

The silver dollar Draped Bust obverse with the Small Eagle reverse was made from 1795 through 1798, with most examples being dated 1796 or 1797. Long-published mintage figures on these two dates, showing the 1797 to be much rarer, are not correct, as today both the 1796 and 1797 exist in about the same numbers. Although mintage figures refer to the quantities produced in the given calendar year, these do not necessarily refer to the dates on the coins themselves. Silver dollars of this type are fairly scarce. Sharpness of strike presents difficulty, and usually there are weaknesses in details, particularly on the reverse eagle. Then follows the 1798 to 1804 type with Draped Bust obverse and Heraldic Eagle reverse. Many such coins exist, again mostly in grades from VF through lower Mint State ranges. Striking can be indifferent, but the population is such that you will have more opportunities from which to select.

The Gobrecht silver dollars of 1836 (starless obverse, stars on reverse, plain edge) and 1839 (stars on obverse, starless reverse, reeded edge) present a special challenge in the formation of a type set. For quite a few years, these were considered to be *patterns*, and thus anyone forming a type set of regular-issue United States coins did not have to notice them. However, in recent decades research by R.W. Julian (in particular), Walter Breen, and others, has revealed that the majority of 1836 and 1839 silver dollars originally produced went into circulation at face value. Accordingly, they were coins of the realm at the time, were freely spent, and are deserving of a place among regular coinage types.

The 1836 Gobrecht dollar is easy enough to find, although expensive. The original coinage amounted to 1,600 to which an unknown number of restrikes can be added. The main problem arises with the 1839, made only to the extent of 300 originals plus perhaps a couple hundred restrikes. These are as rare as can be, and the originals that exist nearly always have abundant signs of circulation. Whether to include this issue or to avoid it is up to you. However, if you do include it you may be interested in knowing that this is the rarest of all major United States silver design types, even outclassing the 1796 and 1797 half dollar.

In 1840 the regular Liberty Seated dollar made its appearance, with the reverse depicting a perched eagle holding an olive branch and arrows. This style was continued through 1865. In 1866 the motto IN GOD WE TRUST was added to the reverse. Generally, both of these types can be easily enough found in circulated grades from VF up, as well as low Mint State ranges. Choice and gem Mint State pieces are in the minority, particularly of the 1840 to 1865 type.

Morgan silver dollars, made by the hundreds of millions from 1878 through 1921, are easily found, with the particular variety of 1881-S being at once the most common of all varieties existing today in gem condition and, happily, also usually seen with sharp strike and nice appearance.

Peace silver dollars can be collected as a single type, 1921 through 1935, easy enough to obtain as examples abound. However, it is interesting to select the first year of issue, 1921, as a separate type, as the design is in high relief, and in this book I set it apart as a distinct type. The 1921 is plentiful in Mint State, but rarely comes sharply struck. A compromise needs to be made, but select the best quality you can find. Later, Peace dollars with shallow relief abound in choice and gem preservation, although striking can be a problem.

Beyond a Type Set

Generally, silver dollars of the 1794 to 1803 years are collected by dates and major types, some of which are described in the *Red Book*. However, the presentation there needs some analysis, as, for example, I do not recall anyone ever sending in a want list for a *Red Book*-listed "1800 'Dotted Date' from die breaks," unless they were a variety collector. A *basic collection* of early dates and major varieties would consist of the following, this being what I would try to track down if I were forming a display (of course, as always, opinions can differ):

1794
1795 Flowing Hair (either with two leaves beneath each wing or three leaves beneath each wing, or take your pick and have just a single coin)
1795 Draped Bust
1796
1797 10 Stars left, 6 right
1797 9 Stars left, 7 right
1798 Small Eagle reverse, 15 obverse stars
1798 Small Eagle reverse, 13 obverse stars
1798 Heraldic Eagle reverse
1799, 9 Over 8, Overdate
1799 7 stars left, 6 right (normal arrangement)
1799 8 stars left, 5 stars right
1800
1801
1802, 2 Over 1, Overdate
1802
1803

Although the 1794, of which an estimated 135 or so exist today, is famous and expensive, the other varieties on the above list are eminently affordable in such decent grades as VF and EF. Beyond the *Red Book* listings, full or abbreviated, there is a rich panorama of die varieties. In many instances among early dollars the number of aficionados desiring a particularly rare die combination, say one with ten known, may be exceeded by even the small population of specimens—with the result that not much premium has to be paid.

The 1804 silver dollar is a study in itself. These were first struck in 1834 from 1804-dated dies prepared at that time, as no originals were ever made. Later, probably circa

1859, a new reverse die was made up, and combined with the earlier 1804 obverse (made in 1834 as noted). Those made in 1834 and around that time are today known as Class I dollars, whereas those made with a different reverse, beginning in 1859 and continuing perhaps through the 1870s, are known as Class III. An intermediate variety, from the Class III die combination but with plain instead of lettered edge, is in the Smithsonian and is known as Class II. All varieties combined comprise 15 different specimens. This has been called the "King of American Coins" for well over a century and has achieved great fame.

After the 1804-dated dollar, it is a long jump date-wise to 1836, when silver dollars were again struck for circulation, these being of the Gobrecht design. In 1839 more Gobrecht dollars were struck, with the design modified, both the 1836 and 1839 being discussed above as types. Accompanying these dollars in the *Red Book* listing and elsewhere are a number of other die combinations, and edge and metal varieties, including pieces of the year 1838, most of which are pattern restrikes. These are avidly desired and collected.

Forming a specialized collection of Liberty Seated dollars from 1840 through 1873 has been a pursuit of quite a few collectors over the years. Generally, the Philadelphia Mint dates are available without difficulty, although the 1851 and 1852 are typically acquired as Proof restrikes, originals of both years being prohibitively rare. Most difficult to find in higher grades are the branch mints, including the famous 1870-S, of which only 10 are known to exist and for which no mintage quantity figure was ever listed in the reports. Branch-mint pieces, beginning with the 1846-O, were placed into circulation and used extensively. Beginning in 1870, dollars of this type were struck at Carson City, also usually seen with evidence of circulation. The only exceptions to this are certain dollars of 1859-O and 1860-O, which turned up in very "baggy" preservation among Treasury hoards, to the extent of several thousand pieces of both dates combined.

Morgan silver dollars from 1878 through 1921 are one of the most active and popular areas in American numismatics. Approximately 100 different major varieties can be collected, per *Red Book* listings, although certain unusual varieties (not basic dates and mintmarks) can be dropped or added as desired. The majority of these pieces can be found in Mint State grade. When these were first minted there was little need for them in circulation, and hundreds of millions of coins piled up in Treasury and other vaults. Although many were melted in 1918, enough remained that untold millions exist today in the hands of the public. For a detailed synopsis of this series, see my Whitman *Guide Book of Morgan Silver Dollars*, as well as other references on the series.

Morgan silver dollars, when first introduced, also attracted the attention of popular writers, who lost no time describing the eagle as a "British grouse," "pelican-bat of the wilderness" (whatever that is!), "buzzard," "turkey," "sick bird," and "hen." Lots of fun to read today!

Morgan silver dollars are large, impressive, and very beautiful when in Mint State grade. Although varieties such as the 1881-S are common and are normally seen in high grades with sharp strike, others with high mintages, the 1886-O and 1896-O being examples, are quite rare in choice and gem Mint State, and when seen usually have rather poor eye appeal. Accordingly, quite a bit of discernment is recommended if you really jump into the series. On a casual basis, it is pleasant to contemplate that 50% to 75% of the different varieties could be obtained in grades such as MS-63 for inexpensive prices.

Peace silver dollars minted from 1921 through 1935 include the High Relief style of 1921, and the shallow-relief motif of 1922 to 1935. A basic set of 24 different dates and mintmarks is easily enough obtained, including in Mint State. The most elusive is the 1934-S. Although thousands exist of this particular variety, the demand is such that dealers can hardly keep them in stock, and basic grades such as MS-63 through MS-65 are highly appreciated whenever they come on the market, usually one at a time.

Flowing Hair (1794-1795)

Circulation-Strike Mintage: *163,811*

Field Population: Circulated, 4,000 to 7,500; Mint State, 150 to 250

Engraver: Robert Scot. **Weight:** 26.96 grams.
Composition: .900 silver, .100 copper (net weight 0.78011 oz. pure silver).
Diameter: Approximately 39–40 mm. **Edge:** HUNDRED CENTS ONE DOLLAR OR UNIT with decorations between words. **Mint:** Philadelphia.

Key to Collecting: The first silver dollar design comprises the years 1794 and 1795. Just 1,758 were struck of 1794, making it a rarity today, while an estimated 162,053 or more were struck of the 1795, probably 4,000 to 7,500 or so existing. Accordingly, a 1795, from G to F, will be the object of your search. EF and AU grades are elusive in regard to the total population, although they are much more available that half dimes or half dollars of the same design. Interestingly, the Flowing Hair silver dollar is also the easiest to locate in any and all grades. However, well-struck pieces without adjustment marks are another subject altogether, and such coins can be called *rare.*

Probably somewhere between 150 to 250 Mint State coins exist, the vast preponderance being of the 1795 date, and nearly all in lower Mint State levels. Perhaps five to ten 1794 dollars (from a total surviving population estimated at about 135) qualify at Mint State.

Aspects of Striking and Appearance: There were many different die combinations of this type, some of which lacked detail when made—such as on the hair of Miss Liberty. Finding a coin from a well-detailed die, and showing such features as hair details, sharp star centers, and sharp breast feathers on the eagle, will be a challenge—not in the league of the challenge facing you for the half dollar of the Flowing Hair type, but still requiring quite a bit of effort. It is precisely such a challenge, which translates to an enjoyable procedure that contributes to the fascination of early type coins. Then there is the matter of adjustment marks. All 1794 dollars I've ever seen have some light striking on the lower left stars, and nearly all have adjustment marks. For the 1795 dollars, the situation is better, and pieces without adjustment marks can be found, but not easily.

Market Value: Circulation Strikes

AG-3	G-4	VG-8	F-12	VF-20	EF-40	AU-50
$1,100	$2,250	$2,500	$4,100	$5,500	$12,000	$19,500
AU-55	**AU-58**	**MS-60**	**MS-62**	**MS-63**	**MS-64**	**MS-65**
$24,500	$37,500	$65,000	$100,000	$160,000	$265,000	$550,000

Retail Price Trends

Year	F-12	EF-40	MS-63
1946	$25	$65	$120
1950	$25	$90	$225
1960	$60	$150	$400
1970	$285	$1,000	$3,500
1980	$675	$1,850	$28,000
1990	$1,400	$4,250	$66,000
2000	1,500	$4,500	$80,000
2010	$3,100	$12,000	$110,000
2019	$4,100	$12,000	$160,000

Draped Bust, Small Eagle Reverse (1795–1798)

Circulation-Strike Mintage: 450,970

Field Population: Circulated, 3,000 to 4,000; Mint State, 80 to 140

Designer: Robert Scot. **Weight:** 26.96 grams. **Composition:** .8924 silver, .1076 copper (net weight .77352 oz. pure silver). **Diameter:** Approximately 39–40 mm. **Edge:** HUNDRED CENTS ONE DOLLAR OR UNIT with decorations between words. **Mint:** Philadelphia.

Key to Collecting: Inaugurated in 1795, the Draped Bust silver dollar type with Small Eagle reverse represents the first appearance of this popular obverse portrait—a depiction of Miss Liberty that later extended to other silver denominations as well as copper half cents and cents. The visage was said to have been by Gilbert Stuart, well known for his unfinished portrait of George Washington, a familiar decoration on schoolroom walls. Silver dollars of this motif were produced through early 1798. An example for type set purposes is easily enough found, but is somewhat on the scarce side. Typical grades are VF and EF. AU coins are rare, and Mint State pieces are especially so. When seen they are often dated 1795, the first year, and can be quite attractive. Some of the 1795 coins have prooflike surfaces. True Mint State examples, particularly in the choice and gem categories, are scarcely ever seen of 1796, 1797, or 1798.

Aspects of Striking and Appearance: Striking is usually fairly decent, unless you take out a magnifying glass and check certain details. Look over the star centers, hair details of Miss Liberty, eagle details on the reverse, and the denticles. While perfection may be more of a goal than a reality, there are some nice coins out there, even if every little detail is not needle-sharp. Many have Mint-caused planchet adjustment marks, most noticeable at the centers and/or near the rims.

Market Value: Circulation Strikes

AG-3	G-4	VG-8	F-12	VF-20	EF-40	AU-50
$825	$1,850	$2,100	$3,800	$5,500	$9,500	$14,000

AU-55	AU-58	MS-60	MS-62	MS-63	MS-64
$20,000	$30,000	$62,500	$87,500	$150,000	$350,000

Retail Price Trends

Year	F-12	EF-40	MS-63
1946	$17.50	$32	$90
1950	$25	$80	$175
1960	$52.50	$175	$325
1970	$265	$500	$1,500
1980	$525	$1,350	$20,000

Year	F-12	EF-40	MS-63
1990	$1,100	$3,000	$30,000
2000	$1,000	$3,100	$45,000
2010	$3,000	$8,100	$90,000
2019	$3,800	$9,500	$150,000

Draped Bust, Heraldic Eagle Reverse (1798–1804)

Circulation-Strike Mintage: **1,153,709**

Proof Mintage (restrikes): ***Fewer than 40***

Field Population: Circulated, 35,000 to 55,000; Mint State, 250 to 400

Designer: Robert Scot. **Weight:** 26.96 grams. **Composition:** .8924 silver, .1076 copper (net weight .77352 oz. pure silver). **Diameter:** Approximately 39–40 mm. **Edge:** HUNDRED CENTS ONE DOLLAR OR UNIT with decorations between words. **Mint:** Philadelphia.

Key to Collecting: Many exist in circulated grades, and most often seen are the dates 1798 and 1799. At least a couple hundred or so different examples have been described as Mint State over the years. Some of these represent wishful thinking more than anything else. Still, select examples do exist. If you are contemplating the purchase of one, pick a coin that is lightly toned and shows generous amounts of mint luster.

Aspects of Striking and Appearance: Relatively few pieces are sharply struck in all areas. Places to check include on the obverse the hair details of Miss Liberty, the star centers, and the denticles. On the reverse, the eagle details, the upper right area of the shield, the stars above the eagle (often a few are weak), and the clouds are points of observation. It will repay you to go slowly on this one.

Proof Coins: Proof "restrikes" from new dies, backdated 1801, 1802, and 1803, were made at the Mint in the third quarter of the nineteenth century.

Market Value: Circulation Strikes

G-4	VG-8	F-12	VF-20	EF-40	AU-50	AU-55
$850	$1,050	$1,450	$2,600	$4,500	$7,500	$10,500

AU-58	MS-60	MS-62	MS-63	MS-64	MS-65
$15,000	$22,000	$33,000	$70,000	$105,000	$155,000

Market Value: Proof Strikes

PF-63	PF-64	PF-65
$250,000	$450,000	$750,000

Retail Price Trends

Year	VF-20	EF-40	MS-65	PF-65
1946	$12.50	$25	$75	$300
1950	$17.50	$60	$90	$1,000
1960	$27.50	$110	$180	$4,500
1970	$150	$500	$2,000	$90,000
1980	$415	$800	$5,000	$250,000
1990	$500	$1,300	$8,000	$600,000
2000	$550	$1,300	$15,000	$900,000
2010	$1,800	$3,900	$140,000	$950,000
2019	$2,600	$4,500	$155,000	$750,000

Gobrecht, No Stars on Obverse, Stars on Reverse (1836)

Proof Mintage (1836–1837 only): 1,600

Field Population: Impaired Proof, 300 to 450; Proof, 400 to 600

Designer: Christian Gobrecht. **Weight:** 26.96 grams. **Composition:** .8924 silver, .1076 copper (net weight .77352 oz. pure silver). **Diameter:** 39–40 mm. **Edge:** Plain. **Mint:** Philadelphia.

Key to Collecting: As the 1836-dated Gobrecht silver dollars were placed into commerce, they quickly saw service, and today it is not particularly unusual to find examples in VF or EF grade, although they are not seen as often as Proofs or impaired Proofs. Some have had holes (for use as jewelry or on a teething cord for infants) skillfully repaired.

December 1836 saw 1,000 pieces struck; a further 600 were struck from the same dies in January 1837, but with a different die alignment. In addition, restrikes were made from the spring of 1859 onward to circa the 1870s. Hundreds exist, and as most auction firms offer at least a few during the course of a year, there will be many purchase opportunities. This variety is also listed in the Judd book on patterns as J-60. Originals have Die Alignment I (dies 180° apart), restrikes occur in the same alignment as well as in Alignment III (both dies in the same direction). All originals, regardless of orientation, have a *perfect* (not cracked) reverse die. Restrikes are in 90% silver composition.

Aspects of Striking and Appearance: Most examples are well struck. Although they were intended for circulation, or at least many ended up there, they seem to have been produced with great care, including a mirror Proof finish. No doubt, any one could have been placed with good effect in a numismatic cabinet, and the owner would have been delighted with all aspects of it!

Proof Coins: Quality varies from impaired Proof to gem, with some of the latter being quite beautiful. The total number extant may be on the long side of 500.

Market Value: Circulation Strikes

VF	EF-40	EF-45	AU-50
$12,500	$15,000	$17,000	$18,000

Market Value: Proof Strikes

PF-60	PF-62	PF-63	PF-64	PF-65
$25,000	$27,000	$40,000	$75,000	$125,000

Retail Price Trends

Year	PF-60	PF-63	PF-64
1946	$150	$200	$225
1950	$150	$200	$225
1960	$690	$850	$1,050
1970	$1,900	$3,000	$4,000
1980	$4,500	$5,000	$7,000

Year	PF-60	PF-63	PF-64
1990	$7,000	$8,000	$10,000
2000	$7,750	$12,250	$19,000
2010	$19,000	$32,000	$40,000
2019	$25,000	$40,000	$75,000

Gobrecht, Stars on Obverse, No Stars on Reverse (1838–1839)

Proof Mintage (1839 only): 300

Field Population: Impaired Proof, 50 to 75; Proof, 200 to 350

Designer: Christian Gobrecht. **Weight:** 26.73 grams.
Composition: .900 silver, .100 copper (net weight .77345 oz. pure silver).
Diameter: 39–40 mm. **Edge:** Reeded. **Mint:** Philadelphia.

Key to Collecting: For a long time, the 1839 Gobrecht dollar of this type was considered to be a pattern and was thus in the purview of pattern specialists, although the *Guide Book of United States Coins* included this and some patterns among its listings. Now it is known that in 1839 the mintage of 300 coins of this type was mostly placed into circulation. Today, *original* examples are so rare as to be almost impossible to find in anything approaching choice preservation.

The 1839 Gobrecht dollar stands today as the rarest of all types in silver—handily eclipsing even the famous 1796 and 1797 half dollar with Draped Bust obverse, Small

Eagle reverse. Most specimens that come on the market are restrikes made beginning in the spring of 1859.

Aspects of Striking and Appearance: Generally well struck. Check the details of Miss Liberty and the higher-relief areas of the eagle.

Proof Coins: Examples are rare today. Most if not all have been classified as restrikes made in spring 1859 and later. An original, unequivocally attributed as such and properly and extensively described, would be a numismatic landmark if offered at auction!

Originals vs. Restrikes: On the *original* issues the reverse die is *not* cracked, and the eagle flies *horizontally* after rotation along the *vertical* axis. The head of Miss Liberty is opposite the space between F in OF and first A in AMERICA on the reverse. Dollars with cracked reverse die are restrikes and are known in this alignment as well as with the head of Miss Liberty is opposite the N in ONE on the reverse. Both originals and restrikes are also listed as patterns.

Market Value: Circulation Strikes

VF	EF-40	EF-45	AU-50
$15,000	$17,500	$20,000	$22,500

Market Value: Proof Strikes

PF-60	PF-62	PF-63	PF-64	PF-65
$55,000	$65,000	$75,000	$85,000	$150,000

Retail Price Trends

Year	PF-60	PF-63	PF-64
1946	$150	$200	$225
1950	$150	$200	$225
1960	$750	$1,000	$1,150
1970	$3,750	$4,000	$6,000
1980	$5,000	$6,000	$8,000

Year	PF-60	PF-63	PF-64
1990	$5,000	$6,000	$8,000
2000	$13,000	$15,000	$22,000
2010	$26,000	$42,000	$80,000
2019	$55,000	$75,000	$85,000

Liberty Seated, No Motto (1840–1865)

Circulation-Strike Mintage: 2,890,563

Proof Mintage: Fewer than 5,500

Field Population: Circulated, 35,000 to 50,000; Mint State, 10,000 to 15,000; Proof, 3,500 to 4,200

Designer: Christian Gobrecht. **Weight:** 26.73 grams. **Composition:** .900 silver, .100 copper (net weight .77344 oz. pure silver). **Diameter:** 38.1 mm. **Edge:** Reeded. **Mints:** Philadelphia, New Orleans, San Francisco.

Key to Collecting: Examples are readily found today in grades such as VF and EF and are typically dated in the 1840s. Beginning extensively in 1850, such coins were hoarded and mainly exported, and later dates are rare. Finding an attractive circulated example for a type set will be no problem, and the same can be said for low Mint State ranges.

Aspects of Striking and Appearance: Most Liberty Seated dollars of this type are well struck, but there are exceptions. Places to check on the obverse include the higher areas of Miss Liberty and her hair details, the stars, and the border denticles. On the reverse, the eagle is a focal point, particularly at the lower left.

Proof Coins: Proofs were struck in the years indicated for all dates except 1851 and 1853. Later, the Mint accommodated collectors by restriking the Proof 1851 and 1853, as well as restriking a number of other dates, in the latter instance, adding to the supply of originals. Proofs remain rare today, but examples from the early 1860s can be obtained fairly readily.

Market Value: Circulation Strikes

VG-8	F-12	VF-20	EF-40	AU-50	AU-55	MS-60	MS-62	MS-63	MS-64	MS-65
$350	$450	$650	$1,100	$1,300	$2,350	$3,200	$5,250	$7,250	$11,000	$85,000

Market Value: Proof Strikes

PF-60	PF-63	PF-64	PF-65
$2,400	$4,750	$6,500	$11,500

Retail Price Trends

Year	VF-20	EF-40	MS-65	PF-65
1946	$5	$7.50	$15	$30
1950	$6.50	$9	$18	$37.50
1960	$16	$30	$60	$115
1970	$37.50	$70	$175	$5,000
1980	$110	$130	$3,000	$10,500

Year	VF-20	EF-40	MS-65	PF-65
1990	$200	$350	$7,500	$11,000
2000	$200	$275	$9,000	$11,000
2010	$350	$475	$58,000	$16,000
2019	$650	$1,100	$85,000	$11,500

Liberty Seated, With Motto (1866-1873)

Circulation-Strike Mintage: 3,597,184

Proof Mintage: 6,060

Field Population: Circulated, 30,000 to 45,000; Mint State, 3,000 to 4,000; Proof, 4,200 to 5,000

Designer: Christian Gobrecht, with motto added by James B. Longacre or someone else on the Mint staff.. **Weight:** 26.73 grams. **Composition:** .900 silver, .100 copper (net weight .77344 oz. pure silver). **Diameter:** 38.1 mm. **Edge:** Reeded. **Mints:** Philadelphia, Carson City, San Francisco.

Key to Collecting: Finding a circulated example for type will not be difficult, with 1871 perhaps being the most plentiful. In the Mint State category choice and gem pieces are more available than for the preceding type, but still are rare in proportion to the demand for them, but when found are apt to be dated 1871 or 1872. Usually these are relatively free of bagmarks (in stark contrast to the earlier type).

Aspects of Striking and Appearance: The striking is usually quite good. Check the obverse features including the hair of Miss Liberty. On the reverse, check the eagle, the motto, and other details.

Proof Coins: Proofs exist of all years and are available in relation to their mintage figures. Choice and gem coins can be found. Some, from old-time collections, have attractive iridescent toning and are especially desired. As always, careful inspection is recommended for any coin contemplated for purchase.

Market Value: Circulation Strikes

VG-8	F-12	VF-20	EF-40	AU-50	MS-60	MS-63	MS-65
$400	$425	$500	$575	$1,025	$2,050	$4,600	$49,000

Market Value: Proof Strikes

PF-60	PF-63	PF-64	PF-65
$2,100	$3,800	$5,750	$11,500

Retail Price Trends

Year	VF-20	EF-40	MS-65	PF-65
1946	$4.50	$5.50	$10.50	$18
1950	$7.50	$9	$17	$27
1960	$14	$20	$90	$75
1970	$30	$100	$2,000	$3,000
1980	$100	$140	$4,000	$8,500
1990	$200	$350	$8,500	$9,000
2000	$200	$300	$17,500	$9,700
2010	$300	$450	$27,000	$12,000
2019	$500	$575	$49,000	$11,500

Morgan (1878–1921)

Circulation-Strike Mintage: 656,979,299

Proof Mintage: 23,482

Field Population: Circulated, more than 100,000,000; Mint State, more than 100,000,000; Proof, 14,000 to 16,000

Designer: George T. Morgan. **Weight:** 26.73 grams. **Composition:** .900 silver, .100 copper (net weight .77344 oz. pure silver). **Diameter:** 38.1 mm. **Edge:** Reeded. **Mints:** Philadelphia, New Orleans, Carson City, Denver, San Francisco.

Key to Collecting: Abundant opportunities exist to obtain a single coin for a type. The 1881-S, which at once is the most common Morgan dollar in gem grade and also is one of the sharpest struck, is an obvious candidate. However, it might be fun to add a Carson City coin (such dates as 1882-CC, 1883-CC, and 1884-CC are inexpensive) or one or another of a variety of special interest.

Aspects of Striking and Appearance: Striking can vary widely. The best-struck pieces are those made at San Francisco. Check Miss Liberty's hair above her ear, and, on the reverse, the breast feathers of the eagle. The hair of Miss Liberty might not be completely needle-sharp, but it should be close. Once these two points are checked, examine lettering, denticles (usually decent), and other characteristics. Many coins were made from "tired" dies and show graininess or dull surfaces. Eye appeal can vary considerably from deeply rich and frosty to rather flat and insipid.

Proof Coins: Proofs were made of all years in the series. Quality can vary. Especially desired are certain pieces with frosty or "cameo" portraits and devices, often seen in the 1880s and 1890s. Many Proofs have been cleaned and thus have hairlines, others are rather dull in appearance. Take your time to select a truly nice one.

Market Value: Circulation Strikes

VF-20	EF-40	AU-50	MS-60	MS-63	MS-63DMPL
$30	$33	$35	$40	$45	$190

MS-64	MS-64DMPL	MS-65	MS-65DMPL	MS-66
$50	$425	$125	$900	$200

Market Value: Proof Strikes

PF-60	PF-63	PF-64	PF-65
$1,300	$3,200	$3,750	$5,500

Retail Price Trends

Year	MS-63	MS-65	PF-65
1946	$2.50	$3	$12
1950	$2.50	$3	$15
1960	$2.50	$3	$75
1970	$30	$35	$750
1980	$70	$85	$1,300

Year	MS-63	MS-65	PF-65
1990	$50	$95	$3,000
2000	$25	$100	$4,750
2010	$50	$165	$6,000
2019	$45	$125	$5,500

Peace, High Relief (1921–1922)

Circulation-Strike Mintage: *1921:* 1,006,473; *1922:* 34,401 (nearly all melted)

Proof Mintage: Fewer than 50

Field Population: Circulated, well over 100,000; Mint State, tens of thousands; Proof, fewer than 50

Designer: Anthony de Francisci. **Weight:** 26.73 grams.
Composition: .900 silver, .100 copper (net weight .77344 oz. pure silver).
Diameter: 38.1 mm. **Edge:** Reeded. **Mint:** Philadelphia.

Key to Collecting: You can opt not to include the 1921 Peace dollar as a separate type, but I recommend that you add this interesting issue. The obverse and reverse are both in high relief, quite unlike the later issue, and thus even at quick glance constitute, in my opinion, a different type. Circulated coins are available easily enough, but I suggest that a low-grade Mint State piece is a better option. Most pieces have deep rich luster. Typical grades are up through and including MS-63 and MS-64, with finer pieces being elusive.

Aspects of Striking and Appearance: All examples seen have some lightness of strike at the hair details at the center of the obverse, the portion of the hair that covers the ear. Sometimes the outlines of the neck truncation can be irregular or lightly struck as well. On the reverse, the details of the eagle, particularly the areas in the higher relief just behind the eagle's neck, are often indistinct.

Proof Coins: A few Sand Blast Proofs were made of this year, perhaps a couple dozen. Be very careful, and if you are contemplating a purchase, consult with a trusted professional numismatist. In addition to the foregoing, somewhat fewer than a dozen Proof 1922 High Relief pieces of this design exist.

Market Value: Circulation Strikes

VF-20	EF-40	AU-50	MS-60	MS-62	MS-63	MS-64	MS-65	MS-66
$110	$135	$150	$270	$370	$440	$825	$1,800	$5,800

Market Value: Proof Strikes

PF-65
$45,000

Retail Price Trends

Year	MS-63	MS-65	PF-65
1946	$2.50	$3.25	$70
1950	$4.50	$6	$80
1960	$13	$16	$1,000
1970	$75	$400	$15,000
1980	$200	$900	$12,000
1990	$350	$1,500	$30,000
2000	$225	$2,000	$30,000
2010	$430	$2,500	$49,000
2019	$440	$1,800	$45,000

Peace, Low Relief (1922–1935)

Circulation-Strike Mintage: 189,570,806

Proof Mintage: *Fewer than 20*

Field Population: Circulated, tens of millions; Mint State, tens of millions; Proof, 10 to 15

Designer: Anthony de Francisci. **Weight:** 26.73 grams.
Composition: .900 silver, .100 copper (net weight .77344 oz. pure silver).
Diameter: 38.1 mm. **Edge:** Reeded. **Mints:** Philadelphia, Denver, San Francisco.

Key to Collecting: Millions of these coins exist in just about every grade desired. For type-set purposes a choice or gem example of one of the inexpensive dates will be ideal. Most are richly lustrous and quite attractive. The quality of the luster varies considerably, from "deeply frosty" for certain earlier issues to rather "creamy and satiny" for certain varieties of the 1930s—a curious aspect.

Aspects of Striking and Appearance: Generally good, in view of the design modifications. Check the central hair features and the feathers on the eagle. These will not be needle-sharp, as they were not in the original die. However, they should show no areas of flatness and no blank areas.

Proof Coins: More than 10 *authentic* Sand Blast Proofs exist, plus more that are phony pretenders, sometimes with "papers." Be super careful!

Market Value: Circulation Strikes

VF-20	EF-40	AU-50	MS-60	MS-62	MS-63	MS-64	MS-65	MS-66
$25	$27	$28	$30	$32	$33	$45	$110	$375

Market Value: Proof Strikes

PF-60	PF-63	PF-64	PF-65
$15,000	$30,000	$50,000	$75,000

Retail Price Trends

Year	MS-63	MS-65	PF-65
1946	$2.25	$3	$70
1950	$2.50	$3	$80
1960	$3	$3.75	$1,000
1970	$8	$9	$15,000
1980	$10	$13	$20,000

Year	MS-63	MS-65	PF-65
1990	$45	$75	$30,000
2000	$20	$145	$30,000
2010	$35	$175	$50,000
2019	$33	$110	$75,000

19

Modern Dollars

1971 to Date

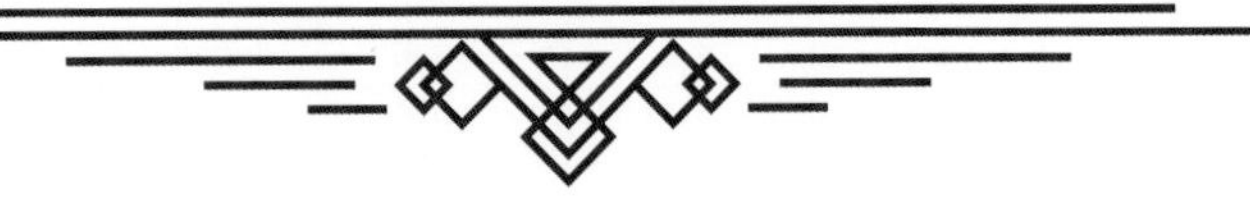

In 1971 dollars were again made, there being a request for these for use on the gaming tables in Nevada. By this time, silver dollars of all kinds had disappeared from circulation, including the familiar Morgan and Peace dollars of yesteryear. In Las Vegas, Reno, and other gambling centers, chips and tokens were used, but metal dollars were desired. Certain other demand was felt as well. The Treasury Department tapped Chief Engraver Frank Gasparro to create what became known as the Eisenhower dollar, depicting on the obverse the portrait of the late president facing left, and on the reverse a symbolic American eagle landing on the surface of the moon, a tribute to the Apollo missions of the previous decade. The composition was metal consisting of copper and nickel, although some silver-content dollars were produced for collectors. Eisenhower dollars were minted through and including 1978, except for the year 1975. The type was interrupted by the 1776–1976 Bicentennial dollar, featuring a double date on the obverse and, on the reverse, a depiction of the Liberty Bell and the moon in small sizes, a motif viewed as rather insipid by many numismatic observers. At the time, of the three Bicentennial designs (quarter, half dollar, and dollar), only the quarter received thumbs-up praise.

In 1979 the Susan B. Anthony dollar came into being, also designed by Frank Gasparro. Of reduced size, the coin, it was hoped, would take the place of paper dollars in circulation and would effect a significant economy. A paper dollar was apt to last just 18 months in circulation, while a metal dollar could last for many years. Depicted on the obverse was women's rights advocate Susan B. Anthony, while the reverse showed an eagle landing on the moon, somewhat similar to that used on the Eisenhower dollar. The reduced diameter of just 26.5 mm was confusing to the public, as such pieces were easily mistaken for quarters (of 24.3 mm diameter). Production was very high in 1979, lower in 1980, and then in 1981 consisted of pieces only for the collecting fraternity. Years later in 1999, for reasons related to anticipated demand ahead of Y2K, more than 40 million more Susan Anthony dollars were made, plus some Proofs.

A more recent entry in the metallic dollar field is the Sacagawea "golden dollar," so-called from its manganese brass surfaces. Again, it was hoped that these pieces would capture the fancy of the public and replace the paper dollar. However, Sacagawea dollars remained largely as curiosities. The mintage dropped sharply in 2001 and in 2002 was limited to pieces only for collectors. Relatively small quantities were made in later years as well, to date. From 2007 to 2016, former presidents of the United States were honored on a series of coins in the "golden dollar" format. Since 2009 an annual program of coins in the same format memorializes Native Americans and the important contributions made by Indian tribes and individual Native Americans to the development and history of the United States. Another coinage program debuted in 2018: the American Innovations dollars celebrate one invention or other innovative development from each state and territory.

Collecting a Type Set of Modern Dollars

Among the Eisenhower, Susan B. Anthony, Sacagawea, and other "golden dollar" types, large supplies are in the hands of dealers and collectors, and finding an example that is just right will be easy enough to do.

Beyond a Type Set

Eisenhower dollars from 1971 through 1978 are easily obtained in choice and gem grades, although some of the circulation strikes, especially the early years, tend to be bagmarked. There are many different varieties made especially for collectors, including Proofs and some in silver.

In 1979 the Susan B. Anthony dollar was introduced, and high hopes prevailed, but the public reacted unfavorably. The series was thus short lived, beginning in 1979 and ending in 1981, and comprising strikings from the Philadelphia, Denver, and San Francisco mints. Then—surprise!—in 1999, to have coins on hand ahead of Y2K in case of increased public demand, additional Susan B. Anthony dollars were struck. Accordingly, the series was expanded to include the 1999-P and 1999-D varieties, plus Proofs of 1999-S. For want of a better term, Susan Anthony dollars are quite *cute*, small in size and with the portrait sufficiently small to give the obverse a cameo-like appearance. However, upon close inspection, the visage of Miss Anthony is not particularly warm or pleasant. The designer, Frank Gasparro, mentioned to me that nicer portraits could have been used, but he was commanded to stick to the one given to him.

On the other hand, Sacagawea, as portrayed on the "golden dollar" issued beginning in 2000, seems to be smiling, a happy camper, or trailblazer, carrying her little baby. On the reverse, the soaring eagle seems to be particularly realistic—one can envision such a bird hovering overhead in a clearing in a pine forest. Numismatists enjoy these coins immensely, but they were a dud for general use in circulation. This matters not, and from a collecting viewpoint, a set can be put together easily and is fun to own.

More recently, the Presidential, Native American, and American Innovation dollars provide a bounty of collecting opportunities. Folders, albums and display cases offer attractive means of protecting and exhibiting the coins in this historic series.

Modern dollars are covered in detail in the *Guide Book of Modern United States Dollar Coins* (Whitman Publishing).

Eisenhower, Copper-Nickel (1971–1978)

Circulation-Strike Mintage: 466,001,887

Proof Mintage: 11,751,840

Field Population: Circulated, hundreds of millions; Mint State, tens of millions; Proof, 10,000,000 to 11,000,000

Designer: Frank Gasparro. **Weight:** 22.68 grams. **Composition:** Outer layers of .750 copper, .250 nickel bonded to inner core of pure copper. **Diameter:** 38.1 mm. **Edge:** Reeded. **Mints:** Philadelphia, Denver, San Francisco.

Key to Collecting: Coins of the Eisenhower type were made from 1971 through 1978, except that none were dated 1975 (the Mint was busy pre-striking coins that year for the Bicentennial). Circulation strikes were produced for use in casinos and elsewhere, while silver pieces were sold at a premium to numismatists. In the present text, I have included the silver coins as a separate type, but you may opt to just get one Eisenhower dollar. In any event, such coins are not expensive. Circulated coins are abundant but not of consideration for you as Mint State pieces abound, although many show extensive bagmarks, this being particularly true for the earlier dates.

Aspects of Striking and Appearance: Generally good, but check the high parts of the portrait on the obverse and, on the reverse, the details of the eagle.

Proof Coins: In the copper-nickel metal, Proofs were made at the San Francisco Mint beginning in 1973. Quantities ran into the millions, and pieces are easily obtained today.

Market Value: Circulation Strikes

EF-40	MS-63	MS-65	MS-66
$2	$5	$18	$60

Market Value: Proof Strikes

PF-65	PF-67Cam	PF-67DC	PF-68DC
$7	$10	$15	$20

Retail Price Trends

Year	MS-63	MS-65	PF-65
1980	$1.50	$2	$6
1990	$2.25	$8	$5
2000	$2	$8	$5

Year	MS-63	MS-65	PF-65
2010	$5	$14	$10
2019	$5	$18	$7

Eisenhower, Silver (1971–1974)

Circulation-Strike Mintage: 12,844,882

Proof Mintage: 8,397,090

Field Population: Circulated, several million; Mint State, several million; Proof, 7,300,000 to 8,000,000

Designer: Frank Gasparro. **Weight:** 24.59 grams. **Composition:** 40% silver, 60% copper, consisting of outer layers of .800 silver, .200 copper bonded to inner core of .209 silver, .791 copper (net weight .3161 oz. pure silver). **Diameter:** 38.1 mm. **Edge:** Reeded. **Mints:** Philadelphia, Denver, San Francisco.

Key to Collecting: These silver issues were produced in large quantities and were generally well preserved by the recipients. Whether to include them as a separate type is up to you, but as the cost is inexpensive, and most pieces are quite attractive, it is easy to do so. Circulated issues are not relevant as Mint State coins are available and usually quite attractive.

Aspects of Striking and Appearance: Usually well struck and attractive.

Proof Coins: Usually in gem preservation. Common.

Market Value: Circulation Strikes

EF-40	MS-63	MS-65	MS-66
$5	$7	$22	$75

Market Value: Proof Strikes

PF-65	PF-67Cam	PF-67DC	PF-68DC
$10	$20	$25	$40

Retail Price Trends

Year	MS-63	MS-65	PF-65
1980	$2	$4.25	$7
1990	$6	$10	$8
2000	$4	$20	$5
2010	$5	$18	$10
2019	$7	$22	$10

Eisenhower, Bicentennial, Copper-Nickel (1776–1976)

Circulation-Strike Mintage: 220,565,274

Proof Mintage: 6,995,180

Field Population: Circulated, tens of millions; Mint State, tens of millions; Proof, 6,000,000 to 6,700,000

Designers: ***Obverse:*** Frank Gasparro; ***Reverse:*** Dennis R. Williams. **Weight:** 22.68 grams. **Composition:** Outer layers of .750 copper, .250 nickel bonded to inner core of pure copper. **Diameter:** 38.1 mm. **Edge:** Reeded. **Mints:** Philadelphia, Denver, San Francisco.

Key to Collecting: The 1776–1976 Eisenhower dollar is the largest of the three denominations given special reverses to observe the Bicentennial of American Independence. Made in large quantities in anticipation of great demand, sales did not come up to expectations as the coin market was in a slump at the time, and the coinage did not capture the imagination of the general public. A couple hundred million or so were made, and as a result examples are easy enough to find today. Circulation strikes are common but not relevant to building a type set as Mint State pieces are plentiful and usually well struck, though bagmarks can be a problem.

Aspects of Striking and Appearance: Usually fairly well struck, but check the higher parts of the design. Eye appeal is usually good as well.

Proof Coins: Abundant in proportion to their mintages. Two varieties of reverse lettering were made, "low relief, bold" and "sharp, delicate," this per *Red Book* terminology.

Market Value: Circulation Strikes

EF-40	MS-63	MS-65	MS-66
$2	$5	$28	$60

Market Value: Proof Strikes

PF-65	PF-67Cam	PF-67DC	PF-68DC
$8	$12	$15	$30

Retail Price Trends

Year	MS-63	MS-65	PF-65
1980	$2	$2	$4
1990	$2.25	$12	$5.50
2000	$2.50	$20	$6
2010	$7	$30	$9
2019	$5	$28	$8

Eisenhower, Bicentennial, Silver (1776–1976)

Circulation-Strike Mintage: 11,000,000

Proof Mintage: 4,000,000

Field Population: Circulated, several hundred thousand; Mint State, nearly 11,000,000; Proof, 3,300,000 to 3,600,000

Designers: ***Obverse:*** Frank Gasparro; ***Reverse:*** Dennis R. Williams. **Weight:** 24.59 grams. **Composition:** Outer layers of .800 silver, .200 copper bonded to inner core of .209 silver, .791 copper (net weight .3161 oz. pure silver). **Diameter:** 38.1 mm. **Edge:** Reeded. **Mints:** Philadelphia, Denver, San Francisco.

Key to Collecting: The commentary for this variety is generally the same as the preceding, except that these pieces were struck on planchets of silver and copper and went only to numismatists and souvenir hunters, not into general circulation (such as at

Nevada casinos). Coins such as this help fill in the later parts of a type set quickly and inexpensively. All were struck at the San Francisco Mint and bear an S mintmark.

Aspects of Striking and Appearance: Usually well struck.

Proof Coins: Plentiful in proportion to the mintage, typically of the variety with "low relief, bold lettering" on reverse. A few were made of the "sharp design, delicate lettering" style.

Market Value: Circulation Strikes

MS-63	MS-65	MS-66
$16	$20	$29

Market Value: Proof Strikes

PF-65	PF-67Cam	PF-68DC
$18	$19	$34

Retail Price Trends

Year	MS-63	MS-65	PF-65
1980	$2	$4.50	$9
1990	$8	$9	$13
2000	$8	$9	$9.50
2010	$16	$26	$19
2019	$16	$20	$18

Susan B. Anthony (1979–1999)

Circulation-Strike Mintage: 886,808,452

Proof Mintage: 7,617,889

Field Population: Circulated, more than 100,000,000; Mint State, hundreds of millions; Proof, well over 10,000,000

Designer: Frank Gasparro. **Weight:** 8.1 grams. **Composition:** Outer layers of copper-nickel (.750 copper, .250 nickel) bonded to inner core of pure copper. **Diameter:** 26.5 mm. **Edge:** Reeded. **Mints:** Philadelphia, Denver, San Francisco.

Key to Collecting: Reviews of the Susan B. Anthony dollars, sometimes called "Susies" by numismatists, are quite mixed. The public did not like them at all, and the Treasury Department found that these pieces were disappointing, as they did not take the place of paper dollars in circulation. However, numismatists generally liked them or even loved them, as the format was new, most pieces were well struck, and it became easy enough to form a complete collection of the different varieties made in 1979, 1980, and 1981. Then, unexpectedly, some more were made in 1999. Circulated coins are not relevant due to the plentitude of Mint State and Proof pieces.

Aspects of Striking and Appearance: Usually well struck.

Proof Coins: Very attractive, usually with cameo finish, and well reviewed by numismatists.

Market Value: Circulation Strikes

EF-40	MS-63	MS-64	MS-65	MS-66
$2	$3	$5	$7	$15

Market Value: Proof Strikes

PF-65	PF-67Cam	PF-68DC	PF-69DC
$6	$8	$10	$20

Retail Price Trends

Year	MS-63	MS-65	PF-65
1980	$1.50	$1.50	$5
1990	$1.75	$3	$7
2000	$1.45	$4	$5

Year	MS-63	MS-65	PF-65
2010	$3	$4	$9
2019	$3	$7	$6

Sacagawea (2000–2008)

Circulation-Strike Mintage: 1,462,491,610

Proof Mintage: 27,853,342

Field Population: Circulated, hundreds of millions; Mint State, hundreds of millions; Proof, tens of millions

Designers: ***Obverse:*** Glenna Goodacre; ***Reverse:*** Thomas D. Rogers Sr. **Weight:** 8.1 grams. **Composition:** Pure copper core with outer layers of manganese brass (.770 copper, .120 zinc, .070 manganese, and .040 nickel). **Diameter:** 26.5 mm. **Edge:** Plain. **Mints:** Philadelphia, Denver, San Francisco; 22-karat gold experimental specimens dated 2000-W were struck at West Point in 1999.

Key to Collecting: The Sacagawea dollar, called the "Golden Dollar" in United States Mint publicity, was launched with much enthusiasm in 2000. Then-Mint Director Jay Johnson went on the road to promote its use as a substitute for paper dollars, a replay of the failed Susan B. Anthony dollar concept, but this time around with the new hope that the yellow appearance would make it more easily distinguishable from the similarly sized quarter dollar. Canada had enjoyed the success of its gold-colored dollar coins picturing a loon, nicknamed "loonies," since 1987. Johnson's stops included numismatic conventions where he was well received, as were the coins. However, in time the scenario played out similar to that of the Anthony dollars: numismatists loved them, but the public had little interest. Circulated coins are available easily enough, but not relevant to what you want. Choose a Mint State coin instead. Today, a nice little collection can be formed of the different date and mint varieties, including Proofs.

Aspects of Striking and Appearance: Usually well struck and of very pleasing appearance. Spotting has occurred on some pieces, a reaction of the outer manganese brass metal with the atmosphere, and such pieces should be avoided. Generally most have excellent aesthetic appeal. Some pieces given by the Mint to designer Glenna Goodacre have a special finish and are especially prized, having entered the secondary market; apparently the lagniappe was unintended by the Mint.

Proof Coins: Plentiful and attractive.

Market Value: Circulation Strikes

MS-64	MS-65	MS-66
$2	$4	$6

Market Value: Proof Strikes

PF-65	PF-69DC
$6	$15

Presidential (2007–2016)

Circulation-Strike Mintage: Millions, or tens of millions, each

Proof Mintage: 1,000,000 to 4,000,000 each

Field Population: Circulated, hundreds of millions; Mint State, tens of millions; Proof, tens of millions

Designers: ***Obverse:*** See image captions for obverse designers; ***Reverse:*** Don Everhart. **Weight:** 8.1 grams. **Composition:** Pure copper core with outer layers of manganese brass (.770 copper, .120 zinc, .070 manganese, and .040 nickel). **Diameter:** 26.5 mm. **Edge:** Lettered. **Mints:** Philadelphia, Denver, San Francisco.

Key to Collecting: In addition to the regular Uncirculated or Mint State coins produced in large quantities, smaller numbers of Satin Finish dollars were made of the 2007 to 2010 years, Philadelphia and Denver Mints. In December 2011, Secretary of the Treasury Timothy Geithner directed that the U.S. Mint suspend minting and issuing circulating Presidential dollars. Collector formats, however, continued to be issued. Presidential dollars are very common in Mint State. Most have from a few to many bagmarks, with true MS-65 and better coins in the minority.

Some error coins have been discovered without edge lettering.

The *Guide Book of Modern United States Dollar Coins* includes history, mintages, and other detailed information on each issue.

Aspects of Striking and Appearance: Most examples are very well struck. Check the higher points of the design. Special issues are uniformly sharply struck.

Proof Coins: Proofs have been made each year and are readily available. The 2015 releases (Truman, Eisenhower, Kennedy, L.B. Johnson) and the 2016 Reagan issue were also struck as Reverse Proofs at Philadelphia.

2007, Washington
Obverse designer: Joseph Menna.

2007, J. Adams
Obverse designer: Joel Iskowitz.

2007, Jefferson
Obverse designer: Joseph Menna.

2007, Madison
Obverse designer: Joel Iskowitz.

2008,
Monroe
Obverse designer:
Joseph Menna.

2008,
J.Q. Adams
Obverse designer:
Don Everhart.

2008,
Jackson
Obverse designer:
Joel Iskowitz.

2008,
Van Buren
Obverse designer:
Joel Iskowitz.

2009,
W.H. Harrison
Obverse designer:
Joseph Menna

2009,
Tyler
Obverse designer:
Phebe Hemphill.

2009,
Polk
Obverse designer:
Susan Gamble.

2009,
Taylor
Obverse designer:
Don Everhart.

2010,
Fillmore
Obverse designer:
Don Everhart.

2010,
Pierce
Obverse designer:
Susan Gamble.

2010,
Buchanan
Obverse designer:
Phebe Hemphill.

2010,
Lincoln
Obverse designer:
Don Everhart.

2011,
A. Johnson
Obverse designer:
Don Everhart.

2011,
Grant
Obverse designer:
Don Everhart.

2011,
Hayes
Obverse designer:
Don Everhart.

2011,
Garfield
Obverse designer:
Phebe Hemphill.

2012,
Arthur
Obverse designer:
Don Everhart.

2012,
Cleveland, 1st Term
Obverse designer:
Don Everhart.

2012,
B. Harrison
Obverse designer:
Phebe Hemphill.

2012,
Cleveland, 2nd Term
Obverse designer:
Don Everhart.

2013,
McKinley
Obverse designer:
Phebe Hemphill.

2013,
T. Roosevelt
Obverse designer:
Joseph Menna.

2013,
Taft
Obverse designer:
Barbara Fox.

2013,
Wilson
Obverse designer:
Don Everhart.

2014,
Harding
Obverse designer:
Michael Gaudioso.

2014,
Coolidge
Obverse designer:
Phebe Hemphill.

2014,
Hoover
Obverse designer:
Phebe Hemphill.

2014,
F.D. Roosevelt
Obverse designer:
Joseph Menna.

2015,
Truman
Obverse designer:
Don Everhart.

2015,
Eisenhower
Obverse designer:
Joseph Menna.

2015,
Kennedy
Obverse designer:
Don Everhart.

2015,
L.B. Johnson
Obverse designer:
Michael Gaudioso.

2016, Nixon
Obverse designer:
Don Everhart.

2016, Ford
Obverse designer:
Phebe Hemphill.

2016, Reagan
Reverse designer:
Richard Masters.

Market Value: Circulation Strikes

MS-64	MS-65	MS-66
$2	$3	$5

Market Value: Proof Strikes

PF-65	PF-69DC
$4	$15

Native American (2009 to Date)

Circulation-Strike Mintage: Millions annually

Proof Mintage: Usually 1,000,000 to 2,000,000 annually

Field Population: Circulated, tens of millions; Mint State, tens of millions; Proof, millions

Designers: ***Obverse:*** Glenna Goodacre; ***Reverse:*** See image captions for reverse designers. **Weight:** 8.1 grams. **Composition:** Pure copper core with outer layers of manganese brass (.770 copper, .120 zinc, .070 manganese, and .040 nickel). **Diameter:** 26.5 mm. **Edge:** Lettered. **Mints:** Philadelphia, Denver, San Francisco.

Key to Collecting: Since 2009, the reverse of the golden dollar has featured an annually changing design that memorializes Native Americans and, in the words of the authorizing legislation, "the important contributions made by Indian tribes and individual Native Americans to the development [and history] of the United States." The coins are marked (incuse) on their edges with the year of minting, the mintmark, and the legend E PLURIBUS UNUM. The Native American $1 Coin Act also specified that at least 20% of the total mintage of dollar coins in any given year (including Presidential dollars) will be Native American dollars. Production of all dollar coins minted after 2011 has been limited to numismatic sales (Proofs and other collector formats, and circulation strikes in rolls and bags available directly from the U.S. Mint); none are issued for circulation, as they have proven unpopular in commerce.

The obverse of the Native American dollar coin is a modified version of the Sacagawea dollar, featuring that coin's central portraits (of Sacagawea and Jean Baptiste), and the legends LIBERTY and IN GOD WE TRUST. The date and mintmark, as noted above, are on the coin's edge. Each new reverse design is chosen by the secretary of the Treasury following consultation with the Senate Committee on Indian Affairs, the Congressional Native American Caucus of the House of Representatives, the Commission of Fine Arts, the National Congress of American Indians, and the Citizens Coinage Advisory Committee.

In addition to the regular Uncirculated or Mint State coins produced in large quantities, smaller numbers of Satin Finish dollars were made of the 2009-P, 2009-D, 2010-P, and 2010-D issues. Sold at an additional premium, most of these exist today in grades of MS-67 and upward and are designated SP (Specimen) or SMS (Special Mint Set) by the commercial grading services. 50,000 2014-D coins were made with Enhanced Uncirculated finish and were sold at an extra premium. Most of these grade MS–68 to 70. In 2015 at the West Point Mint 90,000 2015-W dollars were struck with Enhanced Uncirculated finish. These are unique up to this time as the only collectible West Point dollars in any of the three "golden dollar" series (Sacagawea, Native American, and Presidential). Nearly all are in grades MS–68 to 70.

Some error coins have been discovered without edge lettering.

Native American dollars are common in high grades, being struck in the millions annually, and are usually collected in MS and Proof.

These coins are studied in depth in the *Guide Book of Modern United States Dollar Coins* (Whitman Publishing).

Aspects of Striking and Appearance: Most examples are very well struck. Check the higher points of the design. Special issues are uniformly sharply struck.

Proof Coins: Proofs have been made each year and are readily available.

2009, Three Sisters
Reverse designer: Norman E. Nemeth.

2010, Great Law of Peace
Reverse designer: Thomas Cleveland.

2011, Wampanoag Treaty
Reverse designer: Richard Masters.

2012, Trade Routes in the 17th Century
Reverse designer: Thomas Cleveland.

2013, Treaty With the Delawares
Reverse designer: Susan Gamble.

2014, Native Hospitality
Reverse designer: Chris Costello.

2015, Mohawk Ironworkers
Reverse designer: Ronald D. Sanders.

2016, Code Talkers
Reverse designer: Thomas D. Rogers Sr.

2017, Sequoyah
Reverse designer: Chris Costello.

2018, Jim Thorpe
Reverse designer: Michael Gaudioso.

2019, American Indians in Space
Reverse designer: Emily Damstra.

Market Value: Circulation Strikes

MS-64	MS-65	MS-66
$2	$4	$6

Market Value: Proof Strikes

PF-65	PF-69DC
$5	$15

American Innovation (2018 to Date)

Circulation-Strike Mintage: Millions

Proof Mintage: Millions

Field Population: All of current mintages

Designers: ***Obverse:*** Justin Kunz; ***Reverse:*** See image captions for reverse designers. **Weight:** 8.1 grams. **Composition:** Pure copper core with outer layers of manganese brass (.770 copper, .120 zinc, .070 manganese, and .040 nickel). **Diameter:** 26.5 mm. **Edge:** Lettered. **Mints:** Philadelphia, Denver, San Francisco.

Key to Collecting: In 2018 the U.S. Mint issued the first coin in a new, 15-year series: the American Innovation $1 Coin Program. Authorized by Public Law 115-197, each of the golden dollars in the program features a reverse design that "symbolizes quintessentially American traits—the willingness to explore, to discover, and to create one's own destiny." Four new designs, in Uncirculated and Proof finishes, are issued each year from 2019 through 2032—one for each state, in the order in which the states ratified the Constitution or were admitted to the Union, and then for the District of Columbia and each of the five U.S. territories (Puerto Rico, Guam, American Samoa, the U.S. Virgin Islands, and the Northern Mariana Islands). Like all dollar coins minted after 2011, they are issued for numismatic sales only; none are distributed for circulation.

The reverse designs are selected by processes similar to those the Mint has followed for other recent coin programs. Each state, district, or territory is involved in the selection of its coin's potential themes, with the secretary of the Treasury having final decision-making authority. The U.S. Commission of Fine Arts and the Citizens Coinage Advisory Committee review designs and advise the Mint's artists and the Treasury secretary.

The American Innovation dollars bear the following required inscriptions: on the obverse, IN GOD WE TRUST and the denomination; on the reverse, the name of the state, district, or territory (as appropriate), along with UNITED STATES OF AMERICA; and incused into the edge, the date, the mintmark, and the inscription E PLURIBUS UNUM. The obverse common to all coins in the series depicts a left-facing profile of the Statue of Liberty, as designed by Justin Kunz and sculpted by Phebe Hemphill.

While each issue from 2019 through 2032 represents an individual state, district, or territory, the 2018 inaugural issue (designed by Donna Weaver and sculpted by Renata Gordon) represents the American Innovations program in general. A pattern of gears and cogs represents American industry; below, a facsimile of George Washington's signature with SIGNED FIRST PATENT beneath it together represent the presidential signature on the first-ever U.S. patent, issued July 31, 1790. On a cartouche at the right, an eagle crouches on an angled shield, its wings spread behind it, with tools representing innovation (hammer, plow, wheel, etc.) below it.

American Innovation dollars are common in high grades, and are typically collected in Mint State and Proof.

Aspects of Striking and Appearance: These coins are well struck and visually attractive.

Proof Coins: Proofs are made each year and are readily available directly from the Mint and from secondary-market coin dealers.

2018, American Innovators
Reverse designer: Donna Weaver

Market Value: Circulation Strikes

MS-69
$3

Market Value: Proof Strikes

PF-69
$15

20
Trade Dollars
1873-1885

Overview of the Denomination

The majority of Liberty Seated dollars minted after 1850 had been shipped to China, so the Treasury Department in the early 1870s decided to create a special coin for that commerce. Called at first the commercial dollar, then the trade dollar, the denomination became a reality in 1873. The obverse design by chief engraver William Barber depicted Miss Liberty seated on a bale of merchandise, facing to the left, toward Asia, with an expanse of ocean at her feet, symbolic of the trade to the west with China. On the reverse a perched eagle and inscriptions were used, including the weight and fineness of the coin, unusual: 420 GRAINS, 900 Fineness.

From this time until 1878, trade dollars were made in large quantities, primarily at San Francisco (the most active port servicing the China trade). In Canton they were readily accepted and earned high praise from merchants and officials alike. By any accounting the denomination was a resounding success.[21] However, such pieces were made only when silver depositors specifically requested trade dollars. Accordingly, mintage figures tended to be erratic. The silver-producing states in the West were having great difficulty, and through influence with senators and congressmen they succeeded in having the Bland-Allison Act passed on February 28, 1878, which signaled the end of the trade dollar and replaced it with the new "Morgan" dollar, the latter made specifically to the account of the government, not to outside depositors. Now, at long last, Uncle Sam bought millions of ounces of silver, whether needed or not, a practice that continued for years afterwards, much to the satisfaction of citizens and businesses in the West.

The production of trade dollars continued for several years after 1878, with sales of Proofs to collectors through 1883, followed by a small number secretly made in 1884 and 1885.

Selecting a Coin for Your Type Set

Choosing a trade dollar for a type set is easy enough to do, the choices being a circulation strike, which requires some connoisseurship, or else a Proof, most of which are sharply struck and attractive. Enough exist in both formats that there will be no problem obtaining one that is just right, except that gem Mint State pieces are elusive.

Beyond a Type Set

Collecting trade dollars by date and mint took a giant step forward in popularity after the publication in 1993 of my two-volume study, *Silver Dollars and Trade Dollars of the United States: A Complete Encyclopedia.*

There are two great rarities among trade dollars, both at the tail-end of the series, the Proof-only 1884, of which just ten were struck, and the Proof-only 1885, of which only five were made. Neither was produced openly, and examples were sold for the private profit of Mint officials, going to John W. Haseltine, a Philadelphia dealer who was a favored outlet for such things. The existence of these coins was not generally known to numismatists until 1907 and 1908 when examples began popping up on the market. As to the mintage figures, the numbers five and 10 have no official origin, but are said to represent the number once held by Haseltine. Relatively few numismatists have been able to afford examples of these two dates.

Beyond the above, a complete collection of trade dollars of the 1873 to 1883 years can be formed with some effort. Proofs were made of each year during this span, and beginning in 1878 only Proofs were made at the Philadelphia Mint, with no branch issues. Accordingly, the 1878 to 1883 years are Proof-only. These had greater appeal to collectors of an earlier era, and more were saved, with the curious result that Proofs of the otherwise common dates 1873 to 1877 are much harder to find today, especially in choice condition.

Circulation strikes were regularly produced from 1873 through 1878, with emphasis on the San Francisco and Carson City mints, these being closest to Asia, where such pieces were used. Some coins went into domestic circulation (they were legal tender until this provision was repealed on July 22, 1876). Later, after 1876, when coins were traded in the United States, they were valued on their silver content, not their face value. In 1878 America had the very curious situation in which the lighter-weight 412.5 grain Morgan dollar of 90% silver was worth a dollar in circulation, while the 420 grain trade dollar, also of 90% silver, was worth only its melt-down value of about 90 cents! Such things are often beyond understanding.

Very few of the circulating issues were saved by numismatists, with the result today that assembling a collection in choice or gem Mint State can be a great challenge. The key issue, standing high above all others, is the 1878-CC, the lowest mintage in the series. This variety is scarce in any and all grades. As trade dollars became numismatically popular in the United States, thousands were repatriated from China, often bearing Chinese characters, called "chopmarks," applied by bankers and merchants. More often than not the imported coins were harshly cleaned in China, as the owners thought this would make them more desirable. However, many choice and undamaged pieces have been imported as well. The pieces with chopmarks are collectable in their own right in view of their historical significance.

The specialist may want to explore the *varieties* (misleadingly called *types* in the literature) that exist in the trade dollar series, with the Type I issue, minted from 1873 through 1876, having the ribbon ends on the obverse (on the ribbon inscribed LIBERTY) pointing toward the left, and Type II, made from 1876 to 1885, having the ribbon ends pointing downward. There are some other differences as well. The reverses were made in two varieties. Type I, with a berry on the stem below the eagle's claw on the right, was produced from 1873 through 1876, while the Type II, without berry in this position, was produced from 1876 to 1885. For the year 1876 the various dates and mints, including Proofs, can be collected as follows: Type I/I, Type I/II, and Type II/II. Although specialists are quite aware of these, they are not generally known in a wider sense, and the *Guide Book of United States Coins* does not mention them.

Trade Dollar (1873–1885)

Circulation-Strike Mintage: 35,954,535

Proof Mintage: 11,404

Field Population: Circulated, 75,000 to 125,000; Mint State, 15,000 to 25,000; Proof, 7,000 to 8,500

Designer: William Barber. **Weight:** 27.22 grams. **Composition:** .900 silver, .100 copper (net weight .7874 oz. pure silver). **Diameter:** 38.1 mm. **Edge:** Reeded. **Mints:** Philadelphia, Carson City, San Francisco.

Key to Collecting: Circulated trade dollars are relatively common, with typical grades being EF and AU. Many have been cleaned, often with abrasive substances. Many have Chinese chopmarks, considered in this instance to be an advantage (although a deduction is typically made from the price) rather than an impairment, as these are marks of commerce. Mint State coins are fairly scarce, particularly if unimpaired, and are mostly in grades from MS-60 to MS-62 or MS-63. Truly choice examples as well as gems are in the distinct minority.

Aspects of Striking and Appearance: Most trade dollars were made in strictly utilitarian fashion. Weaknesses are often seen, including on Miss Liberty, her hair details, and the obverse stars. On the reverse the eagle should be checked, particularly the lower areas including the feathers on the legs.

Proof Coins: Most Proofs on the market are dated from 1878 through 1883, these being the pieces most cherished by numismatists in the early days (in view of the Proof-only status of these years). There was a market speculation in Proofs in late 1879 and early 1880, resulting in the extraordinary production of 1,987 Proofs for the latter year. Today Proofs are on the market in all states of preservation, and some care must be taken to select a choice one.

Market Value: Circulation Strikes

VG-8	F-12	VF-20	EF-40	AU-50	MS-60	MS-62	MS-63	MS-64	MS-65
$165	$185	$225	$300	$350	$875	$1,200	$1,600	$2,900	$8,500

Market Value: Proof Strikes

PF-40	PF-60	PF-63	PF-64	PF-65
$1,250	$1,500	$3,000	$3,800	$6,500

Retail Price Trends

Year	EF-40	MS-65	PF-65
1946	$3	$9	$16
1950	$4.50	$9	$22.50
1960	$10	$25	$75
1970	$37.50	$900	$2,500
1980	$85	$2,000	$9,500

Year	EF-40	MS-65	PF-65
1990	$175	$4,000	$8,000
2000	$135	$6,000	$7,500
2010	$190	$8,250	$6,000
2019	$300	$8,500	$6,500

21
Gold Dollars
1849-1889

Overview of the Denomination

Eureka! "I've found it!" This exclamation, a dramatization of John Marshall's discovery of a gleaming nugget of gold in the tail race of Sutter's Mill on the American River on January 24, 1848, ignited the Gold Rush. Soon, the world was electrified, and tens of thousands of fortune seekers headed to California by land and sea. The prospects of vast quantities of gold continuing to arrive from this land of treasure spurred the passage of the Coinage Act of March 3, 1849. This legislation provided for two new denominations, the gold dollar and the double eagle. Heretofore the smallest value had been the $2.50 quarter eagle.

It fell to Chief Engraver James B. Longacre, in his post since 1844, to create new designs for circulating coinage for both coins. As it developed, the obverse design of each was similar, featuring a female head facing left, with LIBERTY inscribed on the coronet or tiara. Interestingly and not widely known today, Longacre later used the same facial outline on the 1854 $3 gold coin and the 1859 Indian Head cent.

The double eagle design was put on the shelf, to be addressed closely in December. In the meantime work proceeded apace on the gold dollar. Soon, all was in place, and the first pieces were struck for general circulation. These featured what is now known as the *Small Head*, surrounded by 13 stars, with the field plane or flat, rather than basined or curved upward toward the borders. The earliest pieces did not have any indication of the designer, but soon the initial L was added to the neck truncation. The reverse depicted an open wreath enclosing the denomination and the date. It seems that the master dies of 1849 included the date, a departure from earlier practices in which the date was punched in separately with a four-digit logotype. Venturing into this area of efficiency did not prove worthwhile, so it seems, and later years of gold dollars had the dates added separately.

Subsequently, in 1849, the head of Miss Liberty was enlarged and the fields were basined, creating a new style that was used through the balance of this type to 1854. On the reverse, the wreath was lengthened on both sides, changing from what is called the early or Open Wreath style to the later Close Wreath, the latter being used through 1854.

Production was accomplished at the Philadelphia, Charlotte, Dahlonega, and New Orleans mints, joined by San Francisco in 1854. In 1850 silver coins became scarce in circulation as their bullion value exceeded their face value, making them unprofitable to coin except for use at exchange brokers and for sale at a premium. Filling the void in everyday commerce was the gold dollar, which saw great service and went on in the next several years to achieve record production, mostly at the Philadelphia Mint, but with significant quantities at the branches as well. Finally, the Act of March 21, 1853, reduced the silver content of the half dime, dime, quarter, and half dollar, after which these circulated again, relieving the pressure on the gold dollar. The weight of silver dollars was not changed, and thus silver dollars did not circulate until many years later. Except in the year 1849, the gold dollar and silver dollar never competed head-on in circulation.

Although the gold dollar was popular and useful, the small diameter of just 13 mm was complained of, and partway through 1854 a change was made, creating what is known today as the Type II dollar, at 15 mm. Miss Liberty was restyled, still facing left, but with a more delicately arranged portrait and wearing a headdress decorated with *ostrich* plumes, sometimes called an *Indian* headdress in the literature, but in real life few if any Native Americans had access to the plumage of this huge land-bound bird from Africa. Around the obverse UNITED STATES OF AMERICA was placed instead of the stars earlier used. The reverse was restyled with an "agricultural wreath" of cotton, corn, wheat, and tobacco, enclosing the denomination. This reverse remained unchanged for the rest of the series and was also used on the $3 gold of 1854 and the Flying Eagle cent of 1857 (and the famous pattern of 1856).

Great problems arose with the striking of the Type II gold dollars, as the small head of Miss Liberty was in high relief. In the coining press, the deepest parts of the obverse die were opposite the two central digits in the date on the reverse die. The metal could not flow effectively in both directions, with the result that nearly all pieces of this design were lightly struck on the central numerals 85. Often striking was light in other areas as well.

Although the Type II gold dollar was intended to be more convenient with its larger size, the difficulties of having pieces strike up sharply prompted the motif to be modified in 1856 to the so-called Type III design. The obverse featured a larger, shallower head of Miss Liberty, again with ostrich feathers, while the reverse remained unchanged. Gold dollars of this motif were produced continuously through 1889.

Beginning in early 1862, when the outcome of the Civil War became increasingly uncertain, gold coins of all kinds were hoarded, soon followed by silver. Gold dollars were no longer seen in circulation in the East and Midwest, and after 1862 production fell off sharply. Although it was hoped that gold coins would soon be used in commerce after the Civil War, this did not prove to be the case. Many political discussions and arguments ensued, and despite hopes and expectations, gold coins did not circulate at par (in terms of Legal Tender notes and other federal paper money) until December 17, 1878. After that time, it was soon learned that the wide availability of newly minted "Morgan" silver dollars, plus the acceptance of paper dollars, made the gold dollar redundant. Accordingly, mintages remained small, and coins were not readily available at banks. In fact, they traded for a small premium and were in demand by jewelers and investors. In 1889 the denomination was discontinued along with the nickel three-cent piece and $3 gold.

COLLECTING A TYPE SET OF GOLD DOLLARS

Although a case could be made for designating the Small Head, Open Wreath gold dollar as a separate type, it is not generally collected as such. Instead, pieces dated from 1849 through 1854 are collectively designated as Type I, with a single piece being sufficient. Examples today are readily available in all grades, although truly choice and gem Mint State pieces are in the minority. To my eye, if you want just one of the Type I style, an 1849 Small Head is a great choice, for nearly all examples are sharply struck and have excellent eye appeal.

In contrast, the Type II design, produced at the Philadelphia Mint in part of 1854, and at the Philadelphia, Charlotte, Dahlonega, and New Orleans mints in 1855, and only at the San Francisco Mint in 1856, is a great challenge. Examples are scarcer in all grades than are those of Type I and III. Choice and gem coins are especially rare. Striking is a great problem, and while some sharp pieces exist, probably 80% or more have areas of weakness, typically at the 85 (center two digits) of the date, but often on the headdress and elsewhere. Further, the borders are sometimes imperfect. Some are downright miserable! As certification services do not take note of such things, cherrypicking is recommended.

Type III gold dollars, made from 1856 through 1889, offer a clear sky and smooth sailing, and you can acquire a specimen in just about any grade you desire, including choice and gem Mint State, most of which are well struck and have excellent eye appeal. Among Type III gold dollars the dates from 1879 through 1889 inclusive are most often seen, as these were widely saved by the public at the time and did not circulate to any appreciable extent. Some of these have enticingly low mintage figures, making them very appealing.

BEYOND A TYPE SET

Forming a specialized collection of gold dollars is a fascinating pursuit, one that has drawn the attention of many numismatists over the years. A complete run of date and mintmark issues from 1849 through 1889 includes no impossible rarities, although the 1875, with just 20 Proofs and 400 circulation strikes reported to have been made, is the key date. Interestingly, while the dollars of 1879 through 1889 often have remarkably low mintages, as mentioned earlier these were saved in quantity, and certain of these dates are easily obtainable, although not necessarily inexpensive.

The early year branch-mint gold dollars are a special challenge. Among the Charlotte Mint varieties, the 1849 comes with an Open Wreath (of which just five are presently known, with a rumor of a sixth) and with a Close Wreath, the latter being scarce but available. Later Charlotte gold dollars, extending through 1859, range from scarce to rare.

Gold dollars were struck at the Dahlonega Mint from 1849 through 1861. In the latter year, the facility was under the control of Confederate States of America forces, and thus the 1861-D gold dollars, rare in any event, are even more desirable as true Confederate coins. The New Orleans Mint also produced gold dollars, which in general are better struck than those at the Charlotte and Dahlonega mints. From 1854 intermittently to 1860, and then in 1870, gold dollars were struck in San Francisco. These Western issues are usually sharply defined and range from scarce to rare. In particular, choice and gem Mint State pieces of the San Francisco Mint are elusive.

Liberty Head (1849–1854)

Circulation-Strike Mintage: 12,565,273

Proof Mintage: Fewer than 20

Field Population: Circulated, more than 200,000; Mint State, 30,000 to 45,000; Proof, 10 to 14

Designer: James B. Longacre. **Weight:** 1.672 grams. **Composition:** .900 gold, .100 copper (net weight .04837 oz. pure gold). **Diameter:** 13 mm. **Edge:** Reeded. **Mints:** Philadelphia, Charlotte, Dahlonega, New Orleans, San Francisco.

Key to Collecting: A representative example can be obtained with ease in just about any grade desired from VF upward. Coins of the first year, 1849 "Small Head," not often collected as a separate type, are frequently seen in Mint State, probably because they were saved as souvenirs or curiosities but are not inexpensive. These combine the first year of issue together with the distinctive Small Head portrait, flat or plain fields, and open wreath. Generally, Mint State examples are quite choice with superb eye appeal and are well struck. Mint State examples of the Large Head gold dollars from 1849 through 1854 are most available for the higher-mintage dates of the early 1850s. Later in the series, the high-mintage issues of 1851, 1852, and 1853 offer possibilities. It is always interesting to add flavor to a type set, and you may wish to consider a Charlotte, Dahlonega, or New Orleans gold dollar.

Aspects of Striking and Appearance: The quality varies from issue to issue. Points to check include the high parts of Miss Liberty's hair, the wreath details, the date numerals, and the denticles. Also the *fields* of the coin should be checked to be sure they are not grainy or wavy. Some connoisseurship is needed.

Proof Coins: Although a few Proofs were coined in the early years, they are for all practical purposes unobtainable. Only about a dozen are known.[16]

Market Value: Circulation Strikes

VF-20	EF-40	AU-50	AU-55	AU-58	MS-60	MS-62	MS-63	MS-64	MS-65
$200	$225	$240	$250	$275	$325	$350	$500	$750	$2,250

Market Value: Proof Strikes

PF-60
$100,000

Retail Price Trends

Year	EF-40	MS-60	MS-65
1946	$6	$7.50	$10
1950	$6	$7.50	$11
1960	$20	$24	$36
1970	$60	$70	$1,000
1980	$220	$400	$2,500

Year	EF-40	MS-60	MS-65
1990	$225	$800	$4,000
2000	$150	$350	$5,000
2010	$225	$375	$5,000
2019	$225	$325	$2,250

Indian Princess Head, Small Head (1854–1856)

Circulation-Strike Mintage: 1,633,426

Proof Mintage: Fewer than 35

Field Population: Circulated, 25,000 to 35,000; Mint State, 6,500 to 9,000; Proof, 17 to 22

Designer: James B. Longacre. **Weight:** 1.672 grams. **Composition:** .900 gold, .100 copper (net weight .04837 oz. pure gold). **Diameter:** 15 mm. **Edge:** Reeded. **Mints:** Philadelphia, Charlotte, Dahlonega, New Orleans, San Francisco.

Key to Collecting: The Type II gold dollar, minted from the end of 1854 at the Philadelphia Mint, then at various mints in 1855, followed by a San Francisco production in 1856, is the key to a gold dollar type set. Specimens are easily enough found in grades such as VF, EF, and even AU, but Mint State pieces are elusive in comparison to the demand for them. When seen, Mint State pieces are apt to be dated 1854 or 1855, these also being the highest-mintage issues. Branch-mint coins in Mint State are virtually impossible to obtain.

Aspects of Striking and Appearance: Striking typically ranges from indifferent to absolutely miserable. Many have clash marks from die damage. Check the feather details and other portrait elements of Miss Liberty, the two central figures of the date on the reverse, the wreath, and the denticles. Often the denticles can be blurred or even missing. The fields of the coin can be irregular, sometimes even appearing as wavy. In *absolute* terms, the gold dollars of this type are not rare, but in *relative* terms, there is such an extensive demand for coins of this design that market activity is intense.

Proof Coins: Proofs exist of the 1854 and 1855 issues but were made in very small quantities. For all practical purposes, they are uncollectible. Only about 20 are known.[17]

Market Value: Circulation Strikes

VF-20	EF-40	AU-50	AU-55	AU-58	MS-60	MS-62	MS-63	MS-64	MS-65
$325	$425	$500	$625	$750	$1,250	$2,250	$5,750	$7,750	$25,000

Market Value: Proof Strikes

PF-60	PF-63	PF-64	PF-65
$75,000	$165,000	$225,000	$325,000

Retail Price Trends

Year	EF-40	MS-60	MS-65	PF-64
1946	$9.50	$12.50	$18	$130
1950	$9.50	$12.50	$18	$150
1960	$30	$45	$67.50	$400
1970	$275	$425	$8,000	$10,000
1980	$400	$1,900	$20,000	$70,000

Year	EF-40	MS-60	MS-65	PF-64
1990	$575	$5,500	$30,000	$100,000
2000	$350	$2,500	$35,000	$180,000
2010	$450	$1,700	$32,000	$225,000
2019	$425	$1,250	$25,000	$225,000

Indian Princess Head, Large Head (1856-1889)

Circulation-Strike Mintage: 5,327,443

Proof Mintage: *8,700*

Field Population: Circulated, 15,000 to 25,000; Mint State, 25,000 to 40,000; Proof, 5,500 to 7,000

Designer: James B. Longacre. **Weight:** 1.672 grams. **Composition:** .900 gold, .100 copper (net weight .04837 oz. pure gold). **Diameter:** 15 mm. **Edge:** Reeded. **Mints:** Philadelphia, Charlotte, Dahlonega, San Francisco.

Key to Collecting: After having emerged from the Type I and Type II gold dollars, you are home free, so to speak, with dollars of the Type III design minted 1856 to 1889. Actually, this is not true—for chances are good that you will find a nice Type III before you acquire either of the earlier designs. Gold dollars of the Type III style did not circulate extensively (except in the West), and today most pieces grade EF or better. Mint State coins abound, particularly for the dates 1879 through 1889, during which time they were a popular investment and speculation, and despite their being currently minted (only at Philadelphia) they sold for a slight premium in the marketplace.

Aspects of Striking and Appearance: While most Type III gold dollars are well struck, it will pay to check the features, including the portrait of Miss Liberty, the date and wreath on the reverse, and the denticles.

Proof Coins: Proofs were produced of all years and, when seen today, are typically from the 1880s. At the time gold dollars were a popular investment and speculation, and many orders were placed for them. That said, the figures cannot be regarded as proportional to the pieces existing today, for the last year, 1889, of which 1,779 Proofs were reported to have been struck, is today a great rarity and is several times more elusive than are the lower-mintage dollars of 1884 to 1888.

Market Value: Circulation Strikes

VF-20	EF-40	AU-50	AU-55	AU-58	MS-60	MS-62	MS-63	MS-64	MS-65
$245	$250	$265	$285	$300	$350	$425	$525	$750	$1,200

Market Value: Proof Strikes

PF-60	PF-63	PF-64	PF-65
$3,250	$5,000	$7,000	$10,500

Retail Price Trends

Year	EF-40	MS-60	MS-65	PF-64
1946	$6	$7	$10	$27.50
1950	$7	$8.50	$12	$30
1960	$20	$26	$40	$70
1970	$65	$75	$175	$150
1980	$200	$375	$800	$1,500

Year	EF-40	MS-60	MS-65	PF-64
1990	$225	$800	$900	$2,000
2000	$140	$325	$1,500	$4,000
2010	$230	$325	$2,250	$7,200
2019	$250	$350	$1,200	$7,000

22
Quarter Eagles ($2.50 Gold Coins) 1796-1929

Overview of the Denomination

Although $2.50 gold coins or quarter eagles were provided for in the Mint Act of April 2, 1792, they were not struck until 1796. In that year, a curious motif was introduced, at least in comparison to the rest of American coinage. The obverse depicted Miss Liberty wearing a conical cloth cap, facing right, *without stars* to left and right, and simply the date below, giving it a cameo-like appearance without equivalent anywhere else. The reverse introduced the heraldic eagle motif based on the Great Seal of the United States, its first appearance in the gold series (although 1795 $5 pieces with the heraldic eagle are known, these were not struck until 1798, employing a serviceable 1795 obverse die still on hand).

Soon, the motif of the quarter eagle was modified by adding stars to the obverse, a style continued through 1807, with some variations in the star arrangements on the obverse and also on the reverse above the eagle. Early $2.50 pieces bore no mark of denomination. The dies were the same diameter as the silver dime, and, interestingly enough, in the early nineteenth century, certain of the same reverses were used in both series.

In 1808 the Capped Bust design by John Reich made its appearance briefly, as it was discontinued, and no pieces of this denomination were again struck until 1821, at which time a different design was used.

From 1821 through 1834, production of quarter eagles was small. No gold coins of any kind circulated at par in the United States. The largest denomination being produced at the time was the $5 half eagle ($10 pieces had last been made in 1804). Virtually all of the half eagles were shipped overseas. Companies involved in the export trade preferred the easier-to-count half eagles and thus quarter eagle production was quite small. Although $2.50 and $5 pieces did not circulate, they could be purchased from exchange dealers at a premium in terms of paper money. Certain federal legislators had the option of receiving their pay in gold coins and took advantage of this. No doubt many if not most of the quarter eagles were used in this fashion, rather than for export. Accordingly, a higher percentage of them survive today in terms of the original mintage.

By spring 1834, no gold coins had been seen in circulation for nearly a generation. Led by the efforts of Missouri Senator Thomas Hart Benton, the Act of June 28, 1834, was passed. It authorized the weight of gold coins to be reduced, effective August 1, and pieces struck after that date circulated at par. No longer was it profitable to melt or export them. However, the earlier quarter eagles continued to trade at a premium at exchange dealers, and certain banks posted buying prices for them. In time the Second Bank of the United States, in Philadelphia, turned in a stash of pre-1834 gold coins to the Mint, earning a nice profit. These went to the melting pot (otherwise, the rarity ratings of early gold, as we now know them, would be vastly different).

Reflective of the change in weight and intrinsic value of the new quarter eagle, to permit instant identification, the motto E PLURIBUS UNUM was omitted from the reverse. Miss Liberty was restyled to what is now known as the *Classic Head.* Original government correspondence indicates that E PLURIBUS UNUM was supposed to be restored in 1835, as by that time, the date alone would identify the new type. However, this was never done. Quarter eagles of the Classic Head style were produced through 1839, including at the Charlotte, Dahlonega, and New Orleans mints toward the end of the series.

The Classic Head motif is properly attributed to William Kneass, who was chief engraver at the time. However, it seems that the portrait was later modified by Christian Gobrecht, who joined the Philadelphia Mint in September 1835 as *second* engraver (he had far more talent than Kneass, and specifically did not want to be called an *assistant* engraver). By this time, Kneass had suffered an incapacitating stroke. Accordingly, virtually all of the design work in all series after 1835 was done by Gobrecht until Gobrecht's death in 1844.

In 1840 the Liberty Head, sometimes called the Braided Hair or Coronet Head, style made its appearance, generally following the motif first used on the $10 coin in 1838 and then the copper cent and gold half eagle of 1839. The Gobrecht Liberty Head design extended without major change through and including 1907, the longest span of any obverse/reverse combination in the history of American coinage.

In terms of public use, the glory days of the quarter eagle seem to have been from the inception of the Classic Head design in 1834 through the 1850s, with special service recorded from 1850 through early 1853 when there were no silver coins in commerce.

Beginning in early 1862, gold and silver coins disappeared from circulation. It was not until December 17, 1878, that gold coins were again seen in commerce in the East and Midwest. By the latter time, the utility of the denomination had been largely supplanted by paper money, and, accordingly, production remained relatively low. There was always a demand for small denomination gold coins as gifts and souvenirs, particularly around the December holiday season. Gold dollars answered this demand in the 1880s, but after the smaller-denomination was discontinued in 1889, quarter eagles served that purpose.

In 1905 President Theodore Roosevelt intended to have sculptor Augustus Saint-Gaudens redesign the quarter eagle along with other gold denominations. However, the sculptor died in 1907, having largely completed the motifs only for the $10 and $20 pieces. On the recommendation of William Sturgis Bigelow, Boston sculptor Bela Lyon Pratt was tapped to design the quarter eagle and half eagle. The obverse depicted an Indian chief (said to have been modeled after Hollow Horn Bear, a Lakota chief[18]), and the reverse was a copy of the standing eagle used by Saint-Gaudens on Roosevelt's unofficial inaugural medal of 1905 as well as Saint-Gaudens's $10 of 1907. The motifs were incuse or recessed, with the field of the coin being the highest area. Such pieces were very unpopular with collectors, and columns in *The Numismatist* were filled with complaints. Quarter eagles of the Indian Head design were made intermittently from 1908 through 1929, after which coinage ceased, the same year that the half eagle was terminated.

COLLECTING A TYPE SET OF QUARTER EAGLES

Early types in the quarter eagle series range from rare to very rare. The first, the 1796 without stars on the obverse, Heraldic Eagle motif on the reverse, is a classic, one of the most desired of all pieces needed for a type set, and accordingly expensive. Most examples are in such grades as EF and AU.

Quarter eagles with stars on the obverse and with the Heraldic Eagle reverse were produced from 1796 intermittently through 1807. Today, they exist in modest numbers, particularly in grades such as EF and AU, but on an absolute basis are fairly rare.

The stand-alone 1808 Capped Bust type by John Reich, of which only 2,710 were minted, is the rarest single type coin in the entire American copper, nickel, silver, and gold series, possibly excepting the 1839 Gobrecht dollar (in a different category as Proof restrikes were made), and in a close race with the 1796 No Stars quarter eagle. Examples of the 1808 can be found in various grades from VF through AU, only rarely higher. These are necessarily expensive.

The next style of quarter eagle, from 1821 through 1827, is rare but when seen is usually in grades such as EF, AU, or even lower ranges of Mint State. The same can be said for the modified quarter eagle from 1829 through early 1834. The issues of 1821 to 1834 are studied as two types in the text below, but many numismatists opt to combine them and acquire but a single example to illustrate this era.

Finally, with the advent of the Classic Head in late 1834, continuing through 1839, quarter eagles become affordable. Specimens can be found in just about any grade desired from VF on up, including lower ranges of Mint State. Then come the Liberty Head quarter eagles minted continuously from 1840 through 1907, in sufficient numbers and for such a long time that it will not be difficult to obtain a piece, with choice and gem coins being plentiful for the dates of the early twentieth century.

Closing out the design scenario for the quarter eagles is the Indian Head type of 1908 through 1929. These pieces are plentiful today, but grading can be difficult, as the highest part on the coin is the *field*, an area immediately subject to contact marks and wear. Even experts are often far apart on what constitutes, for example, an MS-63 coin. Accordingly, although many opportunities exist in the marketplace, I suggest that you approach with great care the buying of one, an example that has frosty, lustrous fields (remember this is the highest area of the coin and sometimes difficult to find truly lustrous).

BEYOND A TYPE SET

Collecting quarter eagles by dates, mintmarks, and major varieties is a very appealing pursuit. Although there are many scarce and rare coins—this description is applicable for any variety from 1796 through early 1834—none are truly impossible. Then come the Classic Head issues of 1834 to 1839, including mintmarks, the latter especially scarce in higher grades.

Liberty Head quarter eagles, produced continuously from 1840 through 1907, include a number of key issues, among which is the famous 1854-S (usually seen in well circulated grades), the Proof-only 1863 (of which only 30 were struck), and a number of elusive mintmarks. Of particular interest is the 1848 with CAL. counterstamped on the reverse, signifying that such pieces were made from gold bullion brought in a special shipment from California.

Capped Bust to Right, No Stars on Obverse (1796)

Circulation-Strike Mintage: *963*

Field Population: Circulated, 150 to 225; Mint State, 20

Designer: Robert Scot. **Weight:** 4.37 grams. **Composition:** .9167 gold, .0833 silver and copper (net weight .14131 oz. pure gold). **Diameter:** Approximately 20 mm. **Edge:** Reeded. **Mint:** Philadelphia.

Key to Collecting: This particular type is one of the great objects of desire in the American coinage series. It is popularly thought that just 963 were struck, this being from early delivery reports. There is always the possibility that the same die combination could have been used later, but if so the additional number would have been small, as the total production of quarter eagles during this decade was minuscule.

The starless obverse design is unique among gold coins of the period, giving this type a special desirability. The reasons for the omission of stars are not known today. Perhaps it was thought that stars on the Heraldic Eagle reverse, which made its coinage debut with this type, would suffice. Later, stars were added to the obverse design, but not to this die—a different obverse die was made, creating the next type listed here. Examples of the starless obverse type are very scarce in all grades, especially so at higher levels. Circulated coins are very rare, typically EF or AU, often with a generous amount of luster, particularly on the reverse. Mint State examples are also few and far between. Just a few exist, mostly at the entry or MS-60 level or thereabouts.

Aspects of Striking and Appearance: Most pieces are lightly struck in one area or another, and finding an example with sharp details to Miss Liberty's head, the word LIBERTY bold, and with the reverse details sharp, plus sharp denticles on obverse and reverse, is an *impossibility*. However, among those that do exist there are variations, and some selection is recommended.

Notes: There is no indication of the denomination of this coin on the obverse, reverse, or edge.

Market Value: Circulation Strikes

F-12	VF-20	EF-40	AU-50	AU-55	AU-58	MS-60	MS-63	MS-64	MS-65
$57,500	$75,000	$95,000	$125,000	$165,000	$200,000	$250,000	$750,000	$1,000,000	$2,000,000

Retail Price Trends

Year	EF-40	MS-60	Year	EF-40	MS-60
1946	$2.50	$12	1990	$23,000	$45,000
1950	$250	$300	2000	$35,000	$125,000
1960	$950	$1,150	2010	$92,000	$225,000
1970	$6,250	$7,750	2019	$95,000	$250,000
1980	$16,000	$30,000			

Capped Bust to Right, Stars on Obverse (1796–1807)

Circulation-Strike Mintage: 18,524

Field Population: Circulated, 1,200 to 2,000; Mint State, 40 to 60

Designer: Robert Scot. **Weight:** 4.37 grams. **Composition:** .9167 gold, .0833 silver and copper (net weight .14131 oz. pure gold). **Diameter:** Approximately 20 mm. **Edge:** Reeded. **Mint:** Philadelphia.

Key to Collecting: While the 1796 to 1807 type with Capped Bust to Right, now with stars on the obverse, is more available than the starless 1796, examples are still very rare, with the entire mintage falling below 20,000 pieces. Few if any of these were deliberately saved for numismatic purposes. The star arrangements on the obverse vary, as do the star counts on the reverse, but these have not generally been considered as separate types. Most extant examples are circulated, typically in EF and AU grades, rarely lower. As a class, such pieces are rare, this being especially true of the earlier dates of the type. Mint State pieces are quite rare, not in the league of the 1796 without stars, but still very difficult to find. Some at the MS-60 or so level have graduated or moved up from being called AU a generation ago, the same being true of many other coins in different series. Choice and gem pieces are very rare, especially if sharply struck and with good eye appeal.

Aspects of Striking and Appearance: Striking varies. Typically, some weakness is shown at one of more of these areas: central hair details of Miss Liberty, stars at the left and right obverse border, and obverse denticles. On the reverse weakness is often seen at the center as well as on the stars above the eagle and the denticles. Perfection is more of a goal than a reality, but still within the available supply many pieces are better struck than are others.

Notes: There is no indication of the denomination of this coin on the obverse, reverse, or edge. Certain of the same reverse dies were used on both dimes and quarter eagles of this era.

Market Value: Circulation Strikes

F-12	VF-20	EF-40	AU-50	AU-55	AU-58	MS-60	MS-62	MS-63	MS-64	MS-65
$5,250	$8,500	$14,000	$18,000	$21,000	$23,500	$32,500	$55,000	$135,000	$200,000	$250,000

Retail Price Trends

Year	EF-40	MS-60	MS-65
1946	$70	$100	$140
1950	$70	$100	$140
1960	$175	$240	$350
1970	$950	$1,500	$3,000
1980	$3,500	$6,500	$13,000
1990	$6,000	$16,000	$30,000
2000	$5,500	$17,500	$40,000
2010	$12,000	$20,000	$300,000
2019	$14,000	$32,500	$250,000

Draped Bust to Left, Large Size (1808)

Circulation-Strike Mintage: 2,710

Field Population: Circulated, 140 to 220; Mint State, 3 to 4

Designer: John Reich. **Weight:** 4.37 grams. **Composition:** .9167 gold, .0833 silver and copper (net weight .14131 oz. pure gold). **Diameter:** Approximately 20 mm. **Edge:** Reeded. **Mint:** Philadelphia.

Key to Collecting: This single-year type features the Capped Bust Left design by John Reich, an adaptation of the design introduced in 1807 on the half dollar. A couple hundred or so circulated issues exist, not super-rare in the context of early quarter eagle dates, but of special desirability and market interest due to the necessity of having a piece to complete a gold type set. Any specimen is an attention-getter *par excellence!* Only a few Mint State coins exist. These typically have nice eye appeal with great luster.

Aspects of Striking and Appearance: All examples are lightly struck in one area or another, typically around the rim.

Market Value: Circulation Strikes

F-12	VF-20	EF-40	AU-50	AU-55	AU-58	MS-60	MS-62	MS-63	MS-64	MS-65
$27,500	$40,000	$65,000	$90,000	$105,000	$130,000	$175,000	$275,000	$450,000	$750,000	$2,500,000

Retail Price Trends

Year	EF-40	MS-60
1946	$200	$250
1950	$225	$275
1960	$900	$1,200
1970	$5,250	$7,000
1980	$15,000	$30,000
1990	$19,000	$47,500
2000	$21,000	$45,000
2010	$60,000	$175,000
2019	$65,000	$175,000

Capped Head to Left, Large Diameter (1821–1827)

Circulation-Strike Mintage: 17,042

Proof Mintage: Fewer than 40

Field Population: Circulated, 250 to 350; Mint State, 80 to 110; Proof, 20 to 30

Designer: John Reich. **Weight:** 4.37 grams. **Composition:** .9167 gold, .0833 silver and copper (net weight .14131 oz. pure gold). **Diameter:** 18.5 mm. **Edge:** Reeded. **Mint:** Philadelphia.

Aspects of Striking and Appearance: The striking is usually decent, quite unlike the earlier quarter eagle types. Points to check for sharpness include the hair details of Miss Liberty and the details of the eagle. However, for this particular type, sharp striking is the rule, not the exception.

Proof Coins: Proof coins were made on a limited basis for presentation and for distribution to numismatists. All examples are exceedingly rare today and are usually encountered only when great collections are dispersed.

Market Value: Circulation Strikes

F-12	VF-20	EF-40	AU-50	AU-55	AU-58	MS-60	MS-62	MS-63	MS-64
$6,500	$9,500	$13,100	$17,500	$19,500	$32,500	$35,000	$45,000	$65,000	$100,000

Market Value: Proof Strikes

PF-63	PF-64
$275,000	$450,000

Retail Price Trends

Year	EF-40	MS-60	MS-64	PF-63
1946	$70	$100	$140	$300
1950	$80	$125	$175	$350
1960	$120	$160	$225	$450
1970	$1,250	$2,250	$5,000	$10,000
1980	$4,500	$9,000	$15,000	$20,000

Year	EF-40	MS-60	MS-64	PF-63
1990	$7,000	$17,000	$25,000	$40,000
2000	$5,000	$14,000	$30,000	$50,000
2010	$10,000	$30,000	$95,000	$180,000
2019	$13,100	$35,000	$100,000	$275,000

Capped Head to Left, Reduced Diameter (1829–1834)

Circulation-Strike Mintage: 25,023

Proof Mintage: Fewer than 60

Field Population: Circulated, 300 to 500; Mint State, 200 to 300; Proof, 30 to 40

Designer: John Reich. **Weight:** 4.37 grams. **Composition:** .9167 gold, .0833 silver and copper (net weight .14131 oz. pure gold). **Diameter:** Approximately 18.2 mm. **Edge:** Reeded. **Mint:** Philadelphia.

Key to Collecting: Quarter eagles of the 1829 to 1834 style, with smaller diameter, are significantly more available than those of the earlier type. All dates within this range are rare, and if choice and attractive any given coin is of commanding importance. Mint State coins are hard to find, and when seen are usually MS-60 to MS-62, some of which have moved up from AU listings of a generation ago. Circulated coins constitute the majority of examples of this type, typically in AU grade, but EF pieces come up for sale as well. Scarcely anything lower is to be found in the marketplace.

Aspects of Striking and Appearance: The sharpness of strike is generally not as satisfactory on this issue as on the preceding, especially on the portrait of Miss Liberty, but other areas should be checked as well. Luster is often dull or unsatisfactory. Finding a really choice piece will be a great challenge.

Proof Coins: Proofs were minted of the various years, but in small quantities. Examples are rare.

Market Value: Circulation Strikes

F-12	VF-20	EF-40	AU-50	AU-55	AU-58	MS-60	MS-62	MS-63	MS-64	MS-65
$6,000	$7,500	$9,500	$13,000	$17,000	$18,500	$22,500	$27,500	$35,000	$50,000	$85,000

Market Value: Proof Strikes

PF-63	PF-64
$100,000	$150,000

Retail Price Trends

Year	EF-40	MS-60	MS-64	PF-63
1946	$60	$75	$105	$250
1950	$60	$75	$105	$300
1960	$110	$130	$200	$800
1970	$725	$1,000	$2,000	$4,000
1980	$3,000	$7,000	$8,000	$7,000

Year	EF-40	MS-60	MS-64	PF-63
1990	$5,750	$13,500	$15,000	$25,000
2000	$4,500	$9,000	$25,000	$40,000
2010	$8,500	$22,500	$50,000	$125,000
2019	$9,500	$22,500	$50,000	$100,000

Classic Head, No Motto on Reverse (1834–1839)

Circulation-Strike Mintage: 968,228

Proof Mintage: Fewer than 50

Field Population: Circulated, 8,000 to 12,000; Mint State, 2,500 to 3,500; Proof, 20 to 35

Designer: William Kneass. **Weight:** 4.18 grams. **Composition:** ***1834–1836:*** .8992 gold, .1008 silver and copper (net weight .13258 oz. pure gold); ***1834–1836:*** .900 gold, .100 silver and copper (net weight .1327 oz. pure gold). **Diameter:** 18.2 mm. **Edge:** Reeded. **Mints:** Philadelphia, Charlotte, Dahlonega, New Orleans.

Key to Collecting: Quarter eagles of the Classic Head design appeared in circulation in August 1834 and caused many press notices at the time. These and the related half eagles were often called *yellow jackets*, *yellow boys*, or *Benton's yellow jackets*, after Thomas Hart Benton, an advocate of the coinage bill of June 28, 1834.

In comparison to half eagles, quarter eagles were produced in much smaller quantities, but many exist today, mostly in worn grades from VF through EF, occasionally AU, but not often Mint State. The latter such examples are fairly scarce, and when seen are usually dated early in the type. Typical grades are MS-60 to MS-62 or MS-63. True choice and gem pieces exist and are scarce and very highly prized, insuring great competition when they come up for auction.

Aspects of Striking and Appearance: The striking is generally good, but central areas should be checked, particularly the upper part of the shield and the lower part of the eagle's neck. Eye appeal and luster vary widely, and some discrimination is recommended to select an example that is choice.

Proof Coins: Proofs were made in small quantities, and today probably only a couple dozen or so survive, most bearing the 1834 date. Such coins are in the category of numismatic prizes.

Market Value: Circulation Strikes

F-12	VF-20	EF-40	AU-50	AU-55	AU-58	MS-60	MS-62	MS-63	MS-64	MS-65
$365	$600	$800	$1,250	$1,650	$2,100	$3,250	$4,500	$9,500	$14,500	$50,000

Market Value: Proof Strikes

PF-60	PF-63	PF-64	PF-65
$32,500	$125,000	$200,000	$350,000

Retail Price Trends

Year	EF-40	MS-60	MS-64	PF-63
1946	$14	$18	$24	$200
1950	$14	$17.50	$25	$250
1960	$22.50	$29	$42.50	$700
1970	$110	$175	$600	$6,000
1980	$300	$2,250	$1,300	$8,000
1990	$425	$1,800	$2,000	$25,000
2000	$450	$1,750	$5,000	$50,000
2010	$850	$3,750	$16,000	$100,000
2019	$800	$3,250	$14,500	$125,000

Liberty Head (1840–1907)

Circulation-Strike Mintage: 11,921,171

Proof Mintage: *4,250*

Field Population: Circulated, 125,000 to 160,000; Mint State, 130,000 to 180,000; Proof, 2,600 to 3,400

Designer: Christian Gobrecht. **Weight:** 4.18 grams. **Composition:** .900 gold, .100 copper (net weight .12094 oz. pure gold). **Diameter:** 18 mm. **Edge:** Reeded. **Mints:** Philadelphia, Charlotte, Dahlonega, New Orleans, San Francisco.

Key to Collecting: Introduced in 1840, the Liberty Head quarter eagle remained in use with essentially the same design until 1907, the longest such span in American coinage history. Early dates range from scarce to rare, and most circulated coins are in grades VF to AU, while Mint State coins are exceedingly rare. Toward the end of the series, in the first decade of the twentieth century, Mint State pieces abound. These attractive coins, of cameo-like appearance, have long been numismatic favorites.

Aspects of Striking and Appearance: Most pieces are fairly well struck if dated from 1880 onward. Earlier coins, especially of the Charlotte, Dahlonega, and New Orleans mints, are often lightly struck in areas. The main point to check is the eagle, the details of which can be shallow to the lower left of the shield, and also in the lower part of the eagle's neck.

Proof Coins: Proof coins exist in relation to their original mintages. Most attractive are the frosty cameo issues of the late nineteenth century.

Market Value: Circulation Strikes

VF-20	EF-40	AU-50	AU-55	AU-58	MS-60	MS-62	MS-63	MS-64	MS-65
$275	$285	$300	$325	$375	$400	$425	$475	$575	$900

Market Value: Proof Strikes

PF-60	PF-63	PF-64	PF-65
$4,500	$7,500	$12,500	$17,500

Retail Price Trends

Year	EF-40	MS-60	MS-64	PF-65
1946	$10	$12.50	$17	$25
1950	$10	$12.50	$17	$40
1960	$20	$24	$35	$105
1970	$50	$65	$200	$800
1980	$165	$250	$700	$2,000

Year	EF-40	MS-60	MS-64	PF-65
1990	$240	$900	$1,000	$4,000
2000	$155	$285	$1,800	$7,500
2010	$325	$400	$1,250	$20,000
2019	$285	$400	$575	$17,500

Indian Head (1908-1929)

Circulation-Strike Mintage: 7,250,261

Proof Mintage: 1,827

Field Population: Circulated, 120,000 to 225,000; Mint State, 120,000 to 160,000; Proof, 1,200 to 1,450

Designer: Bela Lyon Pratt. **Weight:** 4.18 grams. **Composition:** .900 gold, .100 copper (net weight .12094 oz. pure gold). **Diameter:** 18 mm. **Edge:** Reeded. **Mints:** Philadelphia, Denver.

Key to Collecting: Seeking to complete the gold series, President Roosevelt approved the Indian Head design created by Bela Lyon Pratt, a former student of Augustus Saint-Gaudens. Roosevelt liked it immediately. Pratt adapted the standing eagle motif used on Saint-Gaudens's 1907 $10. As a matter of convenience, the Mint decided to use the same basic motifs for the $2.50, although this was not Pratt's original commission.

When news of the coins was published in 1908 it took the numismatic community by surprise. Collectors and dealers were virtually unanimous in condemning the designs, which seemed to fall far short of the highly acclaimed Saint-Gaudens $10 and $20 issued in the previous year. As might be expected, only a few numismatists collected the series. Years later, when they became popular there were few choice pieces around, this being especially true of those dated 1909 to 1915.

Circulated coins are plentiful in EF and AU grades, often with luster in the recessed areas.

Aspects of Striking and Appearance: Striking varies. Look for weakness on the high parts of the Indian's bonnet and in the feather details in the headdress. On the reverse, check the feathers on the highest area of the wing. Some pieces struck from worn dies are apt to have grainy or granular fields, this being more true of dates in the 1920s than for earlier issues.

Proof Coins: Sand Blast Proofs were made in 1908 and 1911 to 1915, while Satin Finish Proofs were made of 1909 and 1910. When seen, these are usually in higher Proof grades, 64 and above.

Market Value: Circulation Strikes

VF-20	EF-40	AU-50	MS-60	MS-62	MS-63	MS-64	MS-65
$300	$325	$350	$400	$425	$475	$675	$1,500

Market Value: Proof Strikes

PF-60	PF-63	PF-64	PF-65
$4,500	$7,500	$9,000	$17,500

Retail Price Trends

Year	AU-50	MS-60	MS-64	Sand Blast PF-65
1946	$9	$10	$14	$26
1950	$7	$8	$12	$30
1960	$16	$17.50	$25	$70
1970	$80	$50	$600	$3,000
1980	$150	$600	$2,500	$6,000
1990	$250	$425	$1,500	$7,000
2000	$165	$235	$1,200	$10,000
2010	$300	$325	$1,000	$25,000
2019	$350	$400	$675	$17,500

23
$3 Gold Coins
1854-1889

Overview of the Denomination

Gold coins of the $3 denomination were authorized by the Coinage Act of February 21, 1853, the same piece of legislation that reduced the weight of certain silver coins (resulting in arrows being added to the dates). The logic for having a $3 piece escapes most numismatic students today, for the $2.50 quarter eagle, of nearly the same value, was already well established in circulation. It could have been that the owner of a $3 piece could have purchased a sheet of 100 three-cent stamps without requiring change, or could go to a bank and easily obtain 100 silver trimes, but this is a stretch in reasoning.

However, production went forward, and in the first year, 1854, 138,618 were made at the Philadelphia Mint—which would forever stand as the highest production in the series. Afterward, mintages declined, and in 1889 the denomination was abolished (along with the nickel three-cent piece and the gold dollar).

Coins of this denomination circulated in the East and Midwest until 1861, after which they disappeared, although small quantities continued to be made, with 1874 and 1878 registering significantly greater amounts as it was anticipated that these and other gold coins would soon go into circulation. On the West Coast, $3 pieces were used continuously, but it is likely that after the 1860s they were not often seen. Most popular in the West were the San Francisco issues from 1855 through 1860.

Selecting a Coin for Your Type Set

Although many different dates are available at reasonable prices, most numismatists either opt to acquire a circulated or Mint State 1854 (significant as the first year of issue; also, in this year the word DOLLARS is in smaller letters than on later issues) or a Mint State coin from the low-mintage era of 1879 to 1889. Similar to the situation discussed earlier for gold dollars, although the mintages of these later pieces were low, they were popularly saved at the time, and many more exist than might otherwise be the case.

Differences in availability can be dramatic and also illogical to the uninitiated. As an example, I estimate that of the 1857 $3, of which 20,891 were minted, only about 10 to 15 choice and gem coins exist today, and even that range may be on the high side. On the other hand, for 1885, of which only 1,000 were struck (!), I believe that at least 100 are in numismatic hands.

BEYOND A TYPE SET

Collecting $3 pieces by date and mint would at first seem to be a daunting challenge, but on closer view it is eminently achievable except for a handful of pieces. The 1870-S is unique (in the Harry W. Bass Collection on loan to the American Numismatic Association), the 1875 and 1876 were made only in Proof format to the extent of 20 and 45 pieces respectively, and the 1873 is quite rare. Beyond that, examples of coins in grades such as EF and AU can generally be purchased for less than $1,000 each, including some varieties with very low mintages.

Choice examples can be elusive, this being particularly true of mintmarked issues of the 1854 to 1860 years. Generally, Mint State Philadelphia pieces are rare after 1855, but then come on the market with frequency for 1874 and 1878. The low-mintage $3 pieces of 1879 through 1889 were popular at the time of issue, many were saved, and today Uncirculated pieces exist to a greater extent than would normally be the case.

Indian Princess Head (1854–1889)

Circulation-Strike Mintage: 537,824

Proof Mintage: *2,200*

Field Population: Circulated, 25,000 to 35,000; Mint State, 25,000 to 35,000; Proof, 1,400 to 1,800

Designer: James B. Longacre. **Weight:** 5.015 grams. **Composition:** .900 gold, .100 copper (net weight .14512 oz. pure gold). **Diameter:** 20.5 mm. **Edge:** Reeded. **Mints:** Philadelphia, Dahlonega, New Orleans, San Francisco.

Key to Collecting: The panorama of $3 pieces from 1854 through 1889 offers many opportunities for acquiring a coin as a type, including the first year of issue, which also happens to be the highest in mintage. Circulated examples are readily available of most of the higher-mintage dates of the 1850s, also of 1878 (typically in a higher circulated grade such as different levels of AU) and, less often, of dates in the 1880s. In the $3 series the first year of issue, in this instance 1854, is often seen in Mint State. Most examples of this year have somewhat satiny lustrous surfaces. Afterward, a long span of years elapses without Mint State pieces being readily available, until 1879. From that point through 1889, an era of low mintages, quite a few choice and gem examples exist, as at the time $3 pieces were a popular speculation and also had intense numismatic interest. Three-dollar gold pieces of 1878 are also fairly numerous in Mint State but tend to be bagmarked and have luster less attractive than the other dates just mentioned.

Aspects of Striking and Appearance: The typical $3 piece tends to be well struck, but there are exceptions. Points of observation include the tips of the ostrich feathers in the headdress, the hair details below the band inscribed LIBERTY, and, on the reverse, check the wreath details as well as the date numerals. Many of the later issues are prooflike, especially in the early 1880s.

Proof Coins: Proofs were made of all years, but today those most often seen are from the 1880s. Examples are usually fairly choice.

Market Value: Circulation Strikes

VF-20	EF-40	AU-50	AU-55	AU-58	MS-60	MS-62	MS-63	MS-64	MS-65
$850	$1,000	$1,050	$1,150	$1,250	$2,150	$2,750	$4,000	$5,500	$9,500

Market Value: Proof Strikes

PF-63	PF-64	PF-65
$12,500	$18,500	$32,500

Retail Price Trends

Year	EF-40	MS-60	MS-64	PF-65
1946	$17.50	$22.50	$32.50	$65
1950	$18	$20	$30	$75
1960	$80	$90	$120	$500
1970	$275	$340	$1,000	$5,000
1980	$525	$1,500	$2,000	$10,000

Year	EF-40	MS-60	MS-64	PF-65
1990	$800	$3,500	$4,000	$16,000
2000	$600	$1,750	$6,000	$20,000
2010	$1,100	$2,450	$7,000	$32,500
2019	$1,000	$2,150	$5,500	$32,500

24
$4 Gold Stellas
1879–1880

Overview of the Denomination

There is a lot to be said for *tradition*, and this word is responsible for the inclusion of two types of the $4 gold Stella here. By any evaluation, these are patterns, not regular coins, and are in the purview of specialists in the pattern series. However, the wide availability of the 1879 Flowing Hair has made it a stock-in-trade item for coin sales and auctions for over a century, with the majority of buyers being collectors of regular coins, not pattern enthusiasts. Further, the curious $4 patterns have been neatly adopted into nearly all the books that list regular coins but not patterns (or just a few patterns, such as the 1856 Flying Eagle cent and the 1859 transitional half dime, as examples). The old Wayte Raymond *Standard Catalogue* (1934 to 1958 publication run) and the *Guide Book of United States Coins* followed suit.

Whether *you* add one or both types of $4 Stellas to your type set depends a lot on your budget. Accordingly, you might want to linger and read the descriptions below, or jump posthaste to the next section! No matter what your inclination and financial wherewithal, Stellas are certainly *interesting*.

The $4 piece was the brainchild of The Hon. John A. Kasson, who served as United States minister to Austria-Hungary. In Europe coins of slightly lower value than the American $5 piece (the British gold sovereign being but one of many examples) were popular in trade. Kasson thought that an American $4 piece would serve as an international medium of exchange. This stands as one of many such notions that reached pattern coin form, but never resulted in issues made for general circulation. Others include the international $5 of 1868 and Dana Bickford's impressive $10 of 1874.

However, reality dictated that the familiar $20 pieces were more convenient for international trade, easier to count, and were already in place. Besides, although the $4 Stella was set as being worth four American dollars, it still was not of the same value as even a single other current variety of European gold coin, and change would have to be made in transactions, just as it would have to be made for the standard $5 half eagle.

Patterns called the *Stella*, from the five-pointed star on the reverse, were prepared in two styles for Kasson's proposal. The most familiar today is the 1879 with Miss Liberty having flowing hair, the work of Charles E. Barber, son of chief engraver William Barber. The attractive and curious $4 Flowing Hair Stellas, as they are designated today, were distributed in significant numbers to congressmen and others. An early story, true per testimony of the era, is that these became favorite gifts to madams and others in the demimonde of Washington, where certain ladies catered to the pleasure of legislators distant from home. As a result, more than just a few $4 pieces in existence today show evidence of having been used as jewelry. As to how many 1879 Flowing Hair Stellas were struck, no one knows, with 425 being a popular figure. My estimate is about 700.

In the same year, 1879, George Morgan created his version of the Stella, with Miss Liberty having coiled hair. Apparently, no records at all were kept of the quantity made, and later factual-appearing statements as well as guesses have ranged from 10 upward. In 1880 both Flowing Hair and Coiled Hair versions were made, again in small numbers. In 1879 and 1880, information about the three rare varieties (1879 Coiled Hair and both of 1880) was kept under wraps, and it was not until decades later, well into the twentieth century, that illustrations of each of these appeared in print!

Stellas for a Type Set

For type-set purposes, some numismatists opt to acquire a single example of the only issue readily available, the 1879 Flowing Hair style by Charles E. Barber, although these are expensive. However, the Coiled Hair style is a different type, is much rarer, and if you own an oil well or two, or were a founding shareholder in Microsoft, you might want to add one of these as well.

Collecting One of Each Variety

Over the past century perhaps a couple dozen numismatists have put together complete sets of one of each gold striking of the 1879 and 1880 Flowing Hair and Coiled Hair Stella, this being made possible by collections being dispersed and sold to others, as it is unlikely that even as many as 20 complete sets could exist at one time.

Needless to say, a full set of gold Stellas is a show-stopper. The first such display I ever saw was set up by O.L. Harvey at the 1955 ANA convention in Omaha and was one of the main attractions of the show. This was the first ANA show I ever attended, wondrous to my young eyes.

Stella, Flowing Hair (1879-1880)

Proof Mintage:
700

Field Population: Impaired Proofs, 200; unimpaired Proofs, 350 to 500

Designer: Charles E. Barber **Weight:** 7 grams. **Composition:** Approximately .857 gold, .042 silver, .100 copper. **Diameter:** 22 mm. **Edge:** Reeded. **Mint:** Philadelphia.

Key to Collecting: The 1879 Flowing Hair is the standard $4 Stella and is the variety typically acquired for a type set. Several hundred exist today, probably close to 500, all in Proof or impaired Proof finish.

Aspects of Striking and Appearance: All or nearly all examples have some areas of light striking and striations on the high part of Miss Liberty just above her forehead. Otherwise the details are usually sharp.

Proof Coins: All pieces were struck with Proof finish. Survivors today range from impaired Proofs, sometimes polished, to choice and gem examples. All are highly prized.

Market Value: Proof Strikes

PF-40	PF-50	PF-60	PF-63	PF-64	PF-65	PF-66	PF-67
$90,000	$95,000	$120,000	$165,000	$175,000	$225,000	$275,000	$400,000

Retail Price Trends

Year	PF-60	PF-65
1946	$550	$750
1950	$500	$700
1960	$2,000	$3,000
1970	$9,000	$12,000
1980	$25,000	$37,500

Year	PF-60	PF-65
1990	$35,000	$65,000
2000	$32,500	$80,000
2010	$110,000	$200,000
2019	$120,000	$225,000

Stella, Coiled Hair (1879–1880)

Proof Mintage: *35–50*

Field Population: 25 to 32

Designers: ***Obverse:*** George T. Morgan; ***Reverse:*** Charles E. Barber. **Weight:** 7 grams. **Composition:** Approximately .857 gold, .042 silver, .100 copper. **Diameter:** 22 mm. **Edge:** Reeded. **Mint:** Philadelphia.

Key to Collecting: A $4 Coiled Hair Stella, by George T. Morgan, of either the 1879 or 1880 date, represents a great rarity. The number struck is not known, but it was certainly small. Nearly all pieces are arranged in grade from PF-62 upward, with relatively few impaired coins. Most were carefully preserved.

Aspects of Striking and Appearance: Often with some areas of light striking in the high parts of the portrait. Sometimes casually struck in other areas as well—rather remarkable, as one might think these pieces, known to be of great interest to collectors at the time they were made and this being the only reason for striking them, would have been sharp. Planchet flakes and lintmarks are seen on some. Striking was done with less than meticulous care.

Proof Coins: Exceedingly rare, with probably fewer than 30 existing today, with 1880 being the rarer of the two dates.

Market Value: Proof Strikes

PF-60	PF-63	PF-64	PF-65	PF-66	PF-67
$275,000	$450,000	$500,000	$800,000	$1,100,000	$1,250,000

Retail Price Trends

Year	PF-60	PF-65
1946	$1,000	$1,500
1950	$1,000	$1,500
1960	$4,500	$6,750
1970	$19,000	$26,000
1980	$19,000	$26,000
1990	$50,000	$75,000
2000	$100,000	$245,000
2010	$250,000	$550,000
2019	$275,000	$800,000

25
Half Eagles
($5 Gold Coins)
1795-1929

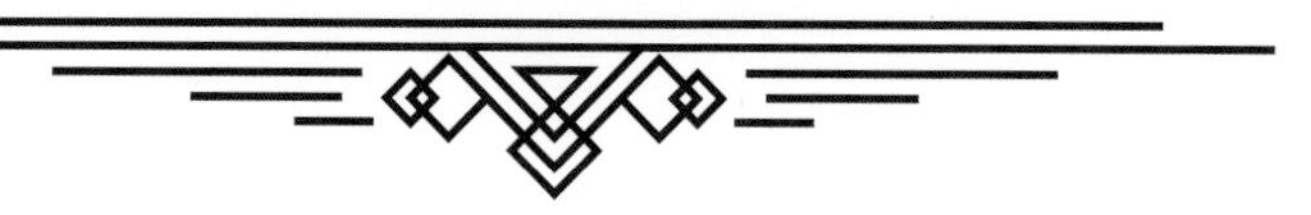

Overview of the Denomination

From the standpoint of longevity and continuity, the $5 gold half eagle denomination is the most extensive series among gold coins in American numismatics.

Around May of 1795, David Rittenhouse, director of the Mint since its inception, assigned engraver Robert Scot to produce half eagle dies. Rittenhouse left the Mint at the end of June and was replaced by Henry William DeSaussure, who ordered that gold coin production should begin. On July 31, 744 half eagles were delivered, followed by subsequent amounts through September totaling 8,707 pieces for the year.

Half eagles of the early years, with Miss Liberty wearing a conical cap and facing right, stars to both sides, and with the reverse illustrating an eagle on a palm branch, circulated extensively in the United States. However, the total mintage of this early type was not sufficient to make an impact on commerce, and little notice was made of them in contemporary newspapers. Instead, the demand for gold coins continued to be filled by Spanish-American doubloons (8-escudo pieces) and their fractional parts.

In 1798 the Heraldic Eagle reverse was introduced in the half eagle series, a style continued through part of 1807. Around this time, a perfectly serviceable 1795-dated half eagle obverse die was combined with the new Heraldic Eagle reverse, creating an oddity—a 1795 of a type that did not exist in that calendar year!

Half eagles of the Heraldic Eagle design were produced in fairly large numbers, again serving in domestic trade. In the early nineteenth century, many if not most of the highest-valued gold coin being made, the $10 eagle, were exported, resulting in the termination of their coinage in 1804, this being considered as an exercise in futility. It then fell to the half eagle to be the largest gold coin of the realm, a position it filled until 1838 when eagles were again minted.

Production of half eagles was fairly extensive through the first decade of the nineteenth century, continuing to 1813. Such coins were mostly used in trade in the Eastern states, but some were sent abroad. This was a time of very great difficulties on the high seas, with French and, later, English vessels seizing American ships, an action which eventually resulted in the 1807 Embargo Act, which, in effect, shut down American maritime commerce and precipitated the War of 1812.

A peace treaty was signed in December 1814, but word did not reach the United States on a timely basis, and the Battle of New Orleans, fought under General Andrew Jackson in January 1815, was regarded as the greatest American triumph of that conflict. This action later projected Jackson into the White House (election of 1828), with vast consequences to the Bank of the United States and the American economic scene.

In the meantime, the half eagle designs were modified, including the Capped Bust to Left style by John Reich (1807) and a new style with stars surrounding the head, introduced in 1813.

After the war, economic conditions fluctuated in the United States, and sometimes gold coins were seen with frequency, exchangeable at par with paper money, and other times they nearly completely disappeared. Communications between Eastern cities were time-consuming, and often different exchange rates and policies were in place in, for example, Charleston, Baltimore, New York, and Boston. Such variations provided opportunities for profit by exchange and bullion brokers.

Beginning in 1821, gold coins disappeared completely from American circulation. During the ensuing decade, protective tariffs were levied against foreign goods, which resulted in great prosperity to American manufacturers. At the same time, the traditional American value of gold in relation to silver, 16 units of silver to 1 unit of gold, was slightly different from the ratio on the international scene, and gold became worth slightly more. Accordingly, United States half eagles shipped to foreign destinations could be melted down at a profit. This was done extensively and absorbed nearly all of the coinage from that point through early 1834.

During the 1821 to 1834 era, mintages were sometimes very extensive, but today relatively few pieces survive. During this period, it was the prerogative of certain legislators to receive their salaries in gold, and this was done, as a profit of a few cents could be realized on every dollar of income. However, the half eagles (mostly) and quarter eagles, received in pay envelopes did not circulate, but were given to exchange brokers where a profit could be pocketed. In turn, the coins were melted.

The Coinage Act of June 28, 1834, promoted by Senator Thomas Hart Benton of Missouri, caused a great political furor at the time. Controversy was still swirling concerning Jackson's 1830 veto against the re-chartering of the Second Bank of the United States (the charter was set to expire in 1836), and during this period, that bank, headquartered in Philadelphia, was winding down its affairs. Many newspapers predicted the downfall of the American economy, envisioning commerce being awash in worthless bank notes instead of bills issued by the Bank of the United States.

In actuality, the situation was vastly overblown, as most bank notes issued by states with good regulations, including nearly all of New England with its Suffolk Bank redemption system, served their purpose well and were exchangeable nearly at par. Bills of the Bank of the United States had been issued primarily in higher denominations and were seldom seen anyway.

The Act of 1834 provided for a reduction in the authorized weight of gold coins, making new issues unprofitable to melt down. This was to take effect on August 1. After that time, there would be two classes of half eagles (and quarter eagles)—the old style, heavier, and worth more than face value if melted down; and the new, not worth more than face value. Quite a bit of discussion took place as to how the two issues should be differentiated. While Secretary of the Treasury Levi Woodbury and Mint Director Samuel Moore both agreed that later, beginning in 1835, the date on the coin would distinguish the difference, there was the problem as to what to do with those dated 1834.

One proposal was that "AUG" be placed in raised letters on the new coins, signifying the weight used in August and later. Woodbury thought if the word "NEW" were added after the date, as 1834 NEW, this would suffice. In another letter, Woodbury stated to Moore:

> A suggestion was made that increasing the number of stars from 13 to 24 (present number of states in the Union) might suffice to tell old coins from new, and permit the number of stars to correspond to the number of states in the Union.[19]

In Rutherfordton, North Carolina, private gold coiner Augustus Bechtler must have learned of some of this, for in step with the government he reduced the weight of his gold coins, and on a new issue of $5 had the inscription, AUGUST 1. 1834.

As to what the Mint did, a new portrait, the *Classic Head*, by William Kneass, now showing Miss Liberty without a cap, was introduced, and the motto E PLURIBUS UNUM was dropped from the reverse.

Beginning in August, the half eagles and quarter eagles appeared in circulation and were quickly given nicknames such as *golden boys*, *Benton's mint drops*, and, especially, *yellow jackets*. It was unfairly claimed by anti-Jackson interests that the new gold coins were made to give out as political bribes during the coming state and regional elections. Quite a bit of ink was spent in this regard, including by Hezekiah Niles, proprietor of *Niles' Weekly Register*, who in earlier years has been virulently against the Bank of the United States, but who had turned against the Jackson interests.

In any event, coinage of the new half eagle design was particularly extensive during the first several years, primarily made from bullion taken from old-style heavier-weight half eagles and eagles that had been hoarded here, but were now sold back to the Mint at a slight profit. Later, indemnities for French spoliations against American shipping during the early nineteenth century resulted in extensive imports of gold, much of which was converted into coins.

Several accounts reached print concerning the alteration of contemporary silver quarters by changing 25 C on the reverse by removing the 2 and the C to show just 5, and gold plating them, to be passed as examples of the new half eagles. By that time there had been much press notice about the new half eagles and the absence of the motto E PLURIBUS UNUM, but few people had seen one. Thus, a quarter dollar, also without the motto (it had been dropped in 1831), plated to appear like a gold coin, and stating "5" on the reverse, could be easily enough passed. On September 27, 1834, *Niles' Weekly Register* noted: "In Cincinnati, J. Washington Mason, as a joke had a jeweler gild six current silver quarter dollars, which he was able to convince others were the new designs of gold coins."

However, this threat was more in the telling than in the execution, and months later Niles reported that he had not seen one in person.

As the new quarter eagles and half eagles were in circulation, it was realized that the gold coins were slightly overvalued in relation to silver, this being in connection with the international market. Accordingly, someone paying a $10 debt in new gold coins would be tendering metal worth slightly less than if the same debt were paid in $10 worth of current silver coins. It was predicted that silver coins would be preferred, and quantities would be exported, as foreign banks and merchants would desire silver. To a degree, this did happen and was widely reported in the press at the time. However, there seems to have been no major disruption of coinage, and for years thereafter silver and gold both circulated effectively side by side in American commerce.

In 1839 the motif of the half eagle was changed to the Liberty Head type by Christian Gobrecht, a variation on the style used by the same engraver for the 1838 $10. Coins of this motif were continued through 1908. In 1866 the motto IN GOD WE TRUST was added to the reverse. James B. Longacre was chief engraver by that time. Mintages of Liberty Head half eagles were extensive, especially during the earlier years. Production was achieved at several mints, with 1854 through 1857 having the distinction that five different mints each struck coins in these years: Philadelphia, Charlotte, Dahlonega, New Orleans, and San Francisco. This record is not seen elsewhere in the gold series.

Half eagles were popular in circulation in the East and Midwest until 1862, after which time they were withdrawn from circulation, not to be seen again until the later days of December 1878. In the meantime gold coins (and also silver coins) continued to be used on the West Coast. After 1878 half eagles were made in large quantities for certain years, hitting a record of 5,708,760 in 1881. Likely, most of these were exported, as such were not common in domestic circulation save for a few areas in the Rocky Mountain States and in California. Even in those locations after 1878, most higher transactions were conducted through paper money.

In 1908 the Indian Head design, with recessed features, by Bela Lyon Pratt, was introduced. The October–November issue of *The Numismatist* included this:

> That which has been anticipated for months is now a fact that a decidedly new and novel departure in United States coinage appears in the new type $2.50 and $5 gold pieces which were just issued—the first was in November. The great novelty in the new coins is that the design is incuse, instead of being raised or embossed, as is the general coinage in the world. The planchets are not milled, the field from edge to edge being one flat surface with a design struck in, or sunk. The periphery (so-called edge) is reeded.
>
> At last we have the features of a real Indian on our coinage. The central design on the obverse presents in profile the strong features of the male Indian, with long extending and wide full feathered headdress.... The design of the reverse is the much commented upon eagle that appears on the Saint-Gaudens $10 piece. The incuse design, even on the smaller planchets, emphasizes or magnifies the characteristics of this muchly feathered and greatly criticized bird. . . . Those who appreciate an innovation certainly have it in the new coins. General comments on the issue will be welcomed from our contributors.

Many comments were published in later issues, generally unfavorable to the design. The Indian Head half eagle was made through 1916. After that point, production ceased, to be revived briefly in 1929, when 662,000 were struck. However, it is probable that most of this later date remained in Treasury storage and were melted in the 1930s, for today, the 1929 is very rare, and it is likely that no more than a couple hundred or so exist (most of which are in various degrees of Mint State).

COLLECTING A TYPE SET OF HALF EAGLES

Forming a type set of half eagles is a daunting challenge but is possible if you have an appropriate checkbook balance and some determination. Examples of the first type, with Capped Bust to Right (conical cap obverse), and with an eagle on a palm branch on the reverse, readily come on the market and are usually of the date 1795. Typical grades range from EF to lower Mint State levels. Such pieces are scarce, and the demand for them is strong. The next type, the Heraldic Eagle motif, first struck in 1798, but also known from a 1795-dated die used later, was produced through 1807, and easily enough to obtain today. Again, typical grades range from EF to Mint State. Choice and gem coins are available, but are in the distinct minority.

The short-lived Capped Bust to Left style, 1807 to 1812, can be found in similar grades, although such pieces did not circulate as extensively, and AU and Mint State levels are the rule, with scarcely a VF piece in sight. Then follows the era of rarities. The Capped Head to the Left, stars surrounding head, large diameter, 1813 to 1829 style is available courtesy of the first date of issue, 1813. This is the only year seen with some frequency, and with an affordable price tag attached. When seen, examples tend to be choice. The later stretch of this series includes some formidable rarities, among which are the famous 1815 and even rarer 1822, along with a whole string of other seldom-seen varieties in the 1820s. The same style, but of reduced diameter, 1829 to 1834, is also rare, but examples of the 1830s turn up with some regularity, but often lack eye appeal. For some reason, half eagles of the early 1830s are often heavily marked and abraded, which it not true at all for coins of the 1820s.

Classic Head half eagles, capless and mottoless, first minted in August 1834, are easily enough obtained, usually of the first several dates, not as often 1837 or 1838. Grades range from VF upward, reflecting the extensive use of such in circulation. Mint State coins can be found on occasion and are scarce. Choice and gem pieces are rare.

Liberty Head half eagles of the 1839 to 1866 type without motto are very plentiful in worn grades, including certain of the higher-mintage issues from the popular Charlotte and Dahlonega mints (permitting interesting varieties to be added to your type set). Mint State coins are scarce, and when seen are usually in lower levels such as MS-60 and MS-62. Gems of any date are rare. Then follow the Liberty Head pieces with motto on the reverse, 1866 through 1908, the earlier years mostly encountered in worn grades, the later ones easy enough to find in Mint State. Proofs of all Liberty Head half eagles were made, and today they are generally collectable from about 1860 onward. Early types are of exquisite beauty and are also rare.

The Indian Head half eagles of 1908 to 1929 are common enough in worn grades as well as low Mint State levels, but true gems, accurately graded and with lustrous, frosty surfaces, are quite rare. The field is the highest area of the coin and thus is quite susceptible to scuffs and marks. Probably the most available dates in higher grades are 1908 and 1909, with the 1909-D being especially plentiful, due to a hoard that came on the market a generation ago.

While in the annals of American numismatics dozens of old-time numismatists collected half eagles by date, less often by date *and* mint, today rarities are so widely scattered and are so expensive that few collectors can rise to the challenge.

Beyond a Type Set

Early half eagles can be collected by dates and basic varieties (such as listed in the *Red Book*), and also by die varieties. The year 1795 in particular is rich in the latter, and years ago several scholars described such varieties, beginning with J. Colvin Randall in the 1870s, continuing to William H. Woodin in the early twentieth century (whose information never reached print), then Edgar H. Adams, Thomas Ollive Mabbott, and Walter Breen. In more recent times *United States Half Eagle Gold Coins 1795-1834*, by Robert W. Miller, Sr., 1997, has added information. John Dannreuther included half eagles in his *Early U.S. Gold Coin Varieties; A Study of Die States, 1795–1834*, which builds on the research of Harry W. Bass Jr.

Among early half eagles there are two unique varieties, the 1797 with 16 star obverse and 1797 with 15 star obverse, both with Heraldic Eagle reverse, likely struck in 1798. So, these are in the "forget it" category. The same can be said for the later 1822, of which just three are known. Of all early half eagles the 1815 was far and away the most famous during the nineteenth century. Indeed, in the 1880s a publication on the Mint Collection stated that the two highlights there were the 1815 half eagle and the unique 1849 $20. At the time, the 1822, rarer than the 1815, had not been recognized for its elusive nature. Today an estimated 11 examples of the 1815 half eagles exist, mostly in higher circulated grades, including in museums. The aforementioned 1822 is the rarity of rarities in the series, with just three known to survive, two of which are in the Smithsonian Collection, with the third, the Eliasberg Collection coin (which I had the pleasure of cataloguing in 1982), being a highlight of a private cabinet. There are only two known of the 1825, 5 Over 4, overdate, but it is not at all famous, probably because it is an overdate variety, not a single date on its own. Half eagles of 1826 through 1829 are all rare, with the 1829 being particularly well known. The latter date includes early pieces with regular diameter and later ones with the diameter reduced. Generally, all half eagles from 1815 through 1834 are scarce, some of them being especially so. A quick perusal of the *Red Book* will illustrate the scenario.

Classic Head half eagles of the 1834 to 1838 include the scarce 1838-C and 1838-D, the first gold issues of the Charlotte and Dahlonega mints respectively, but none are prohibitively rare. Generally, the higher grade pieces are found toward the beginning of the Classic Head series, especially bearing the date 1834.

Liberty Head half eagles are readily available of most dates and mints from 1839 to 1908, save for the one great rarity, the 1854-S, of which just three are known (one is in the Smithsonian). The last example that came on the market I described as part of the Eliasberg Collection of United States Gold Coins, 1982, from which point it went into a private Texas collection. There is a vast panorama of Charlotte and Dahlonega issues through 1861, most of which were made in fairly large quantities, as this was the highest denomination ever struck at each of these mints (larger-capacity presses were not on hand). Accordingly, they are highly collectable today. Some varieties are scarce, but none are out of reach. Typical grades range from VF to EF and AU, occasionally Mint State, not often choice or gem Mint State, however.

Among San Francisco half eagles most of the early issues are scarce, as such pieces circulated extensively, and there was no thought to saving numismatic examples. However, there are not many specialists in the field, and for some varieties it can be said that collectors are harder to find than are the coins themselves, yielding the opportunity to purchase truly rare pieces for significantly lower prices than would otherwise be the case. Carson City half eagles were minted beginning in 1870 and continuing intermittently through 1893, with most of the early issues ranging from scarce to rare, the 1870-CC being particularly well known in this regard. Proofs of the Liberty Head type are generally collectable from the 1860s onward, with most coming on the market being of the higher-mintage dates of the last two decades of the design.

Among Indian Head half eagles 1908 to 1929, the 1909-O is the rarest of the early varieties, and when seen is usually worn. A choice or gem Mint State 1909-O is an incredible rarity. However, enough worn 1909-O half eagles exist, including many brought from overseas hoards in recent decades, that a piece in VF or so grade presents no problem. Half eagles of 1929, of which just 662,000 were minted, were mostly melted, it seems. A couple hundred or so exist today, nearly all of which are Mint State, but nicked and with bagmarks, MS-60 to MS-62 or MS-63. Truly high-quality gems are exceedingly rare.

Capped Bust, Small Eagle Reverse (1795–1798)

Circulation-Strike Mintage: 18,512

Field Population: Circulated, 700 to 1,000; Mint State, 160 to 250

Designer: Robert Scot. **Weight:** 8.75 grams. **Composition:** .9167 gold, .0833 silver and copper. **Diameter:** Approximately 25 mm. **Edge:** Reeded. **Mint:** Philadelphia.

Key to Collecting: All half eagles of this type, with Capped Bust to Right (conical cap) obverse, Small Eagle reverse, are quite scarce. When seen, the typical example is apt to be dated 1795 and in a grade such as VF, EF, or AU. Mint State coins are elusive.

Aspects of Striking and Appearance: Striking varies considerably from coin to coin. Planchet adjustment marks, caused by filing away metal on overweight planchets to reduce them to the appropriate standard, are a problem on this as well as other early half eagles. Such marks are usually seen in the center of the obverse and reverse as well, and/or toward the borders. With regard to striking, check the star centers, the hair details of Miss Liberty, and the eagle feathers. The denticles also should be examined.

There are enough pieces in existence that problem-free coins can be located. The challenge is great, and the accomplishment will yield much satisfaction. As is the case elsewhere in early coinage, certification services make no mention on the holders of planchet-adjustment marks, weak striking, or such other things, making the fields fairly clear for you to seek out such quality, while most of your competition is blissfully unaware of such differences!

Notes: There is no indication of denomination or value on these coins. They were valued by gold content.

Market Value: Circulation Strikes

F-12	VF-20	EF-40	AU-50	AU-55	AU-58	MS-60	MS-62	MS-63	MS-64
$21,500	$25,000	$32,500	$40,000	$52,500	$65,000	$75,000	$115,000	$165,000	$325,000

Retail Price Trends

Year	EF-40	MS-60	MS-64
1946	$110	$150	$200
1950	$110	$150	$200
1960	$300	$385	$525
1970	$2,100	$2,400	$10,000
1980	$6,000	$15,000	$85,000

Year	EF-40	MS-60	MS-64
1990	$11,000	$25,000	$100,000
2000	$12,500	$35,000	$130,000
2010	$28,500	$72,500	$300,000
2019	$32,500	$75,000	$325,000

Capped Bust, Heraldic Eagle Reverse (1795-1807)

Circulation-Strike Mintage: 316,867

Field Population: Circulated, 4,500 to 8,000; Mint State, 2,800 to 3,500

Designer: Robert Scot. **Weight:** 8.75 grams. **Composition:** .9167 gold, .0833 silver and copper. **Diameter:** Approximately 25 mm. **Edge:** Reeded. **Mint:** Philadelphia.

Key to Collecting: Thousands of examples of the 1795 to 1807 Heraldic Eagle type exist in the marketplace, but the demand for them is such that at any given time most dealers only have a few to offer, usually of the dates in the early nineteenth century. Typical grades range from VF to lower Mint State levels. Higher-quality pieces are seldom seen. Truly choice and gem examples are quite difficult to find.

Aspects of Striking and Appearance: Striking varies widely, and it will pay to be selective when buying. Enough pieces exist that with some connoisseurship you can find a nice one. On the obverse, check the higher elements of the hair details, the star centers, and the denticles. On the reverse, which is apt to give more problems than the obverse, check the upper part of the shield, the lower part of the eagle's neck, the eagle's wing, the stars above the eagle, and the clouds—while you're at it, you might as well check *everything*. Mint-caused planchet-adjustment marks are also frequently seen and should be avoided. Certification services take no note of adjustment marks or the quality of the striking, and, similar to the preceding type, you have a fairly clear field as many of your competitors are not aware of such differences in quality.

Notes: There is no indication of denomination or value on these coins. They were valued by gold content.

Market Value: Circulation Strikes

F-12	VF-20	EF-40	AU-50	AU-55	AU-58	MS-60	MS-62	MS-63	MS-64
$4,000	$5,000	$7,000	$10,000	$11,500	$12,500	$15,500	$19,000	$32,500	$47,500

Retail Price Trends

Year	EF-40	MS-60	MS-64
1946	$35	$50	$70
1950	$35	$50	$70
1960	$100	$115	$160
1970	$525	$750	$2,000
1980	$1,700	$4,500	$1,000
1990	$2,750	$9,500	$15,000
2000	$2,350	$5,750	$20,000
2010	$7,000	$15,000	$47,000
2019	$7,000	$15,500	$47,500

Draped Bust to Left (1807–1812)

Circulation-Strike Mintage: 399,013

Field Population: Circulated, 2,200 to 3,200; Mint State, 2,000 to 3,000

Designer: John Reich. **Weight:** 8.75 grams. **Composition:** .9167 gold, .0833 silver and copper. **Diameter:** Approximately 25 mm. **Edge:** Reeded. **Mint:** Philadelphia.

Key to Collecting: The short-lived Capped Bust to Left type exists in sufficient quantities today that examples can be found without problems. The average grade is higher than for the preceding type, with EF and AU most likely and low Mint State levels (MS-60, MS-62, MS-63) being the rule, not the exception. However, in the overall aspect of the American coin market, such coins are indeed scarce.

Aspects of Striking and Appearance: The striking is usually fairly decent, better than on the preceding type. Check the hair details on the obverse and the star centers. On the reverse, check the eagle, particularly at the shield and lower left. Also check the denticles. Planchet-adjustment marks are sometimes seen, while they are not as prevalent as on earlier types.

Market Value: Circulation Strikes

F-12	VF-20	EF-40	AU-50	AU-55	AU-58	MS-60	MS-62	MS-63	MS-64
$3,000	$4,500	$5,500	$8,000	$9,500	$11,000	$13,500	$15,500	$28,500	$35,500

Retail Price Trends

Year	EF-40	MS-60	MS-64
1946	$45	$55	$70
1950	$40	$47.50	$70
1960	$90	$115	$165
1970	$550	$625	$4,000
1980	$1,150	$2,750	$12,000
1990	$2,400	$9,500	$17,000
2000	$2,300	$5,500	$20,000
2010	$5,000	$13,500	$35,000
2019	$5,500	$13,500	$35,500

Capped Head to Left, Large Diameter (1813-1829)

Circulation-Strike Mintage: *717, 409*

Proof Mintage: Fewer than 30

Field Population: Circulated, 1,000 to 2,000; Mint State, 2,000 to 3,000; Proof, 10 to 12

Designer: John Reich. **Weight:** 8.75 grams. **Composition:** .9167 gold, .0833 silver and copper. **Diameter:** 25 mm. **Edge:** Reeded. **Mint:** Philadelphia.

Key to Collecting: This type is impressive for its rarity, this being particularly true for the later-date issues. Happily, enough survive that the type is not in the "impossible" category. However, it will be one of the keys to your set. Circulated coins are in the minority and are usually of a high circulated grade. Mint State is the rule for half eagles of this type. The availability does vary. The rare 1815 usually shows signs of wear, while those of 1818 are nearly all Mint State.

Aspects of Striking and Appearance: Striking is usually fairly decent for this type. Check the hair details at the center, the star centers, and on the reverse, check the eagle. The quality of luster usually ranges from excellent to superb on Mint State pieces. Some are slightly prooflike. Planchet-adjustment marks are generally not a problem and are not often seen.

Proof Coins: Proofs were struck on a limited basis. At widely spaced intervals examples appear on the market. Possibly 10 to 12 authentic Proofs are known. Over the years, some prooflike Mint State pieces have been classified as Proofs.[20]

Market Value: Circulation Strikes

F-12	VF-20	EF-40	AU-50	AU-55	AU-58	MS-60	MS-62	MS-63	MS-64
$4,750	$5,750	$7,000	$10,000	$11,000	$12,500	$15,000	$17,500	$28,500	$36,500

Retail Price Trends

Year	EF-40	MS-60	MS-64
1946	$45	$60	$85
1950	$45	$60	$85
1960	$120	$145	$200
1970	$650	$825	$4,500
1980	$1,750	$3,750	$9,000
1990	$3,000	$11,000	$16,000
2000	$2,400	$6,500	$20,000
2010	$7,000	$15,000	$36,000
2019	$7,000	$15,000	$36,500

Capped Head to Left, Reduced Diameter (1829–1834)

Circulation-Strike Mintage: 668,203

Proof Mintage: Fewer than 30

Field Population: Circulated, 225 to 350; Mint State, 250 to 400; Proof, 10 to 12

Designer: John Reich, as modified by William Kneass.
Weight: 8.75 grams. **Composition:** .9167 gold, .0833 silver and copper.
Diameter: 23.8 mm. **Edge:** Reeded. **Mint:** Philadelphia.

Key to Collecting: This half eagle type is also scarce, as there are really no dates that survive in quantity. Pieces can be rather "scruffy" in appearance, and more connoisseurship is needed to get a quality example of this type than of any of the styles discussed to this point. EF and AU pieces are usually heavily bagmarked. Mint State pieces need to be selected with care, and the finding of a choice or gem one will be an outstanding accomplishment. Get set for a long, difficult search. On the other hand, humdrum-quality MS-60 pieces with many bagmarks and with little eye appeal are easy enough to find. Some of these might better be called AU-50 or AU-58.

Aspects of Striking and Appearance: Striking varies. Check the high parts of the hair (especially the area immediately below LIBERTY) and the higher parts of the eagle, then the peripheral areas and the denticles. Sometimes the obverse is lightly struck at the center while reverse details are sharp. Luster is apt to vary from rather dull and insipid to, rarely, deeply frosty. This is a *very difficult* type to locate in a combination of high grade, sharp strike, and superb eye appeal.

Proof Coins: Proofs were made of the various years and are extreme rarities today. Only about 10 to 12 are known.[21]

Market Value: Circulation Strikes

F-12	VF-20	EF-40	AU-50	AU-55	AU-58	MS-60	MS-62	MS-63	MS-64
$20,000	$27,500	$40,000	$45,000	$55,000	$85,000	$95,000	$110,000	$125,000	$140,000

Market Value: Proof Strikes

PF-63	PF-64
$450,000	$750,000

Retail Price Trends

Year	EF-40	MS-60	MS-64
1946	$200	$275	$400
1950	$225	$325	$450
1960	$400	$500	$650
1970	$1,200	$1,750	$3,000
1980	$4,000	$6,000	$9,000

Year	EF-40	MS-60	MS-64
1990	$5,250	$6,500	$15,000
2000	$6,000	$14,500	$80,000
2010	$37,500	$70,000	$120,000
2019	$40,000	$95,000	$140,000

Classic Head, No Motto on Reverse (1834–1838)

Circulation-Strike Mintage: 2,113,612

Proof Mintage: Fewer than 50

Field Population: Circulated, 18,000 to 23,000; Mint State, 2,000 to 3,000; Proof, 20 to 30

Designer: William Kneass. **Weight:** 8.36 grams. **Composition:** ***1834–1836:*** .8992 gold, .1008 silver and copper; ***1837–1838:*** .900 gold, .100 silver and copper. **Diameter:** 22.5 mm. **Edge:** Reeded. **Mints:** Philadelphia, Charlotte, Dahlonega.

Key to Collecting: The Classic Head half eagle of 1834 to 1838 is the first truly plentiful type of the denomination and also one of the most historically interesting (see introductory half eagle comments). Some collectors opt to start their sets with this era, in the various denominations. The Classic Head half eagles were immensely popular in domestic circulation, the first such pieces to achieve extensive use in commerce since 1820. Today, many examples are seen in such grades as VF and EF, with AU being in the minority and Mint State pieces being somewhat elusive. Most are in lower ranges. True choice and gem coins are seldom seen and are numismatic prizes.

Aspects of Striking and Appearance: Striking varies, but there are enough examples around that you can afford to be particular. Check the hair details below the LIBERTY band and to the lower right. On the reverse, check the details of the eagle.

Proof Coins: Proofs were struck of the various years and are exceedingly rare today. Of the few that exist, most are of the 1834 date.

Market Value: Circulation Strikes

VF-20	EF-40	AU-50	AU-55	AU-58	MS-60	MS-62	MS-63	MS-64	MS-65
$625	$850	$1,350	$1,750	$2,350	$4,500	$6,500	$11,500	$22,500	$70,000

Market Value: Proof Strikes

PF-60	PF-63	PF-64	PF-65
$40,000	$125,000	$175,000	$275,000

Retail Price Trends

Year	EF-40	MS-60	MS-64
1946	$20	$30	$40
1950	$18	$25	$37.50
1960	$30	$37.50	$50
1970	$130	$200	$1,750
1980	$350	$2,000	$4,000

Year	EF-40	MS-60	MS-64
1990	$450	$2,000	$8,000
2000	$450	$2,500	$11,000
2010	$875	$4,500	$23,000
2019	$850	$4,500	$22,500

Liberty Head, No Motto Above Eagle (1839–1866)

Circulation-Strike Mintage: **9,114,049**

Proof Mintage: ***450***

Field Population: **Circulated, 50,000 to 100,000; Mint State, 5,000 to 8,000; Proof, 120 to 160**

Designer: Christian Gobrecht. **Weight:** 8.359 grams. **Composition:** .900 gold, .100 copper (net weight .24187 oz. pure gold). **Diameter:** ***1839–1840:*** 22.5 mm; ***1840–1866:*** 21.6 mm. **Edge:** Reeded. **Mints:** Philadelphia, Charlotte, Dahlonega, Denver, New Orleans, San Francisco, Carson City.

Key to Collecting: These are very plentiful in circulated grades from VF to AU. Mint State pieces are in the minority, and choice and gem pieces are quite rare. Quantities were struck at the Charlotte and Dahlonega mints.

Aspects of Striking and Appearance: Striking varies, and pieces should be examined with care. The first place to look is at the lower area of the eagle on the reverse as well as areas around the shield on the eagle's breast. If these features pass muster and are needle sharp (which often they are not), then turn your attention to the obverse, and check the hair details just below the coronet or tiara of Miss Liberty. After that, check the stars, peripheral letters, and denticles. Generally, coins of the Philadelphia, New Orleans, and San Francisco mints can be found with sharp details.

Proof Coins: Proofs occasionally come on the market and are very rare. Interestingly, the Proofs of the 1860s are usually deeply frosty and cameo-like on the devices, against deep mirror fields, and are of better eye appeal than are those made 40 years later.

Market Value: Circulation Strikes

VF-20	EF-40	AU-50	AU-55	AU-58	MS-60	MS-62	MS-63	MS-64	MS-65
$450	$475	$575	$675	$1,000	$1,750	$3,500	$6,000	$10,500	$35,000

Market Value: Proof Strikes

PF-60	PF-63	PF-64	PF-65
$15,000	$35,000	$75,000	$115,000

Retail Price Trends

Year	EF-40	MS-60	MS-65	PF-64
1946	$20	$30	$45	$200
1950	$18	$27.50	$42.50	$300
1960	$18	$22.50	$35	$400
1970	$65	$80	$3,000	$3,000
1980	$150	$800	$7,000	$12,000
1990	$250	$1,700	$13,000	$20,000
2000	$200	$1,300	$17,000	$25,000
2010	$450	$1,500	$35,000	$55,000
2019	$475	$1,750	$35,000	$75,000

Liberty Head, Motto Above Eagle (1866–1908)

Circulation-Strike Mintage: 51,503,654

Proof Mintage: 2,938

Field Population: Circulated, millions; Mint State, more than 1,000,000; Proof, 1,800 to 2,200

Designer: Christian Gobrecht. **Weight:** 8.359 grams. **Composition:** .900 gold, .100 copper (net weight .24187 oz. pure gold). **Diameter:** 21.6 mm. **Edge:** Reeded. **Mints:** Philadelphia, Charlotte, Dahlonega, Denver, New Orleans, San Francisco, Carson City.

Key to Collecting: With this half eagle type, you are home free, as there are pieces available in the marketplace in just about any grade you desire, from VF to gem Mint State. As the difference between low-grade Mint State and circulated coins is not great, a Mint State coin of one level or another is recommended. Examples abound, and you will have no difficulty finding a choice or gem piece.

Aspects of Striking and Appearance: The sharpness is generally much better than on the earlier type, but still the same points should be checked. The first places to look are at the lower area of the eagle on the reverse as well as areas around the shield on the eagle's breast. If these features are sharp, then check the obverse details.

Proof Coins: Proofs exist in relation to their mintage figures. Those of 1902 have polished portraits, rather than cameo or frosted, and issues of 1903 to 1907 are generally not as attractive as are the earlier dates. Choose carefully, with quality in mind.

Market Value: Circulation Strikes

VF-20	EF-40	AU-50	AU-55	AU-58	MS-60	MS-62	MS-63	MS-64	MS-65
$350	$365	$375	$385	$400	$500	$575	$600	$800	$1,750

Market Value: Proof Strikes

PF-60	PF-63	PF-64	PF-65
$6,000	$12,500	$18,000	$30,000

Retail Price Trends

Year	EF-40	MS-60	MS-65	PF-64
1946	$17.50	$22.50	$32.50	$70
1950	$12	$13.50	$20	$75
1960	$17	$19	$30	$125
1970	$55	$60	$400	$1,500
1980	$145	$210	$800	$3,000
1990	$175	$235	$1,800	$13,000
2000	$200	$375	$1,200	$6,000
2010	$410	$475	$4,000	$21,000
2019	$365	$500	$1,750	$18,000

Indian Head (1908–1929)

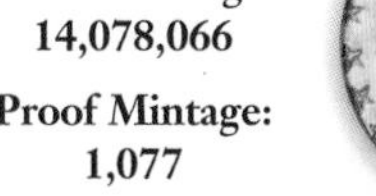

Circulation-Strike Mintage: 14,078,066

Proof Mintage: 1,077

Field Population: Circulated, 150,000 to 250,000; Mint State, 250,000 to 350,000; Proof, 600 to 650

Designer: Bela Lyon Pratt. **Weight:** 8.359 grams. **Composition:** .900 gold, .100 copper (net weight .24187 oz. pure gold). **Diameter:** 21.6 mm. **Edge:** Reeded. **Mints:** Philadelphia, Denver, New Orleans, San Francisco.

Key to Collecting: These half eagles were not popular with collectors at the time of their minting, and few people saved the various issues. There are many coins in EF and AU grades, often with luster in the recessed areas. Mint State examples, when encountered, are usually dated 1908 or 1909-D. Above the MS-63 level examples become scarce, even of these dates, and true gems are rare. Gems of any date and mint are very rare if truly fully frosted in the fields and without significant bagmarks. Quarter eagles and half eagles of this design are subject to wide differences of grading opinion. Be prepared to look at several, or even quite a few pieces, before you find one that is just right.

Aspects of Striking and Appearance: Striking varies. Look for weakness on the high parts of the Indian's bonnet and in the feather details in the headdress. On the reverse, check the feathers on the highest area of the wing. Finding a truly choice example may take some time.

Proof Coins: Sand Blast Proofs were made in 1908 and 1911 to 1915, while Satin Finish Proofs were made in 1909 and 1910. When seen, these are usually in higher Proof levels, 64 and above.

Market Value: Circulation Strikes

VF-20	EF-40	AU-50	AU-55	AU-58	MS-60	MS-62	MS-63	MS-64	MS-65
$400	$420	$440	$460	$475	$500	$650	$1,250	$2,250	$8,000

Market Value: Proof Strikes

PF-60	PF-63	PF-64	PF-65
$7,500	$15,000	$25,000	$45,000

Retail Price Trends

Year	AU-50	MS-60	MS-64	Sand Blast PF-65
1946	$16	$17.50	$27.50	$50
1950	$13	$13.50	$22.50	$45
1960	$17.50	$19	$30	$140
1970	$70	$80	$1,500	$3,000
1980	$185	$1,100	$5,500	$10,000
1990	$325	$900	$7,000	$19,000
2000	$225	$325	$9,000	$19,000
2010	$450	$600	$2,500	$40,000
2019	$440	$500	$2,250	$45,000

26
Eagles
($10 Gold Coins)
1795-1933

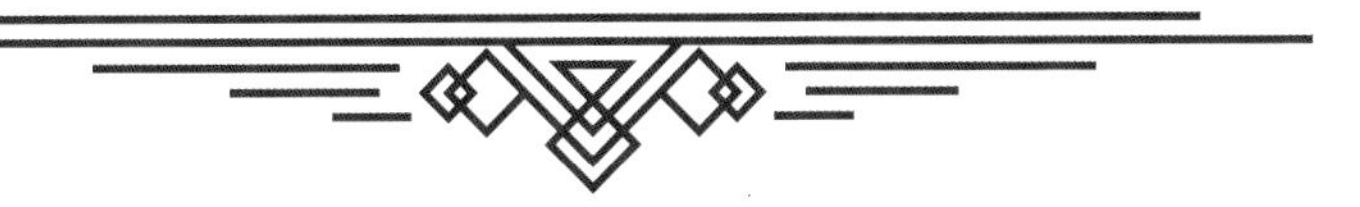

Overview of the Denomination

Eagles or $10 pieces were first struck in 1795. The motif follows that of the half eagles, depicting on the obverse the Capped Bust to right style of Miss Liberty, wearing a conical cap. On the reverse is an eagle perched on a palm branch, holding a wreath aloft in its beak. Coins of this design were produced for the next two years as well, the total quantity, per the annual Mint Reports, being just 5,583 for 1795, 4,146 for 1796, and 3,615 for 1797, the last figure being merely an estimate, as the *Red Book* suggests that in 1797 a further 10,940 pieces were struck of the next type (with Heraldic Eagle reverse). During this era, the Mint furnished reports of coins struck during given *calendar years,* but this did not necessarily coincide with the dates on the dies. Accordingly, such information must be taken with a grain of salt. Today, the 1797 $10 with Small Eagle reverse is quite a bit scarcer than even the low mintage would indicate.

These early eagles were widely used in commerce, being the largest gold denomination authorized under the Act of April 2, 1792. Soon, in 1797, the Heraldic Eagle reverse, copied after the Great Seal of the United States, made its debut. This style was kept in use through and including 1804. Much larger quantities were minted of this type, with the calendar year 1801 registering 44,344 pieces, the all-time high to that point. Most eagles were exported and for this reason, their mintage was discontinued after 1804, with the hope and expectation that the smaller $5, then ascending in rank to become the largest currently issued United States gold coin, would indeed be useful in domestic trade. However, it soon proved that these also were exported, not just casually, but to the extent of nearly their full mintages.

In ensuing years, eagles in domestic circulation largely disappeared, as their meltdown value was worth more than their face value.

In 1838 eagles were again struck, following a long lapse. By this time, the authorized weight of gold coins had been reduced, under the Act of June 28, 1834. The eagles found ready use in domestic commerce as they were not profitable to export. The motif, the Liberty Head or Braided Hair type created by Christian Gobrecht, was later used on other denominations as well. All eagles of 1838 and 1839, 9 Over 8, have the head of Miss Liberty in a slightly different orientation.

That $10 pieces were useful is evidenced by the grade of surviving pieces today, with VF and EF being typical for issues of this era. Although mintages were abundant, peaking at 862,258 in 1847, due to a huge shipment of incoming gold from England, today examples are not often seen at higher-grade levels. The survival of nice pieces is a matter of chance. In 2003 Odyssey Marine Exploration, Inc., had located the SS *Republic*, lost in the Atlantic in 1865. Among the gold coins recovered were many $10 pieces of the early Liberty Head style.

In 1866 the motto IN GOD WE TRUST was added to the reverse of the eagle, constituting a new type that was continued in use through 1907. By this time, the $20 double eagle, inaugurated in 1850, had largely replaced the $10 in the international trade. Mintages for the ensuing decades tended to be considerably lower than for double eagles, although on occasion large quantities of $10 pieces were made, crossing the million mark for 1880, 1881, 1882, 1893, 1894, 1897, 1899, 1901, 1901-S, 1907, and 1907-D. Similar to the situation with $20 pieces, many eagles went overseas, although to the extent of just a small fraction of the quantities shipped of double eagles.

In 1907 the Indian Head eagle by noted sculptor Augustus Saint-Gaudens made its debut. Certain early versions with pellets or periods separating the words in the legend on the reverse, this being per the artist's models, were made in small quantities. A modification was made, and the periods were eliminated, isolating the earlier varieties as numismatic rarities. Today, these are highly appreciated and very valuable. Virtually all exist in Mint State, as none were placed into circulation. Regular Indian Head eagles, without periods, were made of the 1907, 1908, and 1908-D varieties. In the summer of 1908, the motto IN GOD WE TRUST was added to the reverse, after which the new style was employed through 1916, and, intermittently after that until 1933.

COLLECTING A TYPE SET OF EAGLES

The Capped Bust to Right $10 with Small Eagle reverse is the rarest of the early types. However, when seen, they are apt to be in higher grades such as EF, AU, or in low ranges of Mint State. The Heraldic Eagle reverse issues from 1797 through 1804 are much more available, and in slightly higher average grade.

The Liberty Head $10 pieces without motto, minted from 1838 through 1865, are quite elusive in any Mint State range, although VF and EF pieces are plentiful, and there are enough AU coins to easily satisfy demands. Some collectors have considered the 1838 and 1839, 9 Over 8, style, with the head of Miss Liberty tilted forward in relation to the date, to be a separate type. Eagles with IN GOD WE TRUST on the reverse, from 1866 to 1907, are plentiful in high grades, including choice and gem Mint State—no problem at all. Some of these were repatriated from overseas bank vaults beginning in the second half of the twentieth century.

The Saint-Gaudens $10 pieces of 1907 With Periods, existing in the Wire Rim or Regular (Rounded) Rim varieties, can be collected as a type, or ignored—make your choice. Most available is the Wire Rim style, of which somewhat over 400 probably exist today, nearly all in Mint State, often choice or gem. As noted above, these coins were made as regular issues but soon became numismatic delicacies for Treasury officials to distribute as they saw fit. Some were to have gone to museums, but in reality, most were secretly filtered out through favored dealers, including Henry Chapman (Philadelphia) and Thomas L. Elder (New York City). If you have a well-endowed bank-account balance, one of these would be interesting to own.

Then comes the 1907 and 1908 style without periods, easily available in EF, AU, and lower Mint State levels, although gems are elusive.

The final eagle type, the 1908 to 1933 style with IN GOD WE TRUST on the reverse, is readily obtainable in grades from EF through MS-63. Higher pieces are elusive, and when seen are often dated 1932, a year in which 4,463,000 were struck—more than any other coin in the history of the denomination.

Beyond a Type Set

The collecting of $10 coins by varieties is an elite procedure, as the series includes so many scarce and rare coins. However, unlike other denominations none is in the "impossible" category, and with some patience a full set of varieties as listed in the *Red Book* can be obtained.

The early issues with Small Eagle reverse from 1795 through 1797, and those with Heraldic Eagle reverse from 1797 through 1804, can be collected and studied by die varieties. In addition to the regular issues, a few 1804 *restrike* $10 pieces exist from new 1804-dated dies created in 1834.

Liberty Head eagles from 1838 through 1866 (without motto) comprise many scarce dates and mintmarks. Years ago the 1858, of which only 2,521 were minted, was highly acclaimed as a landmark issue, but since then the publicity has faded. In any event, although certain date and mintmark varieties are rare, the number of numismatists collecting them by date sequence is very small, and thus opportunities exist to acquire very elusive pieces at a much smaller proportionate price than would be possible in, say, the gold dollar series. No full set of Mint State early eagles has ever been formed and probably none ever will be. EF and AU are typically the grades of choice, adding Mint State pieces where available.

Later Liberty Head eagles of the 1866 to 1907 style with motto include some low-mintage issues, but again these are not impossible. The most famous is the 1875 Philadelphia variety of which just 100 circulation strikes were made. Although smaller numbers exist for Proof-only mintages, in terms of pieces made for commerce, the 1875 takes the cake. The low-mintage 1879-O (1,500 made) and 1883-O (800) have also attracted a lot of attention. Again, these pieces, while rare, are available to the specialist as there is not a great deal of competition.

Among Indian Head eagles the 1907 With Periods style, Wire Rim, is famous, popular, and rare. Examples come on the market with regularity but are expensive due to the attention they attract. The rounded or regular rim style is much rarer, and when seen is usually in choice Mint State.

The regular without-periods 1907 and 1908 eagles are easy enough to obtain in Mint State, although gems are elusive. The varieties from 1908 through 1916 include no great rarities, although some are scarcer than others. Not many such pieces were saved at the time they were issued, and, accordingly, gems are elusive. However, grades such as AU and low Mint State will present no problem. Among later eagles, the 1920-S, 1930-S, and 1933 are rarities. In particular the 1920-S is difficult to find in choice and gem grade. The 1933 eagle is usually found in Mint State but is expensive due to the publicity given to it. Quite available at reasonable prices are the 1926 and 1932.

Capped Bust to Right, Small Eagle Reverse (1795–1797)

Circulation-Strike Mintage: 13,344

Field Population: Circulated, 250 to 400; Mint State, 180 to 250

Designer: Robert Scot. **Weight:** 17.50 grams.
Composition: .9167 gold, .0833 silver and copper.
Diameter: Approximately 33 mm. **Edge:** Reeded. **Mint:** Philadelphia.

Key to Collecting: Typical grades are EF and AU, with VF coins being in the minority, as such pieces did not circulate actively but tended to be stored in vaults and other cash repositories. Mint State examples come on the market with some regularity, but are usually at lower levels, say MS-60 to MS-63, with those dated 1795 often being somewhat prooflike, this sometimes also seen for 1796, but not often for 1797. Truly choice and gem examples are at once rare and desirable, and if combined with sharp strike and lack of planchet-adjustment marks can be incredible!

Aspects of Striking and Appearance: Many pieces have Mint-caused planchet-adjustment marks visible as parallel lines, often seen at the center of the coin (the high parts of Miss Liberty's hair and on the eagle's breast) as well as at the borders. However, examples exist without this feature, and in securing a piece for type some patience is recommended. With regard to strike, the points to check are the high areas of Miss Liberty, the star centers, the details of the eagle, and the denticles. While many such pieces can be viewed, only a few will ever be chosen by the connoisseur. Once again, certification services pay no attention to planchet-adjustment marks or striking sharpness, giving you an open field of opportunity! *Very few* $10 pieces will emerge with flying colors—sharp and without planchet-adjustment marks, so some compromise might be needed. Perfection can be aspired to, but may not be a reality.

Notes: There is no indication of denomination or value on these coins. They were valued by their gold content with recipients checking "Prices Current" listings in newspapers to establish their worth in relation to bank bills.

Market Value: Circulation Strikes

F-12	VF-20	EF-40	AU-50	AU-55	AU-58	MS-60	MS-62	MS-63	MS-64
$27,500	$35,000	$50,000	$57,500	$72,500	$95,000	$105,000	$150,000	$300,000	$450,000

Retail Price Trends

Year	EF-40	MS-60	MS-64
1946	$175	$200	$275
1950	$175	$200	$275
1960	$350	$415	$575
1970	$1,800	$2,600	$12,000
1980	$7,000	$20,000	$75,000

Year	EF-40	MS-60	MS-64
1990	$12,500	$30,000	$100,000
2000	$12,500	$35,000	$150,000
2010	$47,500	$100,000	$400,000
2019	$50,000	$105,000	$450,000

Capped Bust to Right, Heraldic Eagle Reverse (1797–1804)

Circulation-Strike Mintage: 119,248

Proof Restrike Mintage: *Fewer than 12*

Field Population: Circulated, 3,000 to 5,000; Mint State, 1,200 to 1,600; Proof, 4 restrikes

Designer: Robert Scot. **Weight:** 17.50 grams.
Composition: .9167 gold, .0833 silver and copper.
Diameter: Approximately 33 mm. **Edge:** Reeded. **Mint:** Philadelphia.

Key to Collecting: For type-set purposes, there are enough EF and AU coins around to meet most needs. Mint State specimens are scarce, and when found tend to be of the dates 1799 through 1803. True choice and gem pieces are exceedingly rare.

Aspects of Striking and Appearance: Planchet-adjustment marks continue to be a problem. Typically, these exist as parallel lines observable at the center of the portrait of Miss Liberty as well as at the borders of the obverse and reverse. With regard to sharpness of strike, check the hair details of Miss Liberty, the stars, and, on the reverse, check the details of the shield, the eagle's wings, and the stars. The denticles can also be checked. Again, *very few* $10 pieces will emerge with flying colors—sharp and without planchet-adjustment marks—so some compromise might be needed.

Proof Coins: In 1834 the Mint made up a new die pair with the 1804 obverse date, the "Proof restrike" as it is designated. These were included in sets created for diplomatic presentation. It is believed that just four Proof restrikes are known today.

Notes: There is no indication of the denomination on the reverse dies of this type. There is the possibility that one or more of the same dies may have been used to coin both half dollars (1801 to 1807 years) and eagles (1801 to 1804 years), but no such identification has ever been made by students of the series.

Market Value: Circulation Strikes

F-12	VF-20	EF-40	AU-50	AU-55	AU-58	MS-60	MS-62	MS-63	MS-64
$9,500	$12,500	$16,000	$20,000	$23,500	$26,000	$32,500	$42,500	$67,500	$115,000

Market Value: Proof Strikes

PF-63	PF-64	PF-65
$4,000,000	$4,500,000	$5,000,000

Retail Price Trends

Year	EF-40	MS-60	MS-64
1946	$90	$100	$140
1950	$80	$90	$135
1960	$185	$210	$290
1970	$1,000	$1,200	$2,500
1980	$2,500	$6,000	$15,000

Year	EF-40	MS-60	MS-64
1990	$4,750	$15,000	$30,000
2000	$4,000	$18,750	$40,000
2010	$16,000	$32,000	$110,000
2019	$16,000	$32,500	$115,000

Liberty Head, No Motto Above Eagle (1838–1866)

Circulation-Strike Mintage: 5,292,499

Proof Mintage: *400*

Field Population: Circulated, 25,000 to 50,000; Mint State, 1,800 to 2,500; Proof, 150 to 225

Designer: Christian Gobrecht. **Weight:** 16.718 grams. **Composition:** .900 gold, .100 copper (net weight: .48375 oz. pure gold). **Diameter:** 27 mm. **Edge:** Reeded. **Mints:** Philadelphia, Carson City, Denver, New Orleans, San Francisco.

Key to Collecting: Today, most pieces are in such grades as VF and EF, less often AU, though most are in circulated grades. Mint State examples of this type are rare in all instances. Choice pieces and especially gem pieces are major rarities and are seldom seen. In recent times the finding of long-lost sunken treasures aboard the SS *Central America* (lost in 1857), SS *Brother Jonathan* (1865), and SS *Republic* (1865) has provided some higher-grade pieces but not enough to dramatically change the collecting landscape.

Aspects of Striking and Appearance: Most $10 pieces of this style are fairly well struck, but it will pay to check such features as the hair details of Miss Liberty, the star points, the shield and feathers of the eagle, and the denticles.

Proof Coins: Proofs occasionally come on the market, typically dated from 1858 onward, most often in the early 1860s. Each and every date is exceedingly rare in Proof format especially if choice or gem. Interestingly, such specimens were struck with great care, typically have beautifully frosted surfaces, and represent a triumph of the coinage art that generally faded in quality as the years went by!

Market Value: Circulation Strikes

VF-20	EF-40	AU-50	AU-55	AU-58	MS-60	MS-62	MS-63	MS-64	MS-65
$850	$1,100	$1,300	$1,400	$1,850	$3,750	$8,000	$15,000	$30,000	$95,000

Market Value: Proof Strikes

PF-60	PF-63	PF-64	PF-65
$15,000	$45,000	$85,000	$125,000

Retail Price Trends

Year	EF-40	MS-60	MS-65	PF-65
1946	$40	$50	$75	$175
1950	$37.50	$45	$70	$165
1960	$35	$43.50	$65	$550
1970	$65	$95	$3,000	$5,000
1980	$225	$1,500	$7,000	$20,000

Year	EF-40	MS-60	MS-65	PF-65
1990	$375	$2,400	$13,000	$40,000
2000	$300	$3,000	$19,000	$70,000
2010	$825	$3,250	$92,500	$120,000
2019	$1,100	$3,750	$95,000	$125,000

Liberty Head, Motto Above Eagle (1866–1907)

Circulation-Strike Mintage: 37,391,767

Proof Mintage: 2,327

Field Population: Circulated, millions; Mint State, several million; Proof, 1,400 to 1,700

Designer: Christian Gobrecht. **Weight:** 16.718 grams. **Composition:** .900 gold, .100 copper (net weight: .48375 oz. pure gold). **Diameter:** 27 mm. **Edge:** Reeded. **Mints:** Philadelphia, Carson City, Denver, New Orleans, San Francisco.

Key to Collecting: Circulated coins are readily available. However, for type-set purposes a low-range Mint State coin is likely to be only slightly more expensive than a circulated example. Earlier date and mintmark varieties range from scarce to rare, and in Mint State are especially rare. Beginning with issues of the late 1870s, Mint State coins are plentiful, and for certain issues of the 1890s and early twentieth century choice and gem examples are easy to find.

Aspects of Striking and Appearance: Usually fairly well struck, this being especially true of the later years. Check the hair details of Miss Liberty and the star centers, and, on the reverse, check the eagle details.

Proof Coins: Proofs were struck of all years, and are available in proportion to the mintage quantity. Although quite a few Proofs exist, comparatively speaking, many are impaired. Some connoisseurship will be needed to find a choice example.

Market Value: Circulation Strikes

VF-20	EF-40	AU-50	AU-55	AU-58	MS-60	MS-62	MS-63	MS-64	MS-65
$700	$715	$725	$750	$800	$825	$850	$950	$1,150	$2,750

Market Value: Proof Strikes

PF-60	PF-63	PF-64	PF-65
$7,000	$15,000	$25,000	$45,000

Retail Price Trends

Year	EF-40	MS-60	MS-65	PF-65
1946	$30	$35	$50	$95
1950	$30	$35	$50	$105
1960	$28	$33.50	$50	$225
1970	$55	$70	$200	$1,000
1980	$200	$260	$400	$5,000

Year	EF-40	MS-60	MS-65	PF-65
1990	$275	$425	$800	$10,000
2000	$270	$310	$1,200	$20,000
2010	$775	$850	$5,000	$45,000
2019	$715	$825	$2,750	$45,000

Indian Head, No Motto on Reverse, Periods on Reverse (1907)

Circulation-Strike Mintage:
Wire Rim: 542
Rolled Rim: 32,500

Field Population: Circulated, 15 to 30; Mint State, 400 to 450

Designer: Augustus Saint-Gaudens. **Weight:** 16.718 grams.
Composition: .900 gold, .100 copper (net weight: .48375 oz. pure gold).
Diameter: 27 mm. **Edge:** 46 raised stars. **Mint:** Philadelphia.

Key to Collecting: The eagle with Indian Head obverse and with reverse with periods before and after E PLURIBUS UNUM, available in wire rim (the style usually seen) and rounded (regular) rim styles, can be added to a type set if you have the inclination and finances. Or, the variety can be considered as a subtype and ignored. The choice is yours. All examples known are struck from one of two die pairs and are generally seen in Mint State. Both wire rim and regular rim varieties are nearly always seen in Mint State, as they were never circulated. Choice and gem examples are the rule, not the exception. Today, an estimated 400 or more Wire Rim coins are known, after 70 damaged coins were melted in 1914 and 1915. An estimated 20 or so Rounded Rim issues are known, as all but 50 of the examples struck were melted. No Proofs were made, although this point has been controversial in the past. As all are from the same dies and produced the same way, they are either all Mint State or all Proofs, with most specialists suggesting Mint State.

Aspects of Striking and Appearance: Usually quite good in keeping with the idiosyncrasies of the design—in which certain areas were not sharp in the dies. The surfaces are satiny and lustrous, from a multitude of tiny raised swirls or die finish lines. In the past, some have called these *Proofs*, but in recent times the matter seems to have been laid to rest, and all are considered to be Mint State.

Market Value: Circulation Strikes

VF-20	EF-40	AU-50	AU-55	AU-58	MS-60	MS-62	MS-63	MS-64	MS-65	MS-66
$750	$800	$850	$900	$925	$1,250	$1,850	$2,500	$4,500	$7,000	$12,000

Retail Price Trends

Year	MS-63	MS-65 (wire rim)
1946	$125	$150
1950	$150	$180
1960	$210	$260
1970	$3,000	$4,000
1980	$7,000	$10,000

Year	MS-63	MS-65 (wire rim)
1990	$13,000	$25,000
2000	$18,000	$40,000
2010	$3,250	$12,500
2019	$2,500	$7,000

Indian Head, No Motto on Reverse, No Periods on Reverse (1907–1908)

Circulation-Strike Mintage: 483,448 of regular issue

Field Population: Circulated, 100,000 or more; Mint State, 20,000 to 40,000

Designer: Augustus Saint-Gaudens. **Weight:** 16.718 grams. **Composition:** .900 gold, .100 copper (net weight: .48375 oz. pure gold). **Diameter:** 27 mm. **Edge:** 46 raised stars. **Mints:** Philadelphia, Denver.

Key to Collecting: This is the Indian Head Saint-Gaudens eagle usually seen of the 1907 date, a type also made in early 1908. The design is as above but now without pellets or dots after E PLURIBUS UNUM, as these were removed from the new model by Henry Hering, assistant to the late Augustus Saint-Gaudens. Neither on the present variety nor the earlier described one is the motto IN GOD WE TRUST, for President Theodore Roosevelt personally objected to the name of the Deity on circulating coins. Although many 1907 and 1908 eagles exist of this type, luster and eye appeal tend to vary, and some effort will be needed to find a nice one. The motif has been pleasing to collectors for a long time, and today the design is a numismatic favorite. Circulated examples are plentiful, but probably not of relevance to you as Mint State coins at the lower levels are fairly inexpensive. Mint State are also fairly plentiful, and usually quite attractive. However, quality does vary, and some modest effort will be needed to find one that is just right.

Aspects of Striking and Appearance: Check the central areas of Miss Liberty's portrait details on the obverse and, on the reverse, check the feathers of the eagle.

Proof Coins: Although a few Proofs of the 1907 date may have been made for experimental purposes, none were distributed to the numismatic community. Beware of fakes made later by sandblasting or etching Mint State coins. For all Proof gold coins of this and the next type, do not buy without consulting the advice of a trusted professional.

Market Value: Circulation Strikes

VF-20	EF-40	AU-50	AU-55	AU-58	MS-60	MS-62	MS-63	MS-64	MS-65	MS-66
$700	$725	$750	$775	$800	$875	$900	$950	$1,250	$2,750	$8,000

Retail Price Trends

Year	AU-50	MS-60	MS-65
1946	$32.50	$27.50	$48
1950	$27.50	$30	$45
1960	$40	$45	$70
1970	$200	$100	$900
1980	$300	$750	$2,000

Year	AU-50	MS-60	MS-65
1990	$700	$1,500	$4,000
2000	$450	$525	$6,200
2010	$800	$900	$3,000
2019	$750	$875	$2,750

Indian Head, Motto on Reverse (1908–1933)

Circulation-Strike Mintage: 14,385,139

Proof Mintage: 768

Field Population: Circulated, several million; Mint State, 250,000 to 400,000; Proof, 400 to 500

Designer: Augustus Saint-Gaudens. **Weight:** 16.718 grams. **Composition:** .900 gold, .100 copper (net weight: .48375 oz. pure gold). **Diameter:** 27 mm. **Edge:** ***1908–1911:*** 46 raised stars; ***1912–1933:*** 48 raised stars. **Mints:** Philadelphia, Denver, San Francisco.

Key to Collecting: Examples abound, but as lower-level Mint State coins are only slightly more expensive than are AU coins, Mint State seems to be a better option. At the Mint State level, the quality varies widely, and the typical piece is apt to have problems of one sort or another. Circulated coins can lack eye appeal.

Aspects of Striking and Appearance: Striking can vary. Check the details of the headdress on the obverse and the eagle on the reverse. Luster ranges from somewhat "grainy" on the earlier issues to "creamy" on the 1932. Eye appeal is often independent of grade.

Proof Coins: Proofs of this era can be divided into two categories: the Sand Blast Proofs of 1908 and 1911 to 1915, in which coins from regular dies, but carefully struck on a medal press, were subjected to blasting by sand particles, giving them a rough or sandpaper-like finish; and Satin Finish Proofs, sometimes called Roman Finish Proofs, made in 1909 and 1910 with satiny bright yellow surfaces. Availability is in proportion to the mintage figures. When seen, most examples are in the choice or gem category.

Market Value: Circulation Strikes

VF-20	EF-40	AU-50	AU-55	AU-58	MS-60	MS-62	MS-63	MS-64	MS-65	MS-66
$700	$725	$750	$775	$800	$875	$900	$950	$1,250	$2,750	$8,000

Market Value: Proof Strikes

PF-60	PF-63	PF-64	PF-65
$7,000	$20,000	$32,500	$60,000

Retail Price Trends

Year	AU-50	MS-60	MS-65	Sand Blast PF-65
1946	$32.50	$35	$52.50	$75
1950	$30	$32.50	$50	$80
1960	$32	$35	$50	$240
1970	$200	$1,000	$3,000	$15,000
1980	$400	$1,200	$6,500	$40,000

Year	AU-50	MS-60	MS-65	Sand Blast PF-65
1990	$550	$850	$5,500	$35,000
2000	$400	$450	$4,000	$30,000
2010	$825	$925	$5,000	$60,000
2019	$750	$875	$2,750	$60,000

27
Double Eagles ($20 Gold Coins) 1850-1933

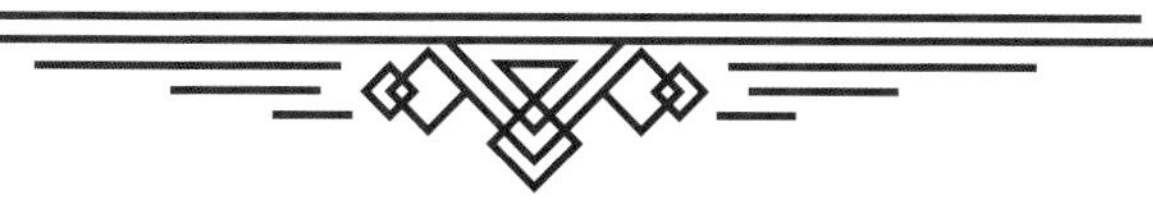

Overview of the Denomination

Beginning in 1849, vast quantities of gold bullion from California reached the East. To convert this influx of precious metal into coins, Congress passed the Act of March 3, 1849, which created two new denominations—the gold dollar and the $20. At the time, the eagle or $10 piece was the highest value, and thus it became logical to call the $20 the *double* eagle.

Chief Engraver James B. Longacre paid attention first to the dollar, which was in circulation by the summer of 1849. Work on the double eagle motifs took longer and was not completed until early 1850. In its final form, the $20 die showed the head of Miss Liberty facing left, somewhat similar to that used on the gold dollar, in combination with an eagle on the reverse, flanked by particularly ornate scrolls, with stars and rays above. In 1850 the first pieces reached circulation, from an astounding mintage of 1,170,261 from the Philadelphia Mint and 141,000 from New Orleans. Immediately, the $20 took the place of the $10 as the coin of choice in large transactions conducted at a distance and with foreign countries. Double eagles made for circulation, from 1850 through 1933, represented well over 75% of the precious metal converted to coin form by the various mints in the United States.

Large quantities were produced for many years. In 1854 the San Francisco Mint opened for business and added to the production of the New Orleans and Philadelphia mints. As the San Francisco Mint was close to the source of gold, production tended to be especially large.

For a short time, in early 1861, a distinctive *variety*, possibly even designated as a *type*, was used, the Paquet Reverse, in which the letters were taller than on the earlier style. The director of the Mint felt that such pieces would not strike, an apprehension that seems to have been unfounded. In any event, only a few were struck at the Philadelphia Mint and just 19,250 at San Francisco. In 1866 the motto IN GOD WE TRUST was added to the reverse, isolating the early style as a separate type.

From 1866 through 1876, the second type of double eagle was produced. Although many were minted, few were saved by numismatists. Today, examples are particularly elusive in gem state, although many EF, AU, and lower Mint State pieces can be found. This particular type saw the advent of the Carson City Mint in 1870, after which production was maintained there intermittently through 1893.

In 1877 the reverse type was changed to display the denomination as TWENTY DOLLARS, instead of TWENTY D. as previously. Double eagles of this type, minted to and including 1907, were made in tremendous quantities, used extensively in commerce, and are plentiful today.

Beginning in the 1870s, the "Silver Question" became prominent in American politics. Mining silver was a mainstay of the economy in Nevada, Colorado, and certain other Western areas. However, the price fell precipitately as European countries abandoned silver in favor of gold as an international standard. In the late 1870s, continuing in the 1880s and peaking by the mid-1890s, European banks and merchants were fearful that Americans would want to settle their international transactions in silver coins, particularly in the "Morgan" dollars made beginning in 1878. Such coins, although marked ONE DOLLAR, had a melt-down value of much less. Accordingly, a tremendous pressure was put upon American financial interests to pay in gold double eagles, which contained full value of metal. This flight of $20 pieces overseas was so great that at one point the Treasury almost ran out of gold! Once these pieces reached foreign destinations, some were melted and converted into coins of particular countries, but many others were simply bagged and tossed into vaults.

In December 1907, the MCMVII High Relief double eagle by Augustus Saint-Gaudens was released into circulation, to the extent of 12,867 pieces, the result of a long collaboration between that artist and President Theodore Roosevelt. These pieces were instantly and immensely popular, and most of them were snatched up by bank tellers and customers. In the same month, the "regular" Saint-Gaudens double eagles, in low relief and with the date expressed as 1907, were also made. Such pieces were produced further in early 1908.

In the summer of the latter year, the motto IN GOD WE TRUST was added to the reverse of the double eagle, creating the sixth major type, which was produced intermittently through and including 1933. Quantities were vast for the international trade, peaking at an incredible 8,816,000 in the year 1928.

In 1933 President Roosevelt prohibited paying out of gold coins in domestic commercial transactions, and soon thereafter the public was requested to turn in all that they had, coins of numismatic value excepted, and a small quantity being allowed for personal use. Foreign banks held on to their long-stored double eagles more tightly than ever, having no interest whatsoever in shipping them to the United States to be exchanged for paper money! Years later, beginning in a large way in the 1940s, overseas hoards were tapped, one country after another, bringing back to the United States millions of double eagles. Such pieces account for most of the coins in the hands of collectors and investors today.

Double eagles minted after 1928 were stored by the Treasury Department and not released into circulation nor shipped overseas, except perhaps for some small quantities. In the 1930s, these were melted. Accordingly, such dates as 1920-S, 1921, all mintmarks after 1924, and all dates after 1929 range from scarce to rare today.

Collecting a Type Set of Double Eagles

Forming a type set of the six major double eagle designs (with the 1861 Paquet reverse added as a sub-type if desired) can be a pleasurable pursuit. Double eagles are large and impressive to own, and in Mint State can be very attractive. Thanks to the aforementioned overseas hoards, finding choice and gem Mint State examples will be no problem at all for the later types.

The first double eagle type, that of 1850 to 1866, is generally available in grades from VF on up, with Mint State pieces being elusive, but being greatly augmented by over 5,000 pieces found by the discovery of the long-lost treasure ship SS *Central America*. Included in that cache were some simply incredible gems. The SS *Brother Jonathan*, lost at sea in 1865, was recovered and yielded hundreds of Mint State 1865-S double eagles, and some dated 1864 and a few earlier. The salvaged wreck of the SS *Republic*, lost in 1865 while on a voyage from New York City to New Orleans, has also yielded some very attractive Mint State double eagles of this first type. In my opinion, if you acquire one of these "treasure" coins it will be equally important to do some reading on the ship involved. In that way you can appreciate the fantastic history of what you have.

The type from 1866 through 1876, with the motto IN GOD WE TRUST above the eagle and with the denomination expressed as TWENTY D., is the rarest type in gem and choice Mint State preservation. Many EF and AU coins have been repatriated from overseas holdings, as have quite a few in such grades as MS-60 through MS-62 or even MS-63. However, true gems are hardly ever seen.

Liberty Head double eagles of the 1877 to 1907 type with motto and with the denomination as TWENTY DOLLARS are exceedingly plentiful in just about any grade desired, with gems being available of certain issues of the early twentieth century. While it is easy to obtain a gem of a common date, some collectors of type coins have opted to add a coin of *special interest*, such as a Carson City issue. The choice is up to you.

The famous MCMVII High Relief double eagle of 1907 was saved in quantity by the public as well as by numismatists, and today it is likely that at least 5,000 to 6,000 exist, representing about half of the mintage. Most of these are in varying degrees of Mint State, MS-60 to MS-63, but with quite a few listed as MS-64 and MS-65. Lower grades such as VF and EF exist, but were often used for jewelry or polished, or have other problems. This particular design is a great favorite with just about everyone, and although pieces are not rarities, they are hardly inexpensive.

The so-called "Arabic Date" 1907 and 1908 Saint-Gaudens design is available in just about any grade desired, with MS-60 through MS-63 or MS-64 pieces being plentiful and inexpensive, a good choice. Double eagles of the final type 1908 to 1933 are abundant in any grade desired, with choice and gem coins being plentiful.

Beyond a Type Set

Collecting double eagles by date and mint is more popular than you might think. Offhand, it would seem that these high denominations, laden with a number of rare dates, would attract few enthusiasts. However, that is not the case, and over a long period of years more people have specialized in double eagles than have specialized in $5 or $10 pieces.

Interestingly, although slightly over 200 dates and mintmarks of $20 pieces were made from 1850 to 1933, 90% of these are relatively available within the budget of most collectors. A quick check at a popular price listing such as *A Guide Book of United States Coins* will verify this.

Two particularly notable collections of double eagles by date and mint, from the earliest times to the latest, were formed by Louis E. Eliasberg of Baltimore, and Jeff Browning of Dallas. Both have been dispersed across the auction block. The first was cataloged by me in 1982 (under the imprimatur of Bowers and Ruddy Galleries), and the second was offered by Stack's and Sotheby's in 2001. In addition, many other collections over the years—dozens in fact—have had large numbers of double eagles, some specializing in the Liberty Head type 1850 to 1907 (such as the "Eagle Collection" sold by Heritage), others only with the Saint-Gaudens type from 1907 onward (such as the Dr. Thaine Price Collection sold by David W. Akers), and others addressing the entire range.

Among rarities in the double eagle series are the 1854-O and 1856-O, each known only to the extent of a few dozen pieces, the 1861 Philadelphia Mint with Paquet reverse (two known), the Proof-only issues of 1883, 1884, and 1887, several other low-mintage varieties of this era, the famous Carson City issue of 1870-CC, and various issues from 1920 onward, including 1920-S, 1921, mintmarks after 1923, and all dates after 1928. Punctuating these rarities are a number of readily available pieces, including the very common Philadelphia issues from 1922 through 1928 inclusive.

A pleasing way to collect double eagles is simply to set a grade goal and to acquire whatever comes to hand, within your budget and within that grade. For example, you could aspire to acquire every Type III $20 (1877 to 1907 Liberty Head) you can find in MS-63 grade for up to a certain price level, ditto for the Saint-Gaudens series. Many dozens of coins are possible, most being quite inexpensive. Such a holding can be very beautiful to own and admire.

Liberty Head, No Motto on Reverse (1849–1866)

Circulation-Strike Mintage: 23,526,676 (including 19,250 1866-S Paquet reverse coins)

Proof Mintage: *375*

Field Population: Circulated, 59,120 to 91,270; Mint State, 6,990 to 8,700; Proof, 80 to 125

Designer: James B. Longacre. **Weight:** 33.436 grams. **Composition:** .900 gold, .100 copper (net weight: .96750 oz. pure gold). **Diameter** 34 mm. **Edge:** Reeded. **Mints:** Philadelphia, New Orleans, San Francisco.

Key to Collecting: Double eagles of the first type are readily available in just about every grade desired. Until the recent era examples of this type were scarcely ever seen in choice Mint State. Today, coins recovered from the SS *Yankee Blade* (lost in 1854),

SS *Central America* (1857), SS *Brother Jonathan* (1865), and SS *Republic* (1865) have provided a generous supply of choice examples. In 1861 a variety or subtype was created by Anthony C. Paquet, using tall letters on the reverse. This can be collected as a separate type, if desired.

Aspects of Striking and Appearance: Striking is usually quite good for dates from 1850 through 1858. In 1859 there was a slight modification, and the hair detail, as per the original dies, is not as sharp. Beyond that, in the context of whatever date you select, check the sharpness of Miss Liberty's hair, not only in the central parts but on the curls down to her neck, and the sharpness of the stars. On the reverse, check the details of the shield and eagle. Denticles can be checked on both sides.

Proof Coins: Proofs are occasionally seen of this type, beginning in this instance with 1859 and continuing through 1865. However, as a class they are exceedingly rare.

Market Value: Circulation Strikes

VF-20	EF-40	AU-50	AU-55	AU-58	MS-60	MS-62	MS-63	MS-64	MS-65
$2,000	$2,250	$2,500	$3,250	$3,750	$5,500	$7,000	$8,500	$10,000	$14,500

Market Value: Proof Strikes

PF-60	PF-63	PF-64	PF-65
$75,000	$125,000	$250,000	$375,000

Retail Price Trends

Year	AU-50	MS-60	MS-65	PF-64
1946	$80	$85	$125	$500
1950	$70	$75	$110	$475
1960	$82.50	$87.50	$135	$1,200
1970	$350	$750	$1,500	$2,000
1980	$700	$1,800	$3,000	$60,000

Year	AU-50	MS-60	MS-65	PF-64
1990	$775	$1,600	$6,000	$45,000
2000	$700	$1,750	$9,000	$70,000
2010	$2,000	$4,000	$14,000	$225,000
2019	$2,500	$5,500	$14,500	$250,000

Liberty Head, Motto on Reverse, TWENTY D. (1866–1876)

Circulation-Strike Mintage: 16,160,758

Proof Mintage: 335

Field Population: Circulated, 104,490 to 159,400; Mint State, 8,790 to 13,490; Proof, 125 to 150

Designer: James B. Longacre. **Weight:** 33.436 grams. **Composition:** .900 gold, .100 copper (net weight: .96750 oz. pure gold). **Diameter** 34 mm. **Edge:** Reeded. **Mints:** Philadelphia, Carson City, San Francisco.

Key to Collecting: This relatively short-lived double eagle type is the scarcest of the six major styles of double eagles. When seen, most pieces show wear, readily available in VF, EF, and AU preservation, although MS-60 through MS-62 are plentiful enough to satisfy demands.

Aspects of Striking and Appearance: Striking can be a problem with these issues. Check the hair detail of Miss Liberty, often unsatisfactory, and the centers of the stars, similarly less than sharp in many instances. The reverses tend to be struck up better, but again check all details including the eagle.

Proof Coins: Proofs are very rare as the low mintage figures indicate. However, when seen they are usually quite attractive.

Market Value: Circulation Strikes

VF-20	EF-40	AU-50	AU-55	AU-58	MS-60	MS-62	MS-63	MS-64
$1,500	$1,550	$1,600	$1,700	$1,750	$2,000	$2,750	$8,500	$32,500

Market Value: Proof Strikes

PF-60	PF-63	PF-64	PF-65
$20,000	$55,000	$75,000	$135,000

Retail Price Trends

Year	AU-50	MS-60	MS-65	PF-65
1946	$70	$75	$110	$375
1950	$65	$70	$105	$340
1960	$75	$80	$120	$1,200
1970	$100	$135	$2,000	$20,000
1980	$500	$650	$4,500	$65,000

Year	AU-50	MS-60	MS-65	PF-65
1990	$650	$800	$9,500	$85,000
2000	$575	$750	$10,000	$80,000
2010	$1,600	$1,850	$170,000	$190,000
2019	$1,600	$2,000	$150,000	$135,000

Liberty Head, Motto on Reverse, TWENTY DOLLARS (1877–1907)

Circulation-Strike Mintage: 64,137,477

Proof Mintage: 2,426

Field Population: Circulated, 1,930,125 to 2,989,600; Mint State, 395,730 to 612,000; Proof, 1,400 to 1,900

Designer: James B. Longacre. **Weight:** 33.436 grams. **Composition:** .900 gold, .100 copper (net weight: .96750 oz. pure gold). **Diameter** 34 mm. **Edge:** Reeded. **Mints:** Philadelphia, Carson City, Denver, New Orleans, San Francisco.

Key to Collecting: Examples are as common as can be and are available in just about any grade desired. Options exist to take the easy way out and acquire a high-mintage variety of the early twentieth century, or else pick something a bit scarcer, perhaps a Carson City issue. Mint State pieces abound, especially for the high-mintage issues near the turn of the twentieth century.

Aspects of Striking and Appearance: The striking is usually much better on this type than on the one before, although the hair details, stars, and reverse features should all be checked. Luster varies widely depending on the date and mint.

Proof Coins: Proofs were minted of all years 1877 through 1907. In 1902 the dies were polished, eliminating the numismatically desirable frosty or cameo effect. From that point through 1907, dies vary in their contrast. Many Proofs are impaired, and for some reason, among a given 10 surviving examples of this type, more are impaired than among a given 10 survivors of the Type 2 style.

Market Value: Circulation Strikes

VF-20	EF-40	AU-50	AU-55	AU-58	MS-60	MS-62	MS-63	MS-64	MS-65
$1,375	$1,385	$1,400	$1,425	$1,450	$1,525	$1,575	$1,650	$1,850	$2,750

Market Value: Proof Strikes

PF-60	PF-63	PF-64	PF-65
$20,000	$40,000	$75,000	$125,000

Retail Price Trends

Year	AU-50	MS-60	MS-65	PF-65
1946	$67.50	$72.50	$105	$300
1950	$65	$70	$100	$350
1960	$60	$65	$100	$900
1970	$110	$400	$900	$12,000
1980	$325	$500	$1,400	$20,000

Year	AU-50	MS-60	MS-65	PF-65
1990	$575	$650	$3,000	$65,000
2000	$525	$550	$3,500	$40,000
2010	$1,600	$1,700	$5,100	$100,000
2019	$1,400	$1,525	$2,750	$125,000

Saint-Gaudens, No Motto, High Relief, MCMVII (1907)

Circulation-Strike Mintage: 12,867 (some in 1908)

Field Population: Circulated, 2,500 to 3,500; Mint State, 3,500 to 5,500

Designer: Augustus Saint-Gaudens. **Weight:** 33.436 grams. **Composition:** .900 gold, .100 copper (net weight: .96750 oz. pure gold). **Diameter:** 34 mm. **Edge:** E PLURIBUS UNUM with words divided by stars. **Mint:** Philadelphia.

Key to Collecting: This is the double eagle that everybody loves! The design showcases the artistry of Augustus Saint-Gaudens to its finest advantage, with the details in sculptured-like high relief, and both obverse and reverse being splendid in their layout. Fortunately, of the 12,867 pieces minted, about half exist today, providing ample opportunities for purchase. However, the demand is such that the pieces are hardly inexpensive. While a fair number of EF and AU pieces exist, often these are polished or have problems. I suggest that you opt for low-grade Mint State. However, if you do select a lightly worn piece, be sure it has no defects. Mint State coins are the rule, not the exception.

Aspects of Striking and Appearance: The striking is usually good, but check the central parts of the figure of *Victory*. Also check her left knee, and the details of the Capitol building. Under magnification the die fields show myriad tiny raised curlicues and other die-finish marks, imparting a matte-like character to the luster. Varieties exist with flat rim and wire rim and do not constitute different types.

Proof Coins: There is no record of any MCMVII double eagles being made as Proofs, nor is there any early numismatic record of any being sold as Proofs.

Market Value: Circulation Strikes

VF-20	EF-40	AU-50	AU-55	AU-58	MS-60	MS-62	MS-63	MS-64	MS-65	MS-66
$9,000	$11,000	$12,000	$13,000	$14,500	$15,000	$19,500	$24,000	$29,000	$45,000	$70,000

Retail Price Trends

Year	AU-50	MS-60	MS-65
1946	$105	$120	$180
1950	$90	$100	$150
1960	$225	$260	$400
1970	$950	$2,000	$14,000
1980	$4,000	$18,500	$35,000
1990	$6,500	$11,000	$40,000
2000	$5,000	$7,000	$35,000
2010	$12,000	$16,500	$47,000
2019	$12,000	$15,000	$45,000

Saint-Gaudens, No Motto, Arabic Numerals (1907–1908)

Circulation-Strike Mintage: 5,296,968

Proof Mintage: Fewer than 5

Field Population: Circulated, 780,000 to 1,100,000; Mint State, 320,000 to 327,500; Proof, 3 or 4

Designer: Augustus Saint-Gaudens. **Weight:** 33.436 grams. **Composition:** .900 gold, .100 copper (net weight: .96750 oz. pure gold). **Diameter:** 34 mm. **Edge:** E PLURIBUS UNUM with words divided by stars. **Mints:** Philadelphia, Denver.

Key to Collecting: Circulated coins are abundant, but not advised for your consideration as Mint State coins are only slightly more costly, and examples abound, including gems from the famous Wells Fargo hoard discovered by Ron Gillio and his associates in the 1990s, and consisting of 19,990 pieces. Most of these are quite attractive. Beyond that, watch out for wide differences of opinion, as the usual light striking of this issue plus other aspects combine so that what one expert can call MS-64, another might call AU. This is a very tricky area, and perhaps to simply go with one holder-certified as "Wells Fargo Hoard" will be the easiest route.

Aspects of Striking and Appearance: The striking is often light on the obverse, particularly the upper part of Miss Liberty. Indeed, poor striking is why the dies were slightly modified later.

Proof Coins: None minted for distribution to collectors.

Market Value: Circulation Strikes

VF-20	EF-40	AU-50	AU-55	AU-58	MS-60	MS-62	MS-63	MS-64	MS-65	MS-66
$1,350	$1,365	$1,375	$1,385	$1,390	$1,400	$1,425	$1,450	$1,475	$1,750	$2,500

Retail Price Trends

Year	AU-50	MS-60	MS-65
1946	$70	$75	$110
1950	$65	$70	$105
1960	$72.50	$77.50	$115
1970	$110	$500	$1,000
1980	$650	$850	$1,800

Year	AU-50	MS-60	MS-65
1990	$725	$850	$1,500
2000	$525	$550	$1,200
2010	$1,550	$1,650	$2,000
2019	$1,375	$1,400	$1,750

Saint-Gaudens, With Motto (1908–1933)

Circulation-Strike Mintage: 64,981,428

Proof Mintage: 687

Field Population: Circulated, 908,530 to 1,601,210; Mint State, 3,157,120 to 4,747,230; Proof, 400 to 500

Designer: Augustus Saint-Gaudens. **Weight:** 33.436 grams. **Composition:** .900 gold, .100 copper (net weight: .96750 oz. pure gold). **Diameter:** 34 mm. **Edge:** E PLURIBUS UNUM with words divided by stars. **Mints:** Philadelphia, Denver, San Francisco.

Key to Collecting: Today, coins of this type are extremely common. Examples are available in just about any grade desired, with EF and AU pieces abounding, but I suggest you ignore them as Mint State coins are readily available. Most are quite attractive, this being particularly true for the issues after 1921 (before then the eye appeal often varies widely).

Aspects of Striking and Appearance: The striking is usually good, but there are exceptions. Check the features of Miss Liberty, the details of the tiny Capitol building at the lower left, and other aspects. Some pieces have arc-like ridges around the periphery, a slight distance in from the edge, seemingly an artifact of extensive die use.

Proof Coins: Proofs of this era can be divided into two categories: the Sand Blast Proofs of 1908 and 1911 to 1915, in which coins from regular dies, but carefully struck on a medal press, were subjected to blasting by sand particles, giving them a rough or sandpaper like finish; and Satin Finish Proofs, sometimes called Roman Finish Proofs, made in 1909 and 1910 with satiny bright yellow surfaces.

Market Value: Circulation Strikes

VF-20	EF-40	AU-50	AU-55	AU-58	MS-60	MS-62	MS-63	MS-64	MS-65	MS-66
$1,350	$1,365	$1,375	$1,385	$1,390	$1,400	$1,425	$1,450	$1,500	$1,750	$2,500

Market Value: Proof Strikes

PF-60	PF-63	PF-64	PF-65
$15,000	$30,000	$45,000	$80,000

Retail Price Trends

Year	AU-50	MS-60	MS-65	Sand Blast PF-65
1946	$68	$70	$105	$160
1950	$55	$60	$90	$500
1960	$52.50	$57.50	$85	$750
1970	$90	$110	$600	$15,000
1980	$250	$350	$1,200	$30,000
1990	$575	$700	$1,800	$40,000
2000	$500	$525	$1,400	$35,000
2010	$1,600	$1,700	$2,000	$70,000
2019	$1,375	$1,400	$1,750	$80,000

APPENDIX A
Bullion Values of Silver and Gold Type Coins

These charts show the bullion values of common-date circulation-strike silver and gold coins. These are intrinsic values—they do not reflect any numismatic premium. The weights indicated for each denomination are actual silver weight (often abbreviated ASW) or actual gold weight (AGW).

Bullion Values of Silver Coins

Silver Price Per Ounce	Wartime Nickel .05626 oz.	Dime .07234 oz.	Quarter .18084 oz.	Half Dollar .36169 oz.	Silver Clad Half Dollar .14792 oz.	Silver Dollar .77344 oz.
$8.00	$0.45	$0.58	$1.45	$2.89	$1.18	$6.19
$8.50	$0.48	$0.61	$1.54	$3.07	$1.26	$6.57
$9.00	$0.51	$0.65	$1.63	$3.26	$1.33	$6.96
$9.50	$0.53	$0.69	$1.72	$3.44	$1.41	$7.35
$10.00	$0.56	$0.72	$1.81	$3.62	$1.48	$7.73
$10.50	$0.59	$0.76	$1.90	$3.80	$1.55	$8.12
$11.00	$0.62	$0.80	$1.99	$3.98	$1.63	$8.51
$11.50	$0.65	$0.83	$2.08	$4.16	$1.70	$8.89
$12.00	$0.68	$0.87	$2.17	$4.34	$1.78	$9.28
$12.50	$0.70	$0.90	$2.26	$4.52	$1.85	$9.67
$13.00	$0.73	$0.94	$2.35	$4.70	$1.92	$10.05
$13.50	$0.76	$0.98	$2.44	$4.88	$2.00	$10.44
$14.00	$0.79	$1.01	$2.53	$5.06	$2.07	$10.83
$14.50	$0.82	$1.05	$2.62	$5.24	$2.14	$11.21
$15.00	$0.84	$1.09	$2.71	$5.43	$2.22	$11.60
$15.50	$0.87	$1.12	$2.80	$5.61	$2.29	$11.99
$16.00	$0.90	$1.16	$2.89	$5.79	$2.37	$12.38
$16.50	$0.93	$1.19	$2.98	$5.97	$2.44	$12.76
$17.00	$0.96	$1.23	$3.07	$6.15	$2.51	$13.15
$17.50	$0.98	$1.27	$3.16	$6.33	$2.59	$13.54
$18.00	$1.01	$1.30	$3.26	$6.51	$2.66	$13.92

Note: The U.S. bullion coins first issued in 1986 are unlike the older regular issues. They contain the following amounts of pure metal: silver $1, 1 oz.; gold $50, 1 oz.; gold $25, 1/2 oz.; gold $10, 1/4 oz.; gold $5, 1/10 oz.

Bullion Values of Gold Coins

Gold Price Per Ounce	$5.00 Liberty Head 1839–1908 Indian Head 1908–1929 .24187 oz.	$10.00 Liberty Head 1838–1907 Indian Head 1907–1933 .48375 oz.	$20.00 1849–1933 .96750 oz.
$1,000	$241.87	$483.75	$967.50
$1,025	$247.92	$495.84	$991.69
$1,050	$253.96	$507.94	$1,015.88
$1,075	$260.01	$520.03	$1,040.06
$1,100	$266.06	$532.13	$1,064.25
$1,125	$272.10	$544.22	$1,088.44
$1,150	$278.15	$556.31	$1,112.63
$1,175	$284.20	$568.41	$1,136.81
$1,200	$290.24	$580.50	$1,161.00
$1,225	$296.29	$592.59	$1,185.19
$1,250	$302.34	$604.69	$1,209.38
$1,275	$308.38	$616.78	$1,233.56
$1,300	$314.43	$628.88	$1,257.75
$1,325	$320.48	$640.97	$1,281.94
$1,350	$326.52	$653.06	$1,306.13
$1,375	$332.57	$665.16	$1,330.31
$1,400	$338.62	$677.25	$1,354.50
$1,425	$344.66	$689.34	$1,378.69
$1,450	$350.71	$701.44	$1,402.88
$1,475	$356.76	$713.53	$1,427.06
$1,500	$362.81	$725.63	$1,451.25
$1,525	$368.85	$737.72	$1,475.44
$1,550	$374.90	$749.81	$1,499.63
$1,575	$380.95	$761.91	$1,523.81
$1,600	$386.99	$774.00	$1,548.00
$1,625	$393.04	$786.09	$1,572.19
$1,650	$399.09	$798.19	$1,596.38
$1,675	$405.13	$810.28	$1,620.56
$1,700	$411.18	$822.38	$1,644.75
$1,725	$417.23	$834.47	$1,668.94
$1,750	$423.27	$846.56	$1,693.13
$1,775	$429.32	$858.66	$1,717.31
$1,800	$435.37	$870.75	$1,741.50
$1,825	$441.41	$882.84	$1,765.69
$1,850	$447.46	$894.94	$1,789.88
$1,875	$453.51	$907.03	$1,814.06
$1,900	$459.55	$919.13	$1,838.25
$1,925	$465.60	$931.22	$1,862.44
$1,950	$471.65	$943.31	$1,886.63
$1,975	$477.69	$955.41	$1,910.81
$2,000	$483.74	$967.50	$1,935.00

Note: The U.S. bullion coins first issued in 1986 are unlike the older regular issues. They contain the following amounts of pure metal: silver $1, 1 oz.; gold $50, 1 oz.; gold $25, 1/2 oz.; gold $10, 1/4 oz.; gold $5, 1/10 oz.

APPENDIX B

Philippine Coins Struck Under the United States 1903–1945

Overview

In April 1899 control of the Philippine Islands was officially transferred from Spain to the United States, as a condition of the treaty ending the Spanish-American War. In July 1901 a civilian government replaced the islands' military administration; one of its first tasks was to sponsor a new territorial coinage. The resulting coins—which bear the legend UNITED STATES OF AMERICA but are otherwise quite different in design from regular U.S. coins—today can be found in many American coin collections, having been brought to the States as souvenirs by service members after World War II or otherwise saved.

The coins, introduced in 1903, also bear the Spanish names for the islands: FILIPINAS. Following Spanish custom, the dollar-sized peso was equivalent to 100 centavos. Silver fractions were minted in denominations of fifty, twenty, and ten centavos, and minor coins (in copper-nickel and bronze) included the five-cent piece, the centavo, and the half centavo.

Dies for the coins were made at the Philadelphia Mint. From 1903 to 1908 the coins were struck at the Philadelphia Mint (with no mintmark) and the San Francisco Mint (with an S mintmark). From 1909 through 1919, they were struck only at San Francisco. In the first part of 1920, one-centavo coins were struck in San Francisco; later in the year a new mint facility was opened in Manila, and from that point into the early 1940s Philippine coins of one, five, ten, twenty, and fifty centavos were struck there. The coins produced at the Manila Mint in 1920, 1921, and 1922 bore no mintmark. No Philippine coins were struck in 1923 or 1924. The Manila Mint re-opened in 1925; from then through 1941 its coinage featured an M mintmark.

Rising silver prices forced the Mint to reduce the fineness and weight for each silver denomination beginning in 1907, and subsequent issues are smaller in diameter.

The Philippine Islands were largely self-governed, as a commonwealth of the United States, from 1935 until full independence was recognized in 1946. Coinage under the Commonwealth began with three commemorative coins in 1936. Circulating issues were minted from 1937 to 1941 (in Manila) and in 1944 and 1945 (in Philadelphia, Denver, and San Francisco).

The Commonwealth coinage retained Melecio Figueroa's obverse design, used on the coinage of 1903 to 1936. Its new reverse design featured a shield derived from the official seal of the government of the Philippines, with three stars symbolizing Luzon, Mindanao, and the Visayas, the islands' three main geographical regions.

After the Manila Mint was destroyed during World War II, in 1944 and 1945, the U.S. Mint again struck coins for the Philippines at its Philadelphia, Denver, and San Francisco mints.

The Philippines became an independent republic after the war, on July 4, 1946. Today the coins of 1903 to 1945, including a set of commemoratives issued in 1936, remain as interesting mementoes of a colorful and important chapter in U.S. history and numismatics, and the special bond between the United States and the Philippines.

The following are general descriptions of Philippine issues by type. For more history, and detailed date-by-date charts with mintages and retail values, see the 1,504-page deluxe edition of the *Guide Book of United States Coins* known as *Mega Red*.

COLLECTING A TYPE SET OF U.S./ PHILIPPINE COINS

Since 1960 Philippines coins struck under United States sovereignty have been featured in the *Guide Book of United States Coins*. This inclusion in the best-selling annual guide marked their significance as part of American numismatics. In the 1960s Whitman Publishing produced a "Philippine Type Set Collection" album in its popular line of blue-leatherette coin albums. In addition to 1903–1945 coin types, the album included openings for pre–United States coins (those minted for the Philippines by the Spanish Empire, 1864 to 1897), and also for types minted for the Republic after 1947.

The coins' coverage in the *Red Book* was dramatically expanded in 1998, in the 52nd edition. It was even more substantially increased in the book's 1,504-page deluxe edition, *Mega Red*, first published in 2015.

A basic type set of U.S./Philippine coins consists of 17 pieces: a single coin to represent the half centavo; two to represent the centavo (pre-Commonwealth and Commonwealth); three each for the 5-centavos, 10-centavos, 20-centavos, and 50-centavos denominations; and two sizes of peso. The three types each of 5- through 50-centavos include the early large-diameter types and later smaller-diameter types, plus one type to represent the Commonwealth coinage of the later 1930s to mid-1940s.

Common-date coins in circulated condition are readily available in the numismatic marketplace, and, as mentioned above, are often found among wartime souvenirs brought back to the United States by military service members in the 1940s and beyond. An attractive circulated type set can be easily and inexpensively assembled. Connoisseurship, meanwhile, can lead to a very nice Uncirculated set. Striking and sharpness varies with each denomination and type. Take your time and look for high-quality coins. Most of the rarities and quite a few higher-grade common coins have been encapsulated in third-party-grading slabs, but many others still exist in their raw, uncertified state.

Beyond a Type Set

There are several scarce pieces within the series, some on par with the great rarities of regular-issue American coins. Also, Proofs were issued for collector sets in the early years of Philadelphia coinage. And in 1936 a set of three commemorative silver coins (two pesos and a 50-centavos piece) was minted to celebrate the dawn of the Commonwealth. All of these avenues offer new collecting possibilities after you build a basic type set.

There are enough interesting die varieties within U.S./Philippine coinage to present challenges and opportunities for advanced collectors.

Beyond legal-tender coinage, numismatists also often collect related tokens and printed leper-colony currency; a 1920 Manila Mint Opening medal; and other Philippine tokens and medals of the era.

Half Centavo (1903–1908)

Circulation-Strike Mintage: 17,738,000

Proof Mintage: 5,384

Designer: Melecio Figueroa. **Weight:** 2.35 grams. **Composition:** .950 copper, .050 tin and zinc. **Diameter:** 17.5 mm. **Edge:** Plain. **Mint:** Philadelphia.

Key to Collecting: In 1903 and 1904 the United States minted nearly 18 million half centavos for the Philippines. By March of the latter year, it was obvious that the half centavo was too small a denomination, unneeded in commerce despite the government's attempts to force it into circulation. In 1908 nearly 8 million coins were melted and made into centavos. Despite the mass melting, type coins are readily available in high circulated grades and in Mint State.

Aspects of Striking and Appearance: Half centavos typically are well struck, except for the 1903 issue, of which some coins may show weak numerals in the date.

Proof Coins: The Philadelphia Mint struck small quantities of Proof half centavos for collectors throughout the denomination's existence, for inclusion in Proof sets (except for 1907, when no Proof sets were issued).

Market Value: Circulation Strikes

EF	MS-60	MS-63
$2.25	$20	$40

Market Value: Proof Strikes

PF-65
$150

One Centavo (1903–1936)

Circulation-Strike Mintage: 195,888,215

Proof Mintage: 5,384

Designer: Melecio Figueroa. **Weight:** 4.7 grams. **Composition:** .950 copper, .050 tin and zinc. **Diameter:** 24 mm. **Edge:** Plain. **Mints:** Philadelphia, San Francisco, Manila.

Key to Collecting: Unlike the half centavo, the bronze centavo was a popular workhorse of Philippine commerce from the start of its production. With millions of coins minted, finding a nice high-grade example will be easy—but a savvy collector will search for a well-struck coin, noting that each mint presents its own challenges and opportunities in terms of quality.

Aspects of Striking and Appearance: On the obverse, the figure's right hand (holding the hammer) is almost always found flatly struck. The reverse, especially of later-date centavos, often shows flattening of the eagle's breast and of the left part of the shield. Issues of the Manila Mint, especially of 1920, often are lightly struck. Those of San Francisco typically are better struck, with only occasional light strikes. On centavos of 1929 to 1936, the M mintmark often is nearly unidentifiable as a letter.

Proof Coins: One-centavo Proofs were struck at the Philadelphia Mint for annual Proof sets in 1903, 1904, 1905, 1906, and 1908. Proof centavos of 1908 bear a date with numerals noticeably larger than those of circulation-strike 1908-S coins.

Market Value: Circulation Strikes

VF	EF	MS-60	MS-63
$2	$4	$20	$45

Market Value: Proof Strikes

PF-60	PF-63
$60	$120

One Centavo, Commonwealth (1937–1944)

Circulation-Strike Mintage: *99,290,492*

Designer: Melecio Figueroa (obverse). **Weight:** 5.3 grams. **Composition:** .950 copper, .050 tin and zinc (except for 1944-S: .950 copper, .050 zinc). **Diameter:** 24 mm. **Edge:** Plain. **Mints:** San Francisco, Manila.

Key to Collecting: The centavo switched over to the Commonwealth shield design in 1937. The Manila Mint struck centavos for the Commonwealth every year from 1937 through 1941. This production was brought to an end by the Japanese invasion that started in December 1941, immediately after the bombing of Pearl Harbor. Part of the United States–Commonwealth plan to retake the islands included the San Francisco Mint's 1944 striking of 58 million one-centavo coins—a quantity greater than all of Manila's centavo output since 1937. Like the federal Lincoln cents of 1944 to 1946, these coins were made of *brass* rather than bronze. The coins were transported to the islands to enter circulation as U.S. and Philippine military forces fought back the Japanese invaders.

The centavo was a popular coin that saw widespread circulation. As a result, many of the coins today are found with signs of wear or damage, exacerbated by corrosion and toning encouraged by the islands' tropical climate. Take time to select an attractive example.

Aspects of Striking and Appearance: Well-struck examples are uncommon. Many 1937-M centavos have a barely readable mintmark. Issues of 1938 to 1941 used a narrow M mintmark, rather than a square version of the letter, resulting in better legibility.

Market Value: Circulation Strikes

VF	EF	MS-60	MS-63
$0.25	$0.50	$1	$2

Five Centavos, Larger-Diameter (1903–1928)

Circulation-Strike Mintage: 24,337,607

Proof Mintage: 4,884

Designer: Melecio Figueroa. **Weight:** 5 grams. **Composition:** .750 copper, .250 nickel. **Diameter:** 20.5 mm. **Edge:** Plain. **Mints:** Philadelphia, San Francisco, Manila.

Key to Collecting: Five-centavo coins were minted under U.S. sovereignty for the Philippines from 1903 to 1935, with several gaps in production over the years. Circulation strikes were made in Philadelphia in 1903 and 1904, then coinage resumed in 1916, this time at the San Francisco Mint. The new Manila Mint took over all five-centavo production starting in 1920, continuing through the end of direct U.S. administration. The Manila Mint coins of 1920 and 1921 bore no mintmark indicating their producer. From 1925 forward they had an M mintmark.

Philippine five-centavo coins are considerably scarcer than their contemporary Liberty Head and Buffalo nickel counterparts minted for mainland United States circulation. However, they remain more affordable while the coins are off the radar of the average U.S. coin collector.

Aspects of Striking and Appearance: The obverse of the 1918 and 1919 San Francisco Mint issues often is weakly struck, with considerable loss of detail. Many 1920 coins lack sharpness in the rims and have weak details overall.

Proof Coins: Five-centavo Proofs were struck at the Philadelphia Mint for annual Proof sets in 1903, 1904, 1905, 1906, and 1908.

Market Value: Circulation Strikes

VF	EF	MS-60	MS-63
$1.25	$2.50	$20	$35

Market Value: Proof Strikes

PF-60	PF-63
$75	$130

Five Centavos, Smaller-Diameter (1930–1935)

Circulation-Strike Mintage: 15,245,562

Designer: Melecio Figueroa. **Weight:** 4.75 grams. **Composition:** .750 copper, .250 nickel. **Diameter:** 19 mm. **Edge:** Plain. **Mint:** Manila.

Key to Collecting: The diameter of the five-centavo coin from 1903 to 1928 was very close to that of the twenty-centavo coin of 1907 to 1929. In 1930, to clearly differentiate their sizes, the diameter of the five-centavo piece was reduced from 20.5 to 19 mm. Five-centavo coinage under U.S. sovereignty continued to 1935, followed by Commonwealth coinage. Struck only in the low single-digit millions, all 1903–1935 Philippine "nickels" are scarcer than their federal U.S. counterparts. Attrition has made high Mint State examples harder to find, but as a type they are affordable thanks to a couple higher-mintage years.

Aspects of Striking and Appearance: Strike is generally good.

Market Value: Circulation Strikes

VF	EF	MS-60	MS-63
$2	$6	$50	$100

Five Centavos, Commonwealth (1937–1945)

Circulation-Strike Mintage: *117,277,872*

Designer: Melecio Figueroa (obverse). **Weight:** ***1937–1941:*** 4.8 grams; ***1944–1945:*** 4.92 grams. **Composition:** ***1937–1941:*** .750 copper, .250 nickel; ***1944–1945:*** .650 copper, .230 zinc, .120 nickel. **Diameter:** 19 mm. **Edge:** Plain. **Mints:** Manila, Philadelphia, San Francisco.

Key to Collecting: The Manila Mint switched its coinage of five-centavo pieces to the Commonwealth reverse design in 1937. Production of the coins increased in 1938, then skipped two years. The 1941 output would be Manila's last for the type; the Japanese invasion at year's end stopped all of its coinage.

Philippine commerce was starved for coins during the war. As part of the broader strategy for liberating the Philippines from Japanese occupation, the U.S. Treasury Department swung its mints into production of five-centavo coins in 1944 (Philadelphia and San Francisco) and 1945 (San Francisco alone). The large mintages make the coins readily available even in Mint State. Search for quality.

Aspects of Striking and Appearance: Most pre-war five-centavo coins are poorly struck.

Market Value: Circulation Strikes

VF	EF	MS-60	MS-63
$0.25	$0.50	$1	$2

Ten Centavos, Larger-Diameter (1903–1906)

Circulation-Strike Mintage: 11,352,658

Proof Mintage: 4,884

Designer: Melecio Figueroa. **Weight:** 2.7 grams. **Composition:** .900 silver, .100 copper. **Diameter:** 17.5 mm. **Edge:** Reeded. **Mint:** Philadelphia.

Key to Collecting: From 1903 to 1906 ten-centavo coins were struck both for circulation and in Proof format for collectors. As a type, the circulation-strike coins are readily available in grades up through Mint State.

Aspects of Striking and Appearance: These generally are well struck, although some show slight weakness.

Proof Coins: Ten-centavo Proofs were struck at the Philadelphia Mint for annual Proof sets in 1903, 1904, 1905, 1906, and 1908. They currently are more affordable than their counterpart Barber dimes of the same era.

Market Value: Circulation Strikes

VF	EF	MS-60	MS-63
$4	$5	$35	$75

Market Value: Proof Strikes

PF-60	PF-63
$100	$150

Ten Centavos, Smaller-Diameter (1907–1935)

Circulation-Strike Mintage: 37,812,275

Proof Mintage: 500

Designer: Melecio Figueroa. **Weight:** 2 grams. **Composition:** .750 silver, .250 copper. **Diameter:** 16.5 mm. **Edge:** Reeded. **Mints:** Philadelphia, San Francisco, Manila.

Key to Collecting: In 1907 the silver ten-centavo coin's fineness was reduced from .900 to .750, and at the same time its diameter was decreased. The Manila Mint took over ten-centavo production from San Francisco in 1920. Production after 1921 consisted of 1 million pieces struck in 1929 and just less than 1.3 million in 1935. The next ten-centavo mintage would be under the Commonwealth.

Aspects of Striking and Appearance: These are generally well struck.

Proof Coins: Smaller-diameter ten-centavo Proofs were struck at the Philadelphia Mint for the 1908 Philippine Proof set. None were minted in 1907.

Market Value: Circulation Strikes

VF	EF	MS-60	MS-63
$2	$3	$20	$45

Market Value: Proof Strikes

PF-60	PF-63
$175	$250

Ten Centavos, Commonwealth (1937–1945)

Circulation-Strike Mintage: *178,550,000*

Designer: Melecio Figueroa (obverse). **Weight:** 2 grams. **Composition:** .750 silver, .250 copper. **Diameter:** 16.5 mm. **Edge:** Reeded. **Mints:** Manila, Denver.

Key to Collecting: The Manila Mint under Commonwealth governance struck ten-centavo coins in 1937 and 1938, followed by a hiatus of two years, and a final coinage in 1941. Normal mint functions were interrupted in 1941. Japan's wartime exportation of Philippine coins resulted in scarcity of coinage in day-to-day commerce. The U.S. Treasury geared up the Denver Mint for a massive production of Philippine ten-centavo coins in 1944 and 1945, to be shipped overseas and enter circulation as American and Philippine troops liberated the islands. The 1945 coinage was particularly heavy: more than 130 million ten-centavo coins, compared to the Denver Mint's production of just over 40 million Mercury dimes that year. This large mintage of silver coins continued to circulate in the Philippines into the 1960s. The coins as a type are readily available today. Search for a well-struck, high-quality example for your collection.

Aspects of Striking and Appearance: Well-struck examples are unusual. Part of Miss Liberty's bust is nearly always flatly struck. The Denver coinage of 1944 and 1945 often is weakly struck on the obverse, with loss of detail.

Market Value: Circulation Strikes

VF	EF	MS-60	MS-63
$1	$2	$2.50	$3.50

Twenty Centavos, Larger-Diameter (1903–1906)

Circulation-Strike Mintage: 9,240,962

Proof Mintage: 4,884

Designer: Melecio Figueroa. **Weight:** 5.385 grams. **Composition:** .900 silver, .100 copper. **Diameter:** 23 mm. **Edge:** Reeded. **Mint:** Philadelphia.

Key to Collecting: The Philippine twenty-centavo coin was minted in a 23 mm diameter from 1903 to 1906, struck both for circulation and in Proof format for collectors. As a type, the circulation-strike coins are readily available in grades up through Mint State.

Aspects of Striking and Appearance: Most are well struck. However, the 1904-S usually shows weaker striking.

Proof Coins: Proofs were struck at the Philadelphia Mint for annual Proof sets in 1903, 1904, 1905, 1906, and 1908.

Market Value: Circulation Strikes

VF	EF	MS-60	MS-63
$3.50	$15	$45	$100

Market Value: Proof Strikes

PF-60	PF-63
$125	$200

Twenty Centavos, Smaller-Diameter (1907–1929)

Circulation-Strike Mintage: 26,354,611

Proof Mintage: 500

Designer: Melecio Figueroa. **Weight:** 4 grams. **Composition:** .750 silver, .250 copper. **Diameter:** 20 mm. **Edge:** Reeded. **Mints:** Philadelphia, San Francisco, Manila.

Key to Collecting: In 1907 the diameter of the twenty-centavo coin was reduced and its silver fineness decreased from .900 to .750. Circulation strikes were made at the Philadelphia and San Francisco mints through 1919. In July 1920, a new "Mint of the Philippine Islands," located in Manila, started production. Its output during the period of U.S. sovereignty included twenty-centavo pieces in 1920, 1921, 1928, and 1929. (Production of the coins later continued under the Commonwealth, with a slightly modified design.) The coins are common enough that you can seek out high quality and a nice strike for your collection.

Aspects of Striking and Appearance: Most show flattening of Liberty's hair, sometimes extending into the area of her left bosom and her left hand.

Proof Coins: Smaller-diameter twenty-centavo Proofs were struck at the Philadelphia Mint for the 1908 Philippine Proof set. None were minted in 1907.

Market Value: Circulation Strikes

VF	EF	MS-60	MS-63
$3	$5	$40	$100

Market Value: Proof Strikes

PF-60	PF-63
$200	$325

Twenty Centavos, Commonwealth (1937–1945)

Circulation-Strike Mintage: *118,565,000*

Designer: Melecio Figueroa (obverse). **Weight:** 4 grams. **Composition:** .750 silver, .250 copper. **Diameter:** 20 mm. **Edge:** Reeded. **Mints:** Manila, Denver.

Key to Collecting: The twenty-centavo piece was the largest circulating coin struck by the Commonwealth of the Philippines at the Manila Mint. Production commenced in 1937 and 1938, followed by a hiatus of two years, and a final year of output in 1941 before Japan's December invasion put a halt to all coinage. During their occupation, the Japanese pulled many twenty-centavo pieces out of circulation and melted them as raw material for new imperial coins. Anticipating driving the Japanese military out of the islands, the United States and Commonwealth governments planned an impressive production of coinage for the Philippines in 1944 and 1945. The Denver Mint was the source for twenty-centavo pieces, and its output was immense, in 1945 exceeding even the Philadelphia Mint's production of Washington quarters for domestic use. 111 million of the coins were shipped overseas to accompany the U.S. military as Americans and Filipinos fought to liberate the islands. With so many coins issued, high-quality examples are easy to find for today's type sets. Seek out quality and an eye-appealing strike.

Aspects of Striking and Appearance: Well-struck coins are a challenge to locate.

Market Value: Circulation Strikes

VF	EF	MS-60	MS-63
$2	$2.75	$3	$5

Fifty Centavos, Larger-Diameter (1903–1906)

Circulation-Strike Mintage: 4,177,061

Proof Mintage: 4,884

Designer: Melecio Figueroa. **Weight:** 13.48 grams. **Composition:** .900 silver, .100 copper. **Diameter:** 30 mm. **Edge:** Reeded. **Mint:** Philadelphia.

Key to Collecting: Early fifty-centavo coins were struck both for circulation and in Proof format for collectors. As a type, the circulation-strike coins are readily available in grades up through Mint State.

Aspects of Striking and Appearance: Many obverses show slight flattening of the frontal hair just above Miss Liberty's ear. The reverses sometimes show slight flattening of the eagle's breast feathers. On the reverse, a high spot on the shield is the result of an unevenness in striking.

Proof Coins: Proofs of the larger diameter were struck at the Philadelphia Mint for annual Proof sets in 1903, 1904, 1905, and 1906.

Market Value: Circulation Strikes

VF	EF	MS-60	MS-63
$12	$15	$125	$225

Market Value: Proof Strikes

PF-60	PF-63
$150	$275

Fifty Centavos, Smaller-Diameter (1907–1921)

Circulation-Strike Mintage: 12,254,757

Proof Mintage: 500

Designer: Melecio Figueroa. **Weight:** 10 grams. **Composition:** .750 silver, .250 copper. **Diameter:** 27 mm. **Edge:** Reeded. **Mints:** Philadelphia, San Francisco, Manila.

Key to Collecting: After four years of coinage, in 1907 the fifty-centavo's silver fineness was lowered from .900 to .750, and its diameter was reduced by ten percent. The smaller coins were minted from 1907 to 1921. The Manila Mint took over their production from the Philadelphia and San Francisco mints in 1920, using coinage dies shipped from Philadelphia. This was the largest denomination produced at the Manila Mint. The coins are available enough that you should seek out appealing quality and a strong strike for your type set.

Aspects of Striking and Appearance: Most show notable flatness of strike in Miss Liberty's hair just above her ear, and sometimes on her left hand. A flat strike on the abdomen and left leg should not be mistaken for circulation wear. The reverses are quite unevenly struck.

Proof Coins: Smaller-diameter fifty-centavo Proofs were struck at the Philadelphia Mint for the 1908 Philippine Proof set. None were minted in 1907.

Market Value: Circulation Strikes

VF	EF	MS-60	MS-63
$7.50	$10	$75	$150

Market Value: Proof Strikes

PF-60	PF-63
$300	$525

Fifty Centavos, Commonwealth (1944–1945)

Circulation-Strike Mintage: 37,307,000

Designer: Melecio Figueroa (obverse). **Weight:** 10 grams. **Composition:** .750 silver, .250 copper. **Diameter:** 27 mm. **Edge:** Reeded. **Mint:** San Francisco.

Key to Collecting: No fifty-centavo coins were struck at the Manila Mint for the Commonwealth of the Philippines. The denomination's first issue was a wartime production of the San Francisco Mint, in 1944, to the extent of some 19 million coins, or double that facility's production of Liberty Walking half dollars for the year. This was followed by a similar mintage in 1945. These coins were intended to enter circulation after being shipped overseas with the U.S. military during the liberation of the Philippines from Imperial Japan's 1942–1945 occupation. They were readily accepted in the coin-starved wartime economy, and continued to circulate in the islands into the 1960s. Today the coins are readily available in any grade desired, but strike can be a challenge. Select quality for your type set.

Aspects of Striking and Appearance: Many are lightly struck, but they typically show flattening less severe than that of the 1907–1921 issues struck under U.S. sovereignty.

Market Value: Circulation Strikes

VF	EF	MS-60	MS-63
$5	$6	$8	$10

One Peso, Larger-Diameter (1903–1906)

Circulation-Strike Mintage: 58,385,256

Proof Mintage: 4,884

Designer: Melecio Figueroa. **Weight:** 26.96 grams. **Composition:** .900 silver, .100 copper. **Diameter:** 38 mm. **Edge:** Reeded. **Mint:** Philadelphia.

Key to Collecting: The Philippine silver peso was struck under U.S. sovereignty in a 38 mm format (the size of the Morgan dollar) from 1903 to 1906. The key date among those struck for circulation is the issue of 1906-S. Although the San Francisco Mint produced more than 200,000 of the coins that year, nearly all of them were held back from circulation. They were instead stored and then later sold as bullion. As a type the silver pesos of 1903 to 1906 are available in circulated grades and to a lesser extent in Mint State.

Aspects of Striking and Appearance: These generally have well-struck obverses, but occasionally with some flattening of Miss Liberty's frontal hair above her ear, and sometimes her left bosom and hand. On the reverse, the feathers on the eagle's breast are indistinctly cut, and the wing tips can sometimes be found slightly flatly struck.

Proof Coins: Proof pesos in this large format were struck at the Philadelphia Mint for annual Proof sets in 1903, 1904, 1905, and 1906.

Market Value: Circulation Strikes

VF	EF	MS-60	MS-63
$35	$40	$150	$325

Market Value: Proof Strikes

PF-60	PF-63
$350	$650

One Peso, Smaller-Diameter (1907–1912)

Circulation-Strike Mintage: 43,107,503

Proof Mintage: *502*

Designer: Melecio Figueroa. **Weight:** 20 grams. **Composition:** .800 silver, .200 copper. **Diameter:** 35 mm. **Edge:** Reeded. **Mints:** Philadelphia, San Francisco.

Key to Collecting: By 1906 market forces were driving the Philippine silver pesos out of commerce and into the melting pot: the rising price of silver made the coins worth more as precious metal than as legal tender. In 1907 the U.S. Mint responded by lowering the denomination's silver fineness from .900 to .800, and reducing its diameter from 38 mm to 35 mm. The smaller coins had about one-third less silver, by actual weight, than those of 1903 to 1906, guaranteeing that they would stay in circulation.

The new smaller pesos were minted every year from 1907 to 1912, with the San Francisco Mint producing them for commerce and the Philadelphia Mint striking a small quantity of Proofs in 1907 and 1908. Millions of the coins were stored as backing for Silver Certificates (and, later, Treasury Certificates) in circulation in the Philippines. Although the Manila Mint started operations in 1920, the silver peso was never part of its production for circulation.

In December 1941, Japan, immediately after attacking Pearl Harbor, began a fierce assault on the Philippines. Manila fell on January 2, 1942, and General Douglas MacArthur fell back to the Bataan Peninsula. In late February President Franklin Roosevelt ordered him to leave the Philippines for Australia, prompting the general's famous promise to the Philippine people: "I shall return!" Not long after the fighting erupted it had become apparent that the Japanese would overtake the islands, and early in 1942 the U.S. military dumped crates holding 15,700,000 silver pesos, mostly of 1907–1912 coinage, into the sea near Corregidor, to avoid their seizure. Many millions of these coins were salvaged by the U.S. Treasury and the Central Bank of the Philippines after the war, with all but about five million pieces being reclaimed by 1958. Today a great majority of the salvaged "war pesos" show clear evidence of their prolonged submersion in saltwater. A typical effect is a dark corrosion strongly resistant to any manner of cleaning or conservation. This damage to so many coins has added to the scarcity of high-grade pre-war silver pesos.

Aspects of Striking and Appearance: Some but not all exhibit flattened frontal hair, and sometimes a flattened left hand. On the reverse, the eagle's breast feathers are not clearly defined. On some examples the reverses are quite unevenly struck.

Proof Coins: Unlike the smaller denominations, Proof pesos of 1907 also are known—but only to the extent of two examples. They were also struck in 1908 for Proof sets.

Market Value: Circulation Strikes

VF	EF	MS-60	MS-63
$10	$20	$225	$425

Market Value: Proof Strikes

PF-60	PF-63
$700	$1,300

NOTES

1. Information from R.W. Julian to the author. This was the third Bank of the United States, chartered by the state of Pennsylvania after the charter of the second Bank of the United States expired.
2. Per conversations with researcher John Dannreuther in the 1990s. Also, my observations of 1849 gold dollars of various dies and mints reveal no minute differences in date placement.
3. This figure includes 500 made in August and September, plus 12, 367 produced later (Roger W. Burdette to author, July 27, 2004).
4. Information from Roger W. Burdette to author, July 27, 2004.
5. Ibid.
6. Ibid.
7. Certain information on the ANA grading system is adapted from *A Guide Book of Double Eagle Gold Coins* (Whitman Publishing).
8. Kenneth Bressett and Abe Kosoff, *Official A.N.A. Grading Standards for United States Coins* (Whitman Publishing). Slightly adapted.
9. Walter Breen, *Walter Breen's Complete Encyclopedia of U.S. and Colonial Coins* (New York: Doubleday, 1988), 177.
10. In Jefferson's memorandum book for 1792 in the Library of Congress. Dr. Joel J. Orosz, letter to author, July 25, 2004.
11. Breen, *Complete Encyclopedia of U.S. and Colonial Coins*, 337.
12. Letter published in *Numismatic News*, January 19, 1999.
13. *Numismatic News*, June 13, 2000.
14. Saul Teichman estimate, letter to author, August 3, 2004.
15. This per Treasury correspondence reviewed by the author. Also see my *Silver Dollars and Trade Dollars of the United States: A Complete Encyclopedia* (Wolfeboro, NH: Bowers and Merena, 1993) and John M. Willem's *The United States Trade Dollar: America's Only Unwanted, Unhonored Coin*, 2nd ed. (Racine, WI: Whitman, 1965). Willem indicates otherwise, but I respectfully disagree with this.
16. Saul Teichman estimate, letter to author, August 3, 2004.
17. Ibid.
18. The chief died on March 15, 1913, per a notice in *The Numismatist*, April 1913. Certain information from Superior Galleries, Elite Coin Auction, August 2004, Lot 965.
19. Letter of July 16, 1834. Earlier quoted ideas are from a letter of July 12, 1834, Woodbury to Moore.
20. Saul Teichman estimate, letter to author, August 3, 2004.
21. Ibid.

BIBLIOGRAPHY

HISTORY OF THE U.S. MINT

Augsburger, Leonard D., and Joel J. Orosz. *The Secret History of the First U.S. Mint*, Atlanta, GA, 2011.

Bierly, William. *In God We Trust*, Pelham, AL, 2019.

Bowers, Q. David. *A Guide Book of the United States Mint*, Pelham, AL, 2016.

Evans, George. *Illustrated History of the U.S. Mint* (various eds.), Philadelphia, 1885–1901.

Lange, David W. *History of the United States Mint and Its Coinage*, Atlanta, GA, 2005.

Mishler, Clifford. *Coins: Questions and Answers* (6th ed.), Pelham, AL, 2019.

Smith, Pete, Joel Orosz, and Leonard Augsburger. *1792: Birth of a Nation's Coinage*, Birmingham, UK, 2017.

Stewart, Frank. *History of the First United States Mint, Its People and Its Operations*, 1924 (reprinted 1974).

HALF CENTS

Bowers, Q. David. *A Guide Book of Half Cents and Large Cents*, Atlanta, GA, 2015.

Breen, Walter. *Walter Breen's Encyclopedia of United States Half Cents 1793–1857*, South Gate, CA, 1983.

Cohen, Roger S., Jr. *American Half Cents—The "Little Half Sisters"* (2nd ed.), 1982.

Manley, Ronald P. *The Half Cent Die State Book, 1793–1857*, United States, 1998.

Large Cents

Bowers, Q. David. *A Guide Book of Half Cents and Large Cents*, Atlanta, GA, 2015.

Breen, Walter. *Walter Breen's Encyclopedia of Early United States Cents 1793–1814*, Wolfeboro, NH, 2001.

Grellman, J.R. *Attribution Guide for United States Large Cents 1840–1857* (3rd ed.), Bloomington, MN, 2002.

Newcomb, H.R. *United States Copper Cents 1816–1857*, New York, 1944 (reprinted 1983).

Noyes, William C. *United States Large Cents* (6 vols.), Ypsilanti, MI, 2006–2015.

———. *United States Large Cents 1793–1814*, Bloomington, MN, 1991.

———. *United States Large Cents 1816–1839*, Bloomington, MN, 1991.

PENNY-WISE, official publication of Early American Coppers, Inc.

Sheldon, William H. *Penny Whimsy (1793–1814)*, New York, 1958 (reprinted 1965, 1976).

Wright, John D. *The Cent Book 1816–1839*, Bloomington, MN, 1992.

Small Cents

Bowers, Q. David. *A Guide Book of Lincoln Cents*, Pelham, AL, 2016.

Lange, David W. *The Complete Guide to Lincoln Cents*, Wolfeboro, NH, 1996.

Snow, Richard. *A Guide Book of Flying Eagle and Indian Head Cents* (3rd ed.), Pelham, AL, 2016.

Two-Cent Pieces

Bierly, William. *In God We Trust*, Pelham, AL, 2019.

Nickel Five-Cent Pieces

Bowers, Q. David. *A Guide Book of Buffalo and Jefferson Nickels*, Atlanta, GA, 2007.

———. *A Guide Book of Shield and Liberty Head Nickels*, Atlanta, GA, 2006.

Fletcher, Edward L., Jr. *The Shield Five Cent Series*, Ormond Beach, FL, 1994.

Lange, David W. *The Complete Guide to Buffalo Nickels*, Virginia Beach, VA, 2006.

Nagengast, Bernard. *The Jefferson Nickel Analyst* (2nd ed.), Sidney, OH, 1979.

Peters, Gloria, and Cynthia Mahon. *The Complete Guide to Shield and Liberty Head Nickels*, Virginia Beach, VA, 1995.

Half Dimes

Blythe, Al. *The Complete Guide to Liberty Seated Half Dimes*, Virginia Beach, VA, 1992.

Bowers, Q. David. *A Guide Book of Liberty Seated Silver Coins*, Atlanta, GA, 2016.

Logan, Russell, and John McClosky. *Federal Half Dimes 1792–1837*, Manchester, MI, 1998.

Newlin, H.P. *The Early Half-Dimes of the United States*, Philadelphia, 1883 (reprinted 1933).

Dimes and Twenty-Cent Pieces

Bowers, Q. David. *A Guide Book of Barber Silver Coins* (2nd ed.), Pelham, AL, 2019.

———. *A Guide Book of Liberty Seated Silver Coins*, Atlanta, GA, 2016.

———. *A Guide Book of Mercury Dimes, Standing Liberty Quarters, and Liberty Walking Half Dollars*, Atlanta, GA, 2015.

Brunner, Lane J., and John M. Frost. *Double Dime: The United States Twenty-Cent Piece*, 2014.

Davis, David, Russell Logan, Allen Lovejoy, John McCloskey, and William Subjack. *Early United States Dimes 1796–1837*, Ypsilanti, MI, 1984.

Greer, Brian. *The Complete Guide to Liberty Seated Dimes*, Virginia Beach, VA, 2005.

Lange, David W. *The Complete Guide to Mercury Dimes* (2nd ed.), Virginia Beach, VA, 2005.

Lawrence, David. *The Complete Guide to Barber Dimes*, Virginia Beach, VA, 1991.

QUARTER DOLLARS

Bowers, Q. David. *A Guide Book of Barber Silver Coins* (2nd ed.), Pelham, AL, 2019.

———. *A Guide Book of Liberty Seated Silver Coins*, Atlanta, GA, 2016.

———. *A Guide Book of Mercury Dimes, Standing Liberty Quarters, and Liberty Walking Half Dollars*, Atlanta, GA, 2015.

———. *A Guide Book of Washington Quarters* (2nd ed.), Pelham, AL, 2017.

Briggs, Larry. *The Comprehensive Encyclopedia of United States Seated Quarters*, Lima, OH, 1991.

Cline, J.H. *Standing Liberty Quarters* (3rd ed.), 1996.

Rea, Rory, Glenn Peterson, Bradley Karoleff, and John Kovach. *Early Quarter Dollars of the U.S. Mint, 1796–1838*, 2010.

Tompkins, Steve M. *Early United States Quarters, 1796–1838*, 2008.

HALF DOLLARS

Bowers, Q. David. *A Guide Book of Barber Silver Coins* (2nd ed.), Pelham, AL, 2019.

———. *A Guide Book of Liberty Seated Silver Coins*, Atlanta, GA, 2016.

———. *A Guide Book of Mercury Dimes, Standing Liberty Quarters, and Liberty Walking Half Dollars*, Atlanta, GA, 2015.

Overton, Al C. *Early Half Dollar Die Varieties 1794–1836* (5th ed.), Murietta, CA, 2014.

Peterson, Glenn R. *The Ultimate Guide to Attributing Bust Half Dollars*, Rocky River, OH, 2000.

Tomaska, Rick. *A Guide Book of Franklin and Kennedy Half Dollars* (3rd ed.), Pelham, AL, 2018.

Wiley, Randy, and Bugert, Bill. *The Complete Guide to Liberty Seated Half Dollars*, Virginia Beach, VA, 1993.

SILVER DOLLARS AND RELATED DOLLARS

Bolender, M.H. *The United States Early Silver Dollars From 1794 to 1803* (5th ed.), Iola, WI, 1987.

Bowers, Q. David. *The Encyclopedia of United States Silver Dollars 1794–1804*, Wolfeboro, NH, 2013.

——. *A Guide Book of Liberty Seated Silver Coins*, Atlanta, GA, 2016.

——. *A Guide Book of Modern United States Dollar Coins*, Atlanta, GA, 2016.

——. *The Rare Silver Dollars Dated 1804*, Wolfeboro, NH, 1999.

——. *Silver Dollars and Trade Dollars of the United States: A Complete Encyclopedia*, Wolfeboro, NH, 1993.

——. *A Guide Book of Morgan Silver Dollars* (6th ed.), Pelham, AL, 2019.

Burdette, Roger W. *A Guide Book of Peace Dollars* (4th ed.), Pelham, AL, 2019.

Crum, Adam, Selby Ungar, and Jeff Oxman. *Carson City Morgan Dollars* (4th ed.), Pelham, AL, 2019.

Fey, Michael S., and Jeff Oxman. *The Top 100 Morgan Dollar Varieties*, Morris Planes, NJ, 1997.

Logies, Martin A. *The Flowing Hair Silver Dollars of 1794*, 2004.

Newman, Eric P., and Kenneth E. Bressett. *The Fantastic 1804 Dollar*, Racine, WI, 1962 (Tribute ed. 2009).

Standish, Michael "Miles," with John B. Love. *Morgan Dollar: America's Love Affair With a Legendary Coin*, Atlanta, GA, 2014.

Van Allen, Leroy C., and A. George Mallis. *Comprehensive Catalogue and Encyclopedia of U.S. Morgan and Peace Silver Dollars*, New York, 1997.

GOLD PIECES ($1 THROUGH $20)

Akers, David W. *Gold Dollars (and Other Gold Denominations)*, Englewood, OH, 1975–1982.

Bowers, Q. David. *A Guide Book of Double Eagle Gold Coins* (2nd ed.), Pelham, AL, 2019.

——. *A Guide Book of Gold Dollars* (2nd ed.), Atlanta, GA, 2011.

——. *A Guide Book of Gold Eagle Coins*, Pelham, AL, 2017.

——. *A Guide Book of Quarter Eagle and Half Eagle Gold Coins*, Pelham, AL, 2019.

——. *United States Gold Coins: An Illustrated History*, Wolfeboro, NH, 1982.

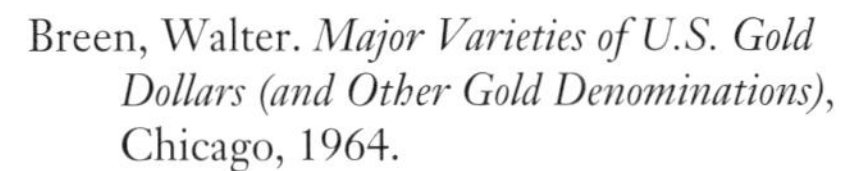

Breen, Walter. *Major Varieties of U.S. Gold Dollars (and Other Gold Denominations)*, Chicago, 1964.

Dannreuther, John W., and Harry W. Bass. *Early U.S. Gold Coin Varieties*, Atlanta, GA, 2006.

Fivaz, Bill. *United States Gold Counterfeit Detection Guide*, Atlanta, GA, 2005.

Schein, Allan. *The $2 1/2 and $5 Gold Indians of Bela Lyon Pratt*, 2016.

Patterns

Judd, J. Hewitt. *United States Pattern Coins* (10th ed.), Atlanta, GA, 2008.

Philippine Coins Struck Under the United States

Allen, Lyman L. *U.S. Philippine Coins*, Oakland Park, FL, 1998.

Shafer, Neil. *United States Territorial Coinage for the Philippine Islands*, Whitman Publishing, 1961.

Yeoman, R.S. *Mega Red*, Whitman Publishing, several editions.

Proof Coins and Proof Sets

Lange, David W. *A Guide Book of Modern United States Proof Coin Sets* (2nd ed.), Atlanta, GA, 2010.

Type Coins

Burdette, Roger W. *The Renaissance of American Coinage 1905–1908*. Great Falls, VA, 2006.

——. *The Renaissance of American Coinage 1909–1915*. Great Falls, VA, 2007.

——. *The Renaissance of American Coinage 1916–1921*. Great Falls, VA, 2005.

Garrett, Jeff, and Ron Guth. *100 Greatest U.S. Coins* (5th ed.), Pelham, AL, 2019.

Guth, Ron, and Jeff Garrett. *United States Coinage: A Study by Type*, Atlanta, GA, 2005.

Die Varieties

Fivaz, Bill, and J.T. Stanton. *The Cherrypickers' Guide to Rare Die Varieties* (various editions and volumes), Atlanta, GA, and Pelham, AL.

ACKNOWLEDGMENTS

The author expresses appreciation to the following for help in the ways indicated:

Eric P. Newman wrote the foreword. The author of many research articles, studies, and books, Newman was a friend of the author for more than 50 years. He earned more Heath Literary Award honors given by the American Numismatic Association than has any other person. He was also a founding member of the Rittenhouse Society group of numismatic writers and researchers.

Richard A. Bagg (manuscript review) • **Andrew V. Bowers** (manuscript review) • **Wynn D. Bowers** (manuscript review) • **Roger W. Burdette** (historical information from his manuscripts on twentieth century coins and designs, manuscript review, suggestions) • **Frank Campbell** (American Numismatic Society librarian; helped with research inquiries) • **Donald J. Carlucci** (information about the Pennsylvania quarter dollar) • **G.C. Carnes** (information concerning the Texas State quarter) • **Daniel Carr** (information about State quarters) • **Jane Colvard** (of the American Numismatic Association Library; assisted with a request) • U.S. Commission of Fine Arts, Washington, DC (provided certain documents) • **Bill Fivaz** (information about the Georgia State quarter) • **Roberta A. French** (extensive research assignments and fulfillment and transcription) • **Paul Jackson** (information concerning State quarters) • **Jay Johnson** (former Mint director; reminiscences and comments concerning coinage) • **R.W. Julian** (information during the course of research for many years) • **Christine Karstedt** (suggestions) • **Melissa Karstedt** (suggestions) • **John Kraljevich** (information on Mint engravers of the 1790s, manuscript review) • **Cynthia Meals** (Office of External Relations, U.S. Mint; assistance and suggestions) • **Karl Moulton** (Mint history information) • **The National Archives and Records Administration,** Washington, DC (provided certain documents) • **Susan Novak** (research and correspondence) • **Joel J. Orosz** (manuscript review, research suggestions) • **Bret Palser** (information on Wisconsin State quarter) • **Spencer Peck** (information concerning the New Jersey State quarter) • **Harry Schultz** shared images of Philippine coinage • **Paul Schultz** offered suggestions • **Michael Serpa** gave feedback on the first edition • **Richard Snow** (information on Wisconsin State quarter) • **David M. Sundman** (suggestions) • **Saul Teichman** (suggestions and help with research and historical information) • **Frank Van Valen** (manuscript review, copy editing, suggestions)

American Numismatic Rarities, Numismatic Guaranty Corporation (NGC), Stack's Bowers Galleries, and **Whitman Publishing** provided use of their staffs and resources including photographs and technical assistance. Most photographs are by **Douglas Plasencia** from important collections including **Oliver Jung** and **Dr. Haig Koshkarian.** Certain staff members of *Coin World*, particularly **Michele Orzano, Beth Deisher,** and **Paul Gilkes**, assisted with information on the State quarters. *Numismatic News* provided information on modern coinage, including State quarters. **Brent Pogue** provided certain photographs taken by **Tom Mulvaney** • **The United States Mint** provided photographs of State quarters and helped in other ways.

In this age of the Internet, many obscure facts and points were checked on various websites, generally credited in the endnotes.

Over the years, the director of the United States Mint has had a profound influence on the panorama of changing coin types and designs. The director when the first edition was written was **Henrietta Holsman Fore.** President George W. Bush appointed Fore director of the United States Mint in 2001. She was front row center in the 50 State Quarters® Program.

Director **Edmund C. Moy** shepherded the Presidential dollars program into national recognition, and oversaw new and exciting commemorative, bullion, and medal series. Director **David Ryder** has also coordinated innovations in U.S. coinage.

ABOUT THE AUTHOR

Q. David Bowers started in the rare-coin business as a teenager, in 1953. He is a founder of Stack's Bowers Galleries and is numismatic director of Whitman Publishing. He and his firms have presented the majority of the most valuable coin collections ever sold at auction. Bowers has served the hobby in many roles and capacities over his long career, including as president of both the American Numismatic Association and the Professional Numismatists Guild. He is the author of more than 60 books, hundreds of auction and other catalogs, and several thousand articles.